Foundations of Linear Algebra

A Series of Undergraduate Books in Mathematics

R. A. ROSENBAUM, Editor

Introduction to Matrices and Linear Transformations
Daniel T. Finkbeiner, II

Introduction to Probability and Statistics, 2nd Edition
Henry L. Alder and Edward B. Roessler

The USSR Olympiad Problem Book: Selected Problems and Theorems of Elementary Mathematics
D. O. Shklarsky, N. N. Chentzov, I. M. Yaglom

Mathematics: The Man-made Universe
Sherman K. Stein

Set Theory and Logic
Robert R. Stoll

Problems in Differential Equations
J. L. Brenner

Computational Methods of Linear Algebra
D. K. Faddeev and V. N. Faddeeva

Foundations of Linear Algebra
A. I. Mal'cev

GOLDEN GATE EDITIONS

A Concrete Approach to Abstract Algebra
W. W. Sawyer

A Modern View of Geometry
Leonard M. Blumenthal

Sets, Logic, and Axiomatic Theories
Robert R. Stoll

An Elementary Introduction to the Theory of Probability
B. V. Gnedenko and A. Ya. Khinchin

The Solution of Equations in Integers
A. O. Gelfond

The Real Number System in an Algebraic Setting
J. B. Roberts

Elements of Astromechanics
Peter van de Kamp

Foundations of Linear Algebra

A. I. MAL'CEV

TRANSLATED FROM THE RUSSIAN BY

THOMAS CRAIG BROWN

Washington University, St. Louis

EDITED BY

J. B. ROBERTS

Reed College

W. H. FREEMAN AND COMPANY

SAN FRANCISCO AND LONDON

Printed in the United States of America.
Library of Congress Catalog Card Number 63-7424.

Second (Russian) Edition published in 1956 by State Technical-theoretical Literature, Moscow B-71, B. Kalyshskaya 15, Minister of Culture USSR, Order No. 1173.

PREFACE TO THE SECOND (RUSSIAN) EDITION

The present edition of this book differs considerably from the first, which appeared in 1948. The principal changes were prompted by a desire to make the book more useful as an aid in teaching various parts of linear algebra in universities and pedagogical institutes.

In connection with this it was necessary to give up the purely geometrical derivation of the Jordan normal forms and to adopt an algebraic treatment; this makes it possible to shorten the exposition and to include a special chapter on the Jordan normal forms.

The topics of quadratic and bilinear forms in the first edition were treated in different chapters; they are now in the same chapter. Besides this, instead of a detailed exposition of some of the more specialized questions of the theory of transformations of unitary spaces there are problems and exercises which formulate these results, which permits without loss of clarity a briefer treatment and the distribution of the material into a smaller number of chapters. This economy allows the inclusion of a large new chapter on multilinear forms and tensors, and a detailed treatment of the fundamental questions of tensor algebra—without altering the previous size of the book.

I take this opportunity to express my gratitude to A. G. Kurosh and the members of the department of the MGY, who discussed the book at a department conference, and to all those persons who, on the occasion of the first edition, encouraged the author to prepare a new one.

A. I. Mal'cev

CONTENTS

1 MATRICES

1. Operations with Matrices

1. Linear Algebra

In linear algebra one studies three kinds of objects; matrices, linear spaces, and algebraic forms. The theories of these objects are so closely related that most problems of linear algebra have equivalent formulations in each of the three theories. The matrix point of view, which underlies the present exposition is the one best adapted to actual calculations. On the other hand, most problems of linear algebra that arise in geometry and mechanics lead to algebraic forms, while the best understanding of the internal connections between different problems of linear algebra is obtained by means of linear spaces. Therefore the ability to pass from are type of formulation to another is one of the most important skills to acquire in the study of linear algebra.

From the point of view of the theory of forms, linear algebra falls naturally into three parts: the theories of linear forms, of bilinear and quadratic forms, and of multilinear forms. Linear algebra proper usually encompasses linear and bilinear forms, and the very beginnings of the theory of multilinear forms as tensor algebras. The more delicate questions of the theory of multilinear forms belong to the theory of invariants and are not included in this book.

Linear algebra is a branch of mathematics as old as mathematics itself. The solving of the equation $ax + b = 0$ may be considered the original problem of this subject. Although this problem presents no difficulty, the method which solves it, together with the properties of the corresponding linear function $y = ax + b$, are the initial models for the ideas and methods of all of linear algebra. For example, the fundamental idea behind the solution of a system of linear equations in several unknowns is that of replacing such a system by a chain of these simple equations.

The study of systems of linear equations acquired new significance after the creation of analytic geometry; it was possible to reduce all the fundamental questions about the arrangements of lines and planes in space to the investigation of such systems. The search in the 18th century for the general solution of n linear equations in n unknowns led Leibnitz and Cramer to the notion of the determinant. In the 19th century, determinants not only found use in algebra and analytic geometry, but also entered analysis in the work of Ostrogradski and Jacobi on functional determinants. At the same time, the problem of the transformation of quadratic forms by linear substitutions acquired great importance in analytic geometry, in the theory of numbers, and especially in theoretical mechanics. The same problem was central also in the geometrical ideas of Lobachevski and Riemann, which led to the study of many-dimensional spaces, including many-dimensional linear spaces (Grassmann). In the middle of the last century, investigations of noncommutative algebras (Hamilton), led to the development of a matrix calculus (Cayley and Sylvester), which played a major role in the subsequent growth of linear algebra. Results which appeared near the end of the 19th century included the normal form of a matrix of a linear transformation (Jordan), elementary divisors (Weierstrass), pairs of quadratic forms (Weierstrass, Kronecker), and Hermitian forms (Hermite). At about the same time the development of differential geometry for many-dimensional spaces and of the theory of transformations of algebraic forms of higher powers led to the creation of the tensor calculus, upon which was built the theory of relativity.

In the present century linear algebra has acquired new richness and versatility through the use of the concepts of group and noncommutative ring in algebra itself, and through the use of infinite-dimensional function spaces in analysis. Applications to quantum mechanics stimulated a still more rapid development of the theory of these spaces, which has become one of the most important parts of contemporary functional analysis.

2. The Base Field

As remarked above, the fundamental objects of study in linear algebra are matrices, linear spaces, and algebraic forms that is, homogeneous polynomials in several indeterminates. These three objects involve a set K of numbers, which is given in advance. The actual selection of K depends on the problem in question and on the scientific discipline. For example, from the standpoint of completeness of algebraic results it is often desirable to take for K the field of complex numbers. But in geometry or mechanics it may be necessary to consider only real numbers, and for the needs of the theory of numbers the field of rational numbers may suffice. Therefore, in order to obtain results applicable to the broadest possible class of problems, it is convenient not to completely specify K beforehand. We will assume only that K is a field; that is, that the sum, difference, product, and quotient of arbitrary elements of K are again in K. However, readers interested only in the physical or geometrical applications of linear algebra may assume in what follows, unless otherwise stated, that K is the field of real numbers or the field of complex numbers.

We do not always insist that K be a number field; we may take for K an arbitrary field, and sometimes even a noncommutative field.* In a considerable part of the theory the formulations of the theorems and of the proofs will hold for any field K. When K is a noncommutative field, the formulations require extra care. In what follows, then, unless otherwise stated, K will be a completely arbitrary field,* which will be called the ***base field***. Its elements will be designated by small Greek letters $\alpha, \beta, \cdots, \tau$, and will sometimes be called scalars.

3. Matrices

A set of mn elements from a field K, arranged in the form of a rectangular table with m rows and n columns, is called a ***matrix*** over K. It is customary to enclose the rectangular array in square brackets (or double lines). Thus the general form of a matrix with m rows and n columns is

$$\begin{bmatrix} \alpha_{11} & \alpha_{12} & \cdots & \alpha_{1n} \\ \alpha_{21} & \alpha_{22} & \cdots & \alpha_{2n} \\ \vdots & \vdots & & \vdots \\ \alpha_{m1} & \alpha_{m2} & \cdots & \alpha_{mn} \end{bmatrix} \quad \text{or} \quad \begin{Vmatrix} \alpha_{11} & \alpha_{12} & \cdots & \alpha_{1n} \\ \alpha_{21} & \alpha_{22} & \cdots & \alpha_{2n} \\ \vdots & \vdots & & \vdots \\ \alpha_{m1} & \alpha_{m2} & \cdots & \alpha_{mn} \end{Vmatrix},$$

where the α_{ij} are elements of the field K. Often, instead of such detail, one uses the abbreviation $\|\alpha_{ij}\|$ or $\|\alpha_{ij}\|_{m,n}$.

If a matrix has the same number of rows as columns, it is called *square*, and this number is the *order* of the matrix. A matrix having only one row is called simply a *row matrix*. In what follows, matrices will be denoted by large Latin letters.

Two matrices are *equal* if they have the same number of rows and the same number of columns and if corresponding elements are equal. Thus a single equality between two matrices each with m rows and n columns is equivalent to a system of mn equalities between their elements.

4. Multiplication by Scalars and Matrix Addition

The basic operations with matrices are addition, multiplication, and multiplication by scalars. The simplest of these is multiplication by scalars. By definition, to multiply the scalar α by the matrix A, or the matrix A by the scalar α, one multiplies each element of A by α. For example,

* The reader should carefully note that the author does *not* subsume his "noncommutative field" under the term "field" (*Ed.*).

$$2\begin{bmatrix}1 & 3\\2 & 4\end{bmatrix}=\begin{bmatrix}1 & 3\\2 & 4\end{bmatrix}2=\begin{bmatrix}2 & 6\\4 & 8\end{bmatrix}.$$

A matrix in which each element is zero is called a ***zero matrix***, and is denoted O. To indicate the number of rows and columns of a zero matrix, one may employ the notation O_{mn}.

The following properties are immediate consequences of the definition of the product of a matrix by a scalar:

1. $1A = A$;
2. $OA = O$;
3. $\alpha(BA) = (\alpha B)A$.

Corresponding to any square matrix $A = ||\alpha_{ij}||$, there is a determinant $|\alpha_{ij}|$, which will be denoted by $|A|$. The value of a determinant is multiplied by α if the elements of any one row are multiplied by α, whereas multiplying a matrix A by α multiplies every element by α. Therefore, for A, a square matrix of order n,

$$|\alpha A| = \alpha^n |A| .$$

The ***sum*** of two matrices A and B, having the same numbers of rows and of columns, respectively, is the matrix with the same number of rows and columns whose elements are the sums of the corresponding elements from A and B. For example,

$$\begin{bmatrix}2 & 1 & 3\\4 & 1 & 2\end{bmatrix}+\begin{bmatrix}2 & -1 & 2\\1 & 2 & 3\end{bmatrix}=\begin{bmatrix}4 & 0 & 5\\5 & 3 & 5\end{bmatrix}.$$

The following properties are immediate consequences of this definition:

4. $A + (B + C) = (A + B) + C$;
5. $A + B = B + A$;
6. $A + O = A$;
7. $(\alpha + \beta)A = \alpha A + \beta A$;
8. $\alpha(A + B) = \alpha A + \alpha B$.

We leave the proofs of these to the reader. In particular, applying 1 and 7, we obtain

$$A + A = 2A , \qquad A + A + A = 3A, \cdots .$$

Introducing the notation $(-1)A = - A$, we also have

$$\begin{aligned}A + (-A) &= O ;\\(-\alpha)A &= - \alpha A ;\\-(A + B) &= - A + (- B) ;\\-(- A) &= A .\end{aligned}$$

For brevity, $A + (- B)$ is usually written $A - B$.

5. Matrix Multiplication

The operation of multiplication of matrices is more complicated than addition and multiplication by scalars. Let there be given two matrices A and B, where the number of columns of A is equal to the number of rows of B. If

$$A = \begin{bmatrix} \alpha_{11} & \alpha_{12} & \cdots & \alpha_{1n} \\ \alpha_{21} & \alpha_{22} & \cdots & \alpha_{2n} \\ \vdots & \vdots & & \vdots \\ \alpha_{m1} & \alpha_{m2} & \cdots & \alpha_{mn} \end{bmatrix}, \qquad B = \begin{bmatrix} \beta_{11} & \beta_{12} & \cdots & \beta_{1p} \\ \beta_{21} & \beta_{22} & \cdots & \beta_{2p} \\ \vdots & \vdots & & \vdots \\ \beta_{n1} & \beta_{n2} & \cdots & \beta_{np} \end{bmatrix},$$

then the matrix

$$C = \begin{bmatrix} \gamma_{11} & \gamma_{12} & \cdots & \gamma_{1p} \\ \gamma_{21} & \gamma_{22} & \cdots & \gamma_{2p} \\ \vdots & \vdots & & \vdots \\ \gamma_{m1} & \gamma_{m2} & \cdots & \gamma_{mp} \end{bmatrix},$$

where $\gamma_{ij} = \alpha_{i1}\beta_{1j} + \alpha_{i2}\beta_{2j} + \cdots + \alpha_{in}\beta_{nj}$, for $i = 1, 2, \cdots, m$ and $j = 1, 2, \cdots, p$, is called the ***product*** of A and B and is written AB. For example,

$$\begin{bmatrix} \alpha & \beta \\ \alpha_1 & \beta_1 \\ \alpha_2 & \beta_2 \end{bmatrix} \begin{bmatrix} \gamma & \delta & \varepsilon \\ \lambda & \mu & \nu \end{bmatrix} = \begin{bmatrix} \alpha\gamma + \beta\lambda & \alpha\delta + \beta\mu & \alpha\varepsilon + \beta\nu \\ \alpha_1\gamma + \beta_1\lambda & \alpha_1\delta + \beta_1\mu & \alpha_1\varepsilon + \beta_1\nu \\ \alpha_2\gamma + \beta_2\lambda & \alpha_2\delta + \beta_2\mu & \alpha_2\varepsilon + \beta_2\nu \end{bmatrix}.$$

The rule for multiplication of matrices is sometimes formulated as follows.

To obtain the element in the i-th row and j-th column of the product of two matrices, multiply the elements of the i-th row in the first matrix by the corresponding elements of the j-th column in the second matrix and add the resulting products.

Generally speaking, the product of two matrices depends on the order of the factors; for example,

$$\begin{bmatrix} 1 & 2 \\ 3 & 5 \end{bmatrix} \begin{bmatrix} 18 & 19 \\ -16 & -13 \end{bmatrix} = \begin{bmatrix} -14 & -7 \\ -26 & -8 \end{bmatrix},$$
$$\begin{bmatrix} 18 & 19 \\ -16 & -13 \end{bmatrix} \begin{bmatrix} 1 & 2 \\ 3 & 5 \end{bmatrix} = \begin{bmatrix} 75 & 131 \\ -55 & -97 \end{bmatrix}.$$

It may also happen that the product of two matrices in one order is meaningful, while the product of the same matrices in the opposite order is not defined.

From the definition of matrix multiplication we prove the property:

9. $\alpha(AB) = (\alpha A)B = A(\alpha B)$.

Let $A = ||\alpha_{ij}||_{m,n}$ and $B = ||\beta_{ij}||_{n,p}$. Using the rule for multiplying matrices, we obtain for the element in the ith row and kth column of the matrix $\alpha(AB)$ the expression

$$\alpha(\alpha_{i1}\beta_{1k} + \alpha_{i2}\beta_{2k} + \cdots + \alpha_{in}\beta_{nk}).$$

Analogously, for the elements in the ith row and kth column of the matrices $(\alpha A)B$, $A(\alpha B)$, we obtain the expressions

$$(\alpha\alpha_{i1})\beta_{1k} + (\alpha\alpha_{i2})\beta_{2k} + \cdots + (\alpha\alpha_{in})\beta_{nk} \, ,$$
$$\alpha_{i1}(\alpha\beta_{1k}) + \alpha_{i2}(\alpha\beta_{2k}) + \cdots + \alpha_{in}(\alpha\beta_{nk}) \, .$$

Since these three expressions are equal, 9 is proved. In the same way it is easy to prove the properties.

10. $(A + B)C = AC + BC$;
11. $C(A + B) = CA + CB$.

From 10 and 11 it is easy to prove the general rule: *To multiply one sum of matrices by a second sum of matrices, multiply each matrix of the first sum by each matrix of the second and add the resulting products.*

We have seen that the commutative law does not hold for matrix products: AB may differ from BA. However, the second arithmetical law—the associativity of multiplication—does hold:*

12. $A(BC) = (AB)\,C$.

To prove this, set

$$AB = M \, , \quad BC = N \, ,$$

and denote the elements of the matrices M, N, respectively, by μ_{ik}, ν_{jl}. By matrix multiplication we have

$$\mu_{ik} = \alpha_{i1}\beta_{1k} + \alpha_{i2}\beta_{2k} + \cdots + \alpha_{in}\beta_{nk} \, ,$$
$$\nu_{jl} = \beta_{j1}\gamma_{1l} + \beta_{j2}\gamma_{2l} + \cdots + \beta_{jp}\gamma_{pl} \, .$$

where α_{ij}, β_{jk}, γ_{kl} are elements of A, B, C. Carrying out the multiplication of M by C, we obtain in the ith row and lth column of $(AB)C$ the sum

$$\mu_{i1}\gamma_{1l} + \mu_{i2}\gamma_{2l} + \cdots + \mu_{ip}\gamma_{pl} = \sum_{k=1}^{p} \sum_{j=1}^{n} \alpha_{ij}\beta_{jk}\gamma_{kl} \, .$$

Analogously, multiplying A by N, we obtain in the ith row and lth column of the product $A(BC)$ the sum

$$\alpha_{i1}\nu_{1l} + \alpha_{i2}\nu_{2l} + \cdots + \alpha_{in}\nu_{nl} = \sum_{j=1}^{n} \sum_{k=1}^{p} \alpha_{ij}\beta_{jk}\gamma_{kl} \, .$$

Since these sums differ only in the order of their terms, 12 is proved.

From 12 it follows that the product of several matrices A, B, C, $\cdots$, D, written in a definite order, does not depend on the arrangement of the parentheses. Therefore it is possible to speak not only of the product of two matrices, but also of the product of a large number of them. For example, it is possible to speak simply of the product $ABCD$ of four matrices, since the same result is given by all five possible ways of computing this product:

* Inasmuch as it is possible to add and multiply matrices only if the numbers of their rows and columns satisfy certain conditions, each of the equalities 10, 11, 12 must be understand to apply only if all the indicated operations are possible.

$$[(AB)C]D, \quad [A(BC)]D, \quad A[(BC)D], \quad A[B(CD)], \quad (AB)(CD).$$

Indeed, each succeeding product is obtained immediately from its predecessor by applying the associative law 12.

Finally, we note that *the determinant of the product of square matrices equals the product of their determinants*:

$$|AB| = |A|\,|B|.$$

This assertion is the well-known theorem on the multiplication of determinants.

6. Powers of Matrices

We have already remarked that not every two matrices can be added or multiplied—for such operations certain relationships among the numbers of rows and columns are necessary. This inconvenience vanishes if we confine ourselves to the consideration only of square matrices of some given order n. The result of adding or multiplying any two such matrices, or multiplying by a scalar, is again a square matrix of order n. In this and the next section all matrices considered will be square and of fixed order n.

A square matrix whose diagonal elements are all equal to 1, and whose other elements are 0, is called the ***identity matrix***. It is denoted by E, where

$$E = \begin{bmatrix} 1 & 0 \cdots 0 \\ 0 & 1 \cdots 0 \\ \vdots & \vdots \quad \vdots \\ 0 & 0 \cdots 1 \end{bmatrix}.$$

By a simple calculation, we obtain for an arbitrary square matrix A the equality

$$EA = AE = A,$$

which expresses a fundamental property of the matrix E. Matrices having the form

$$\begin{bmatrix} \alpha & 0 \cdots 0 \\ 0 & \beta \cdots 0 \\ \vdots & \vdots \quad \vdots \\ 0 & 0 \cdots \gamma \end{bmatrix}$$

are called ***diagonal***.

It is clear that the sum and product of diagonal matrices are again diagonal:

$$\begin{bmatrix} \alpha & & & & \\ & \beta & & & \\ & & \cdot & & \\ & & & \cdot & \\ & & & & \cdot \\ & & & & & \gamma \end{bmatrix} + \begin{bmatrix} \alpha_1 & & & & \\ & \beta_1 & & & \\ & & \cdot & & \\ & & & \cdot & \\ & & & & \cdot \\ & & & & & \gamma_1 \end{bmatrix} = \begin{bmatrix} \alpha+\alpha_1 & & & & \\ & \beta+\beta_1 & & & \\ & & \cdot & & \\ & & & \cdot & \\ & & & & \cdot \\ & & & & & \gamma+\gamma_1 \end{bmatrix},$$

$$\begin{bmatrix} \alpha & & & & \\ & \beta & & & \\ & & \cdot & & \\ & & & \cdot & \\ & & & & \cdot \\ & & & & & \gamma \end{bmatrix} \cdot \begin{bmatrix} \alpha_1 & & & & \\ & \beta_1 & & & \\ & & \cdot & & \\ & & & \cdot & \\ & & & & \cdot \\ & & & & & \gamma_1 \end{bmatrix} = \begin{bmatrix} \alpha\alpha_1 & & & & \\ & \beta\beta_1 & & & \\ & & \cdot & & \\ & & & \cdot & \\ & & & & \cdot \\ & & & & & \gamma\gamma_1 \end{bmatrix}.$$

Consider now an arbitrary square matrix A of order n with elements from a field K. If there exists a matrix X such that

$$XA = AX = E\,,$$

then A is said to be ***invertible***, and X is called the ***inverse*** of A, written $X = A^{-1}$. It is easy to see that an invertible matrix has only one inverse, so the expression A^{-1} is meaningful. To show this, suppose Y is also an inverse of A; then $AY = E$. Multiplying on the left by X, we obtain $XA \cdot Y = X$, from which it follows that $Y = X$. Similarly, multiplying $YA = E$ on the right by X leads to $Y = X$.

Hence, if the matrix A is invertible, then each of the equations

$$XA = E\,, \quad AX = E$$

has one solution, $X = A^{-1}$.

To find the inverse of a matrix, some properties of determinants are useful. Let $A = \|\alpha_{ij}\|$ and let A_{ij} be the cofactor of the element α_{ij} in the determinant of A. Construct from these cofactors the matrix

$$B = \begin{bmatrix} A_{11} & A_{21} & \cdots & A_{n1} \\ A_{12} & A_{22} & \cdots & A_{n2} \\ \vdots & \vdots & & \vdots \\ A_{1n} & A_{2n} & \cdots & A_{nn} \end{bmatrix},$$

placing in its ith row the cofactors from the ith column of the determinant $|A|$. The matrix B is called the ***adjoint*** of A. A fundamental property of this matrix, which we shall prove, is expressed by the equalities

$$AB = BA = |A|E\,. \qquad (1)$$

To slow this we compute the element in the ith row and jth column of product AB. This element is

$$\alpha_{i1}A_{j1} + \alpha_{i2}A_{j2} + \cdots + \alpha_{in}A_{jn}\,,$$

and consequently, by a familiar theorem on the expansion of determinants, equals 0 for $i \neq j$ and $|A|$ for $i = j$. In each case the element is the corresponding element of the matrix $|A| \cdot E$, and this completes the proof.

Since the determinant of the identity matrix is 1, it follows from (1) that

$$|AB| = ||A|\cdot E| = |A|^n |E| = |A|^n .$$

But $|A|\cdot|B| = |AB|$; hence

$$|A|\cdot|B| = |A|^n . \tag{2}$$

We introduce the following definition: a matrix A is ***nonsingular*** if its determinant is not zero. If the determinant of A is zero, then A is called ***singular***.

Let A be a nonsingular matrix and B its adjoint matrix. Since $|A| \neq 0$, both sides of (*2*) may be divided by $|A|$, giving the determinant of the adjoint matrix:

$$|B| = |A|^{n-1} . \tag{3}$$

Multiplying (1) by $|A|^{-1}$, we obtain

$$A\cdot|A|^{-1}B = |A|^{-1}B\cdot A = E . \tag{4}$$

Hence, we have as our result:

$$A^{-1} = |A|^{-1}B . \tag{5}$$

From this it follows, in particular, that all nonsingular matrices are invertible. Moreover, if A is a singular matrix and if $XA = E$, then, passing to determinants $|X|\cdot|A| = 1$ or $|X|\cdot 0 = 1$, a contradiction. This shows that the notions of invertibility and nonsingularity of matrices are equivalent.

Let A be a nonsingular matrix; then $AA^{-1} = E$. Taking determinants of both sides yields

$$|A||A^{-1}| = 1 ,$$

or

$$|A|^{-1} = |A^{-1}| . \tag{6}$$

That is, *the determinant of the inverse of a matrix is the inverse of the determinant of the matrix.* In particular, if A is a nonsingular matrix, then A^{-1} is also nonsingular, and we may construct the matrix $(A^{-1})^{-1}$. By the definition of the inverse of a matrix,

$$A^{-1}(A^{-1})^{-1} = E .$$

Multiplying this relation on the left by A gives

$$(A^{-1})^{-1} = A . \tag{7}$$

Similarly, it is easy to derive an expression for the inverse of a product of matrices. Let A, B, C be nonsingular matrices. Then

$$ABC\cdot C^{-1}B^{-1}A^{-1} = E ,$$

and hence

$$(ABC)^{-1} = C^{-1}B^{-1}A^{-1} . \tag{8}$$

Now let X be an arbitrary square matrix of order n. We define

$$X^0 = E, \quad X^1 = X, \quad X^2 = XX, \quad X^3 = XXX, \cdots.$$

If X is nonsingular, we also write, for m a natural number,

$$X^{-m} = (X^{-1})^m .$$

Using these definitions, and also (7) and (8), the following rules can be obtained without difficulty:

$$X^p X^q = X^{p+q} , \qquad (9)$$

$$(X^p)^q = X^{pq} . \qquad (10)$$

These rules are valid for all integers p, q, positive, negative, and zero.

Two matrices, A and B, are called ***permutable*** if $AB = BA$. Relation (9) shows that *powers of the same matrix always permute with each other.* Indeed, from (9),

$$X^p X^q = X^{p+q} = X^{q+p} = X^q X^p .$$

7. Matrix Polynomials

Consider a polynomial in λ,

$$\varphi(\lambda) = \alpha_0 + \alpha_1\lambda + \cdots + \alpha_n\lambda^n ,$$

where $\alpha_0, \alpha_1, \cdots, \alpha_n$ are elements from a field K. The expression

$$\alpha_0 E + \alpha_1 A + \cdots + \alpha_n A^n ,$$

where A is an arbitrary square matrix with elements from K, is called a ***polynomial in*** A and is denoted by $\varphi(A)$. The expression $\varphi(A)$ is also called the value of $\varphi(\lambda)$ for $\lambda = A$. *The value of a sum of polynomials in λ (for $\lambda = A$) equals the sum of the values of the summands, and the values of a product of polynomials equals the product of the values of the factors.*

To prove these properties, set

$$\varphi(\lambda) = \alpha_0 + \alpha_1\lambda + \cdots + \alpha_n\lambda^n ,$$
$$\psi(\lambda) = \beta_0 + \beta_1\lambda + \cdots + \beta_n\lambda^n .$$

Then

$$f(\lambda) = \varphi(\lambda) + \psi(\lambda) = (\alpha_0 + \beta_0) + (\alpha_1 + \beta_1)\lambda + \cdots + (\alpha_n + \beta_n)\lambda^n ,$$
$$g(\lambda) = \varphi(\lambda)\psi(\lambda) = (\alpha_0\beta_0) + (\alpha_0\beta_1 + \alpha_1\beta_0)\lambda + \cdots + \alpha_n\beta_n\lambda^{2n} .$$

Our assertion in that

$$f(A) = \varphi(A) + \psi(A) ,$$
$$g(A) = \varphi(A)\psi(A) .$$

For the proof it is sufficient to write out $\varphi(A)$, $\psi(A)$, $f(A)$, $g(A)$ and by the rules 1 to 12 of the matrix calculus to carry out the addition and multiplication of $\varphi(A)$ and $\psi(A)$.

As an example let us consider the equality

$$\lambda^2 - 1 = (\lambda - 1)(\lambda + 1) .$$

Evaluating the right and left sides for $\lambda = A$, we obtain the matrix equality

$$A^2 - E = (A - E)(A + E) .$$

Similarly, from the equality

$$\lambda^3 + 1 = (\lambda + 1)(\lambda^2 - \lambda + 1) ,$$

we obtain the relationship

$$A^3 + E = (A + E)(A^2 - A + E) .$$

In general, from each such relation between polynomials in λ one obtains in this way a matrix identity. In particular, since multiplication of polynomials is commutative, we have

$$\varphi(\lambda)\psi(\lambda) = \psi(\lambda)\varphi(\lambda) .$$

Substituting any square matrix A for λ, we obtain

$$\varphi(A)\psi(A) = \psi(A)\varphi(A) .$$

Consequently, *polynomials in one and the same matrix are permutable.*

8. Transposed Matrices

Consider an arbitrary matrix

$$A = \begin{bmatrix} \alpha_{11} & \alpha_{12} & \cdots & \alpha_{1n} \\ \alpha_{21} & \alpha_{22} & \cdots & \alpha_{2n} \\ \vdots & \vdots & & \vdots \\ \alpha_{m1} & \alpha_{m2} & \cdots & \alpha_{mn} \end{bmatrix} .$$

The matrix

$$A' = \begin{bmatrix} \alpha_{11} & \alpha_{21} & \cdots & \alpha_{m1} \\ \alpha_{12} & \alpha_{22} & \cdots & \alpha_{m2} \\ \vdots & \vdots & & \vdots \\ \alpha_{1n} & \alpha_{2n} & \cdots & \alpha_{mn} \end{bmatrix} ,$$

obtained from A by interchanging rows and columns, is called the ***transpose*** of A. In what follows a prime after the symbol for a matrix will always indicate its transpose.

For arbitrary matrices A, B, the following rules of transposition hold:

$$(\alpha A + \beta B)' = \alpha A' + \beta B'$$
$$(AB)' = B'A' ,$$

where α, β are arbitrary scalars.

We prove the second of these as an illustration. The element in the ith row and jth column of the matrix $(AB)'$ is just the element in the jth row and ith column of AB — that is, it equals

$$\alpha_{j1}\beta_{1i} + \alpha_{j2}\beta_{2i} + \cdots + \alpha_{jn}\beta_{ni} ,$$

where α_{ij}, β_{ij} are the elements of the matrices A, B. But this expression is the sum of the products of elements in the ith row of B' with the corresponding elements in the jth column of A'; hence $(AB)' = B'A'$.

If A is a nonsingular square matrix, then from

$$AA^{-1} = E$$

and the rule of transposition it follows that

$$(A^{-1})'A' = E ,$$

or

$$(A^{-1})' = (A')^{-1} .$$

If A is a square matrix and

$$A' = A ,$$

then A is called ***symmetric***; if

$$A' = -A ,$$

then A is called ***skew-symmetric***. Elements symmetric with respect to the main diagonal in a symmetric matrix are equal; in a skew-symmetric matrix they have opposite signs. In particular, all diagonal elements of a skew-symmetric matrix are zero.

From the rule of transposition for a sum it follows that the sum of symmetric matrices is itself symmetric, and the sum of skew-symmetric matrices is skew-symmetric. The product of symmetric matrices may not be symmetric; for example,

$$\begin{bmatrix} 1 & 2 \\ 2 & 3 \end{bmatrix}\begin{bmatrix} 2 & 1 \\ 1 & 1 \end{bmatrix} = \begin{bmatrix} 4 & 3 \\ 7 & 5 \end{bmatrix} .$$

However, if two symmetric matrices A and B permute, then their product is, symmetric, since

$$(AB)' = B'A' = BA = AB .$$

As a consequence, a power of a symmetric matrix is symmetric, and a polynomial in a symmetric matrix is also symmetric,

If

$$AA' = E , \tag{11}$$

that is, if

$$A' = A^{-1} , \tag{12}$$

then A is called an *orthogonal matrix*. It is known from the theory of determinants that the determinant of the transposed matrix equals the determinant of the given matrix. Therefore, comparing the determinants of the matrices on the right and left sides of equality (11), we obtain

$$|A|\cdot|A'| = 1\,, \quad |A|^2 = 1\,, \quad |A| = \pm 1\,.$$

That is, *the determinant of an orthogonal matrix is* ± 1.

Taking the transpose on both sides of (12), we obtain

$$(A^{-1})' = (A')' = A = (A^{-1})^{-1}\,.$$

That is, *the inverse of an orthogonal matrix is again orthogonal.*

The product of orthogonal matrices is orthogonal since from

$$A' = A^{-1}\,, \quad B' = B^{-1}\,,$$

we have

$$(AB)' = B'A' = B^{-1}A^{-1} = (AB)^{-1}\,.$$

We consider one other matrix operation. Let A be an arbitrary matrix whose elements are complex numbers. The matrix obtained by replacing each element in A by its complex conjugate is called the ***complex conjugate*** of A; it is denoted by $\bar{A}$.

The operation of passing to the complex conjugate matrix posseses the following properties:

$$\overline{\alpha A + \beta B} = \bar{\alpha}\bar{A} + \bar{\beta}\bar{B}\,,$$
$$\overline{AB} = \bar{A}\bar{B}\,,$$
$$\overline{A'} = (\bar{A})'\,,$$
$$\overline{A^{-1}} = (\bar{A})^{-1}\,.$$

The proofs for these are very simple and are left to the reader.

The matrices A and $\bar{A}'$ are called ***Hermitian conjugates.*** If $A = \bar{A}'$, then A is called ***Hermitian or Hermitian symmetric.***

A matrix A satisfying the relation

$$A\bar{A}' = E \tag{13}$$

is called ***unitary.***

Just as for orthogonal matrices, it is shown that *the inverse of a unitary matrix is unitary, and the product of unitary matrices is unitary.*

If all the elements of a determinant are replaced by their complex conjugates, then evidently the value of the determinant is replaced by its complex conjugate. Consequently,

$$|\bar{A}| = \overline{|A|}\,.$$

Therefore, taking determinants on both sides of (13), we obtain

$$|A|\cdot\overline{|A'|} = 1\,,$$

or

$$|A|\cdot\overline{|A|} = 1\,.$$

Thus *the square of the modulus of the determinant of a unitary matrix is* 1.

If all the elements of a matrix A are real numbers, then $\bar{A} = A$; consequently, for real matrices the respective notions of symmetric and Hermitian symmetric, unitary and orthogonal, coincide.

● EXAMPLES AND PROBLEMS

1. Let

$$\varphi(\lambda) = -2 - 5\lambda + 3\lambda^2\,, \quad A = \begin{bmatrix} 1 & 2 \\ 3 & 1 \end{bmatrix}.$$

Show that

$$\varphi(A) = \begin{bmatrix} 14 & 2 \\ 3 & 14 \end{bmatrix}.$$

2. Show that the matrix

$$U = \begin{bmatrix} 0 & i \\ i & 0 \end{bmatrix}$$

is unitary. Under what conditions is a diagonal matrix orthogonal? unitary?

3. Find the inverse of the matrix

$$A = \begin{bmatrix} 2 & 2 & 1 \\ 3 & 1 & 5 \\ 3 & 2 & 3 \end{bmatrix}.$$

4. Show that if

$$A = \begin{bmatrix} 1 & 1 & 0 \\ 0 & 1 & 1 \\ 0 & 0 & 1 \end{bmatrix},$$

then

$$A^n = \begin{bmatrix} 1 & n & \frac{1}{2}n(n-1) \\ 0 & 1 & n \\ 0 & 0 & 1 \end{bmatrix}.$$

5. Show that all matrices permutable with

$$A = \begin{bmatrix} 0 & 1 & 0 & 0 \\ 0 & 0 & 1 & 0 \\ 0 & 0 & 0 & 1 \\ 0 & 0 & 0 & 0 \end{bmatrix}$$

have the form

$$B = \begin{bmatrix} \alpha & \beta & \gamma & \delta \\ 0 & \alpha & \beta & \gamma \\ 0 & 0 & \alpha & \beta \\ 0 & 0 & 0 & \alpha \end{bmatrix}.$$

6. If a matrix possesses two of the three properties — *real*, *orthogonal*, *unitary* — then it also posseses the third.
7. Every square matrix may be written as the sum of a symmetric and a skew-symmetric matrix.
8. A matrix I is called ***involutory*** if $I^2 = E$. Show that if a matrix possesses two of the properties — *symmetric*, *orthogonal*, *involutory* — then it also possesses the third.
9. A matrix P is called ***idempotent*** if $P^2 = P$. Show that the matrices

$$\begin{bmatrix} 25 & -20 \\ 30 & -24 \end{bmatrix}, \quad \begin{bmatrix} -26 & -18 & -27 \\ 21 & 15 & 21 \\ 12 & 8 & 13 \end{bmatrix}, \quad \begin{bmatrix} 1 & 0 & 0 \\ 0 & 1 & 0 \\ 0 & 0 & 0 \end{bmatrix}$$

are idempotent.

10. If P is idempotent, then

$$I = 2P - E$$

is involutory; conversely, if I is involutory, then

$$P = \tfrac{1}{2}(I + E)$$

is idempotent.

2. *Characteristic and Minimal Polynomials*

All matrices considered in the present paragraph are assumed to be square and of fixed order n, with elements from an arbitrary fixed field K.

9. Similarity

A matrix A is called ***similar*** to the matrix B if there exists a nonsingular matrix X such that

$$A = X^{-1}BX. \tag{1}$$

In this case, we also say that A is obtained by a transformation of the matrix B by X. Multiplying both sides of (1) on the left by X and on the right by X^{-1}, we obtain

$$B = XAX^{-1} = (X^{-1})^{-1}AX^{-1}.$$

Thus, if A is similar to B, then B is similar to A. Further, if

$$A = X^{-1}BX, \quad B = Y^{-1}CY,$$

then

$$A = (YX)^{-1}C(YX).$$

Consequently, *two matrices similar to a third are similar to each other.* Finally, it is evident that every matrix is similar to itself.

These properties show that the square matrices of given order n with elements from a field K fall naturally into similarity classes. Finding necessary and sufficient conditions for the similarity of matrices is one of the fundamental problems in the theory of matrices. The solution of this problem will be given in Chapter IV. Here we only establish some preliminary properties of similar matrices.

To transform a sum of matrices by a matrix X, one may transform each of the summands by X, as is seen from

$$X^{-1}(A_1 + A_2 + \cdots + A_k)X = X^{-1}A_1X + X^{-1}A_2X + \cdots + X^{-1}A_kX .$$

To transform a product of matrices by a matrix X, one may transform each factor by X, as is seen from

$$X^{-1}A_1XX^{-1}A_2X\cdots X^{-1}A_kX = X^{-1}A_1A_2\cdots A_kX ,$$

since the products XX^{-1} on the left are equal to E and may be omitted.

To transform a power of a matrix, one may transform the first power; that is,

$$X^{-1}A^mX = (X^{-1}AX)^m .$$

For $m \geqq 0$ this formula follows from the preceding one. If $m < 0$, let $k = -m$. Then

$$X^{-1}A^mX = X^{-1}(A^{-1})^kX = (X^{-1}A^{-1}X)^k = (X^{-1}AX)^{-k} = (X^{-1}AX)^m .$$

The transform of a polynomial evaluated for a matrix equals the polynomial evaluated for the transformed matrix; in other words,

$$X^{-1}f(A)X = f(X^{-1}AX) . \tag{2}$$

This assertion follows at once from the preceding ones, since the value of a polynomial at A is obtained from A by means of the operations of raising to a power, multiplication by a scalar, and addition.

These principles of the transformation of expressions often permit significant simplifications in calculations. For example, let

$$A = \begin{bmatrix} 1 & 1 \\ 0 & 1 \end{bmatrix}, \quad X = \begin{bmatrix} 2 & 1 \\ 3 & 2 \end{bmatrix}.$$

By induction it is easily shown that

$$A^n = \begin{bmatrix} 1 & n \\ 0 & 1 \end{bmatrix}.$$

Since

$$X^{-1}AX = \begin{bmatrix} 7 & 4 \\ -9 & -5 \end{bmatrix},$$

by the principle of the transformation of a power we have

$$\begin{bmatrix} 7 & 4 \\ -9 & -5 \end{bmatrix}^n = X^{-1}A^nX = \begin{bmatrix} 1+6n & 4n \\ -9n & 1-6n \end{bmatrix}.$$

10. Characteristic Polynomials

Let A be a square matrix with elements α_{ij}, for $i, j = 1, 2, \cdots, n$. The matrix

$$\lambda E - A = \begin{bmatrix} \lambda-\alpha_{11} & -\alpha_{12} & \cdots & -\alpha_{1n} \\ -\alpha_{21} & \lambda-\alpha_{22} & \cdots & -\alpha_{2n} \\ \vdots & \vdots & & \vdots \\ -\alpha_{n1} & -\alpha_{n2} & \cdots & \lambda-\alpha_{nn} \end{bmatrix},$$

where λ is an indeterminate, is called the ***characteristic matrix*** of A. Its determinant

$$\varphi(\lambda) = |\lambda E - A| \tag{3}$$

is evidently a polynomial in λ; it is called the ***characteristic polynomial*** of A.

In order to find the highest term of this polynomial, we use the fact that the value of the determinant is the sum of products of its elements, one taken from each row and each column, and each summand carrying the proper sign.

Therefore, to obtain the term with the highest degree in λ, it is necessary to take products of elements of the highest degree. In our case there is only one such product — the product $(\lambda-\alpha_{11})(\lambda-\alpha_{22})\cdots(\lambda-\alpha_{nn})$ of the diagonal elements. All remaining products of the determinant have degree not higher than $n-2$, since if one of the factors of such a product is $-\alpha_{ij}$, where $i \neq j$, then this product does not contain the factors $\lambda-\alpha_{ii}$, $\lambda-\alpha_{jj}$. Thus $\varphi(\lambda) = (\lambda-\alpha_{11})\cdots(\lambda-\alpha_{nn})$ + terms of degree not higher than $n-2$, or

$$\varphi(\lambda) = \lambda^n - (\alpha_{11} + \cdots + \alpha_{nn})\lambda^{n-1} + \cdots \tag{4}$$

The sum of the diagonal elements of a matrix is called its ***trace.*** Formula (4) shows that the *degree of the characteristic polynomial is the order of its matrix; the leading coefficient is* 1, *and the coefficient of* λ^{n-1} *is the negative of the trace of the matrix.* Setting $\lambda = 0$ in (3), we obtain

$$\varphi(0) = |-A| = (-1)^n |A|.$$

But $\varphi(0)$ is the constant term of the characteristic polynomial. Therefore the constant term of the characteristic polynomial of a matrix A is the determinant of this matrix multiplied by $(-1)^n$, where n is the order of A.

The following theorem states one of the most important properties of the characteristic polynomial.

THEOREM 1. *The characteristic polynomials of similar matrices are identical.*

To show this, suppose the matrices A and B are similar:

$$A = X^{-1}BX.$$

Then the characteristic polynomial of A is

$$|\lambda E - A| = |\lambda E - X^{-1}BX| = |X^{-1}(\lambda E - B)X| = |X^{-1}|\,|\lambda E - B|\,|X|\,.$$

The product of the determinants $|X^{-1}|$, $|X|$ is 1. Therefore

$$|\lambda E - A| = |\lambda E - B|$$

which was to be proved.

From this theorem it follows in particular that *similar matrices have the same trace and determinant*, since the trace and determinant, with proper signs, appear as coefficients in the characteristic polynomial.

The equality of the characteristic polynomials is a necessary, but in general not a sufficient, condition for the similarity of matrices. For example, the characteristic polynomials of the matrices

$$E = \begin{bmatrix} 1 & 0 \\ 0 & 1 \end{bmatrix}, \quad A = \begin{bmatrix} 1 & 1 \\ 0 & 1 \end{bmatrix}$$

are equal. However, A cannot be similar to E, since for any (invertible) matrix X,

$$X^{-1}EX = X^{-1}X = E\,.$$

The zeros of the characteristic polynomial of a matrix are called ***characteristic numbers*** or ***proper values***. Multiple zeros of the characteristic polynomial are called multiple proper values of the matrix. It is known that the sum of all the real and complex zeros of a polynomial of degree n with leading coefficient 1 is the negative of the coefficient of the term with degree $n-1$. Formula (4) therefore shows that over the field of complex numbers the trace of a matrix is the sum of all its proper values.

We remark that the trace of a sum of matrices is the sum of the traces of the summands, and the trace of the product of a scalar and a matrix is the product of the scalar and the trace of the matrix. Both these assertions may be combined into one formula:

$$\operatorname{tr}(\alpha A + \beta B) = \alpha \operatorname{tr} A + \beta \operatorname{tr} B\,.$$

To prove this it is sufficient to write out the corresponding matrices and compute their traces.

11. The Cayley-Hamilton Theorem

In Section 7 a matrix $\varphi(A)$ was constructed, corresponding to an arbitrary polynomial $\varphi(\lambda)$, and was called the value of the polynomial for $\lambda = A$. If $\varphi(A) = 0$, A is said to be a ***zero*** of $\varphi(\lambda)$.

THE CAYLEY-HAMILTON THEOREM. *Every matrix is a zero of its characteristic polynomial.*

Let A be an arbitrary matrix. Denote by B the adjoint of the characteristic matrix $\lambda E - A$ (compare Section 6). We denote the elements of the matrix B by β_{ij}, for $i, j = 1, 2, \cdots, n$. These elements are cofactors of the determinant $|\lambda E - A|$ and therefore represent polynomials in λ, of degree not exceeding $n-1$. Let

$$\beta_{ij} = \beta_{ij}^{(0)} + \beta_{ij}^{(1)}\lambda + \cdots + \beta_{ij}^{(n-1)}\lambda^{n-1}.$$

We construct the auxiliary matrices

$$\beta^{(k)} = \begin{bmatrix} \beta_{11}^{(k)} & \beta_{12}^{(k)} & \cdots & \beta_{1n}^{(k)} \\ \beta_{21}^{(k)} & \beta_{22}^{(k)} & \cdots & \beta_{2n}^{(k)} \\ \vdots & \vdots & & \vdots \\ \beta_{n1}^{(k)} & \beta_{n2}^{(k)} & \cdots & \beta_{nn}^{(k)} \end{bmatrix} \qquad (k = 0, 1, \cdots, n-1).$$

The matrix B may evidently be represented in the form

$$B = B^{(0)} + B^{(1)}\lambda + \cdots + B^{(n-1)}\lambda^{n-1},$$

and by the fundamental property of the adjoint matrix,

$$B(\lambda E - A) = |\lambda E - A|\,E. \tag{5}$$

Here $|\lambda E - A|$ is the characteristic polynomial of A, which we denote by $\varphi(\lambda)$. Let

$$\varphi(\lambda) = \alpha_0 + \alpha_1\lambda + \cdots + \alpha_{n-1}\lambda^{n-1} + \lambda^n.$$

Equality (5) may be rewritten in more detail:

$$(B^{(0)} + B^{(1)}\lambda + \cdots + B^{(n-1)}\lambda^{n-1})(\lambda E - A) = (\alpha_0 + \alpha_1\lambda + \cdots + \alpha_{n-1}\lambda^{n-1} + \lambda^n)E.$$

Removing parentheses and comparing coefficients of like powers of λ, we obtain

$$\begin{aligned} -B^{(0)}A &= \alpha_0 E, \\ -B^{(1)}A + B^{(0)} &= \alpha_1 E, \\ -B^{(2)}A + B^{(1)} &= \alpha_2 E, \\ &\vdots \\ -B^{(n-1)}A + B^{(n-2)} &= \alpha_{n-1}E, \\ B^{(n-1)} &= E. \end{aligned}$$

Multiplying these equations (on the right), respectively, by $E, A, \cdots, A^n$ and adding, the terms on the left cancel in pairs, and we obtain

$$O = \alpha_0 E + \alpha_1 A + \alpha_2 A^2 + \cdots + A^n.$$

That is, $\varphi(A) = 0$, which was to be proved.

12. Minimal Polynomials

Consider all nonzero polynomials $f(\lambda)$ which have the matrix A as a zero. Such polynomials exist—for example, the characteristic polynomial of the matrix A. The nonzero polynomial of least degree and leading coefficient 1 which has A as a zero is called the ***minimal polynomial*** of the matrix A.

Every matrix A has a unique minimal polynomial. If there were two, say $\psi_1(\lambda)$ and $\psi_2(\lambda)$, then the difference $\psi_1(\lambda) - \psi_2(\lambda)$ would be a nonzero polymial of lower degree that would again have A as a zero. After dividing this difference by its leading coefficient, we would obtain a polynomial with leading coefficient 1, with A as a zero and with degree less than the degree of the minimal polynomials $\psi_1(\lambda)$ and $\psi_2(\lambda)$, which contradicts the definition of minimal polynomial.

Every polynomial $f(\lambda)$ with the matrix A as a zero is divisible without remainder by the minimal polynomial $\psi(\lambda)$ of this matrix.

Indeed, suppose on the contrary that $f(A) = 0$ but that $f(\lambda)$ is not divisible by $\psi(\lambda)$. Denoting by $q(\lambda)$ the quotient and by $r(\lambda)$ the remainder, where $r(\lambda) \neq 0$, we have

$$f(\lambda) = \psi(\lambda)q(\lambda) + r(\lambda) .$$

Substituting $\lambda = A$, and using $\psi(A) = f(A) = 0$, we obtain $r(A) = 0$. But the degree of $r(\lambda)$ is less than the degree of $\psi(\lambda)$. Then $r(\lambda)$ is a nonzero polymial with A as a zero and with degree less than the degree of the minimal polynomial $\psi(\lambda)$, a contradiction. This proves our assertion. In particular, *the minimal polynomial of a matrix is a divisor of the characteristic polynomial of the matrix.*

We know that similar matrices have identical characteristic polynomials. The minimal polynomial possesses the same property: *similar matrices have identical minimal polynomials.* In fact, let A be similar to B: $A = X^{-1}BX$. If $f(\lambda)$ is any polynomial having B as a zero, then, according to Section I.9,

$$f(A) = f(X^{-1}BX) = X^{-1}f(B)X = 0 .$$

Thus the set of polynomials having one of two similar matrices as a zero coincides with the set of polynomials having the other as a zero. Therefore, the polynomial belonging to this set, that has least degree with leading coefficient 1 will be the minimal polynomial for both matrices.

The equality of the minimal polynomials is yet another necessary condition for the similarity of two matrices. However, this condition also is not sufficient. We consider, as an example, the matrices

$$A = \begin{bmatrix} 2 & 0 & 0 \\ 0 & 3 & 0 \\ 0 & 0 & 3 \end{bmatrix}, \quad B = \begin{bmatrix} 2 & 0 & 0 \\ 0 & 2 & 3 \\ 0 & 0 & 3 \end{bmatrix}.$$

Their characteristic polynomials are respectively

$$(\lambda - 2)(\lambda - 3)^2 , \quad (\lambda - 2)^2(\lambda - 3) .$$

Since these polynomials are different, A and B are not similar. But the minimal polynomial of A must be a divisor of its characteristic polynomial—that is, the minimal polynomial of A must coincide with one of the following polynomials: $(\lambda - 2)$, $(\lambda - 3)$, $(\lambda - 3)^2$, $(\lambda - 2)(\lambda - 3)$. Substituting A for λ, we find that 0 is first obtained for the polynomial $(\lambda - 2)(\lambda - 3)$. Consequently, this polynomial is the minimal polynomial for A. In exactly the same way we find that the minimal polynomial of the matrix B is also the polynomial $(\lambda - 2)(\lambda - 3)$. Thus the minimal polynomials of the matrices A and B are equal, but A and B are not similar.

● EXAMPLES AND PROBLEMS

1. Compute the characteristic polynomials and the proper values of the matrices

$$A = \begin{bmatrix} 2 & 3 \\ 1 & 4 \end{bmatrix}, \quad B = \begin{bmatrix} \cos\alpha & \sin\alpha \\ -\sin\alpha & \cos\alpha \end{bmatrix}, \quad C = \begin{bmatrix} 1 & 2 & 3 \\ 2 & 1 & 3 \\ 3 & 3 & 6 \end{bmatrix}.$$

2. Find the minimal polynomials of the matrices

$$\begin{bmatrix} 3 & 1 \\ 0 & 3 \end{bmatrix}, \quad \begin{bmatrix} 3 & 1 & 0 \\ 0 & 3 & 0 \\ 0 & 0 & 3 \end{bmatrix}, \quad \begin{bmatrix} 2 & 0 & 0 \\ 0 & 3 & 1 \\ 0 & 0 & 3 \end{bmatrix}, \quad \begin{bmatrix} 2 & 0 & 0 & 0 \\ 0 & 2 & 0 & 0 \\ 0 & 0 & 3 & 0 \\ 0 & 0 & 3 & 0 \end{bmatrix}.$$

3. Show that a matrix and its transpose have identical characteristic polynomials.
4. Show that the proper values of a diagonal matrix are its diagonal elements.
5. Prove that

$$\operatorname{tr}(AB) = \operatorname{tr}(BA).$$

6. If from some square matrix of order n the rows and columns passing through some m diagonal elements are eliminated, then the determinant of the remaining matrix of order $n - m$ is called a ***principal minor*** of degree $n - m$. Show that the coefficient of λ^m in the characteristic polynomial of a matrix A is the sum of all its principal minors of degree $n - m$ multiplied by $(-1)^{n-m}$.
7. Show that AB and BA have identical characteristic polynomials.
8. If $\zeta_1, \cdots, \zeta_n$ are the proper values of a matrix A, then the proper values of the matrix $f(A)$, where $f(\lambda)$ is a polynomial, are $f(\zeta_1), \cdots, f(\zeta_n)$.

3. *Block Matrices*

Break a matrix A into parts by means of a system of horizontal and vertical lines. These parts are smaller matrices, and may themselves be considered as elements of the matrix A. They are called ***blocks*** of the matrix A.* A matrix divided into blocks is called a ***block matrix***. It is clear that a single matrix may be divided into blocks in different ways, as for example

* The term ***cells*** is sometimes used.

$$\begin{bmatrix} 1 & 8 & 7 & 6 \\ 3 & 5 & 0 & 2 \\ -1 & 4 & 9 & 3 \end{bmatrix} = \left[\begin{array}{cc:cc} 1 & 8 & 7 & 6 \\ 3 & 5 & 0 & 2 \\ \hdashline -1 & 4 & 9 & 3 \end{array}\right] = \left[\begin{array}{c:cc:c} 1 & 8 & 7 & 6 \\ \hdashline 3 & 5 & 0 & 2 \\ \hdashline -1 & 4 & 9 & 3 \end{array}\right].$$

The convenience of the subdivision into blocks lies in the fact that the fundamental operations with block matrices can be carried out formally, just as with ordinary matrices.

13. Operations with Block Matrices

Let a matrix A be divided in some way into blocks:*

$$A = \begin{bmatrix} A_{11} & A_{12} & \cdots & A_{1n} \\ \vdots & \vdots & & \vdots \\ A_{m1} & A_{m2} & \cdots & A_{mn} \end{bmatrix}.$$

Multiplying all the blocks by a scalar α multiplies all the elements of A by α. Consequently,

$$\alpha A = \begin{bmatrix} \alpha A_{11} & \alpha A_{12} & \cdots & \alpha A_{1n} \\ \vdots & \vdots & & \vdots \\ \alpha A_{m1} & \alpha A_{m2} & \cdots & \alpha A_{mn} \end{bmatrix}.$$

Let B be any matrix divided into the same number of blocks as A:

$$B = \begin{bmatrix} B_{11} & B_{12} & \cdots & B_{1n} \\ \vdots & \vdots & & \vdots \\ B_{m1} & B_{m2} & \cdots & B_{mn} \end{bmatrix}.$$

Let us further suppose that corresponding blocks of A and B have respectively the same number of rows and columns.

In order to add the matrices A and B, it is necessary, according to the definition, to add their corresponding elements. However, the same thing happens if we add the corresponding blocks of these matrices. Therefore,

$$A + B = \begin{bmatrix} A_{11} + B_{11} & A_{12} + B_{12} & \cdots & A_{1n} + B_{1n} \\ \vdots & \vdots & & \vdots \\ A_{m1} + B_{m1} & A_{m2} + B_{m2} & \cdots & A_{mn} + B_{mn} \end{bmatrix}.$$

The situation is somewhat less evident with multiplication. Consider the matrices

* The reader should note that this use of the symbols A_{ij} is not to be confused with the use of A_{ij} as a cofactor. The context will always indicate the correct meaning (*Ed.*).

$$U = \begin{bmatrix} u_{11} & \cdots & u_{1n} \\ \vdots & & \vdots \\ u_{m1} & \cdots & u_{mn} \end{bmatrix}, \quad V = \begin{bmatrix} v_{11} & \cdots & v_{1p} \\ \vdots & & \vdots \\ v_{n1} & \cdots & v_{np} \end{bmatrix},$$

divided into blocks u_{ij}, v_{jk} in such a way that the number of columns of u_{ij} equals the number of rows of v_{jk}, where $i = 1, \cdots, m$, $j = 1, \cdots, n$, $k = 1, \cdots, p$. Under these conditions the expression

$$w_{ik} = u_{i1}v_{1k} + u_{i2}v_{2k} + \cdots + u_{in}v_{nk}$$

has a meaning. It is easy to show that

$$UV = \begin{bmatrix} w_{11} & \cdots & w_{1p} \\ \vdots & & \vdots \\ w_{m1} & \cdots & w_{mp} \end{bmatrix}. \tag{1}$$

That is, matrices which are properly divided into blocks may be multiplied in the usual way: *a block of the product is the sum of the products of the blocks of a row of U with the corresponding blocks of a column of V.*

* * *

We* first prove this rule in the following particular case:

$$[A \quad B]\begin{bmatrix} C \\ D \end{bmatrix} = AC + BD\,. \tag{2}$$

Let α_{ij}, β_{ik}, γ_{jl}, δ_{kl} be the elements respectively of the matrices A, B, C, D, where $i = 1, \cdots, m$; $j = 1, \cdots, n$; $k = 1, \cdots, s$; $l = 1, \cdots, t$. Carrying out the operation indicated on the left side of equation (2), we obtain, for the element in the ith row and lth column,

$$\alpha_{i1}\gamma_{1l} + \cdots + \alpha_{in}\gamma_{nl} + \beta_{i1}\delta_{1l} + \cdots + \beta_{is}\delta_{sl}\,.$$

Likewise, computing the corresponding element on the right side, we obtain the same expression, and equation (2) is proved.

Using (2), it is now easy to prove the more general formula

$$[A_1 A_2 \cdots A_n]\begin{bmatrix} B_1 \\ B_2 \\ \vdots \\ B_n \end{bmatrix} = A_1B_1 + A_2B_2 + \cdots + A_nB_n\,, \tag{3}$$

where the A_i, B_i are separate blocks. For $n = 2$ this formula coincides with (2). We proceed by induction. Suppose, for values less than the given n, that (3) has already been proved, and let

* The material set off by triple asterisks—occurring first here to p. 24—is material that appears in fine print in the Russian original and may be omitted on a first reading (*Ed*).

$$C = [A_2 \cdots A_n]\,, \quad D = \begin{bmatrix} B_2 \\ \vdots \\ B_n \end{bmatrix}.$$

Then from (2) we have

$$[A_1 A_2 \cdots A_n] \begin{bmatrix} B_1 \\ B_2 \\ \vdots \\ B_n \end{bmatrix} = [A_1 C] \begin{bmatrix} B_1 \\ D \end{bmatrix} = A_1 B_1 + CD$$

$$= A_1 B_1 + A_2 B_2 + \cdots + A_n B_n \,.$$

In a similar way one obtains the formulas

$$A[B_1 B_2 \cdots B_n] = [AB_1 AB_2 \cdots AB_n]\,, \tag{4}$$

$$\begin{bmatrix} A_1 \\ A_2 \\ \vdots \\ A_n \end{bmatrix} B = \begin{bmatrix} A_1 B \\ A_2 B \\ \vdots \\ A_n B \end{bmatrix}. \tag{5}$$

In order to derive the general formula (1) from the special cases (3), (4), (5), denote the rows of the block matrix U by $U_1, \cdots, U_m$ and the columns of the block matrix V by $V_1, \cdots, V_p$. By (5),

$$UV = \begin{bmatrix} U_1 \\ \vdots \\ U_m \end{bmatrix} v = \begin{bmatrix} U_1 V \\ \vdots \\ U_m V \end{bmatrix}.$$

Replacing V by $[v_1 \cdots v_p]$ and using (4), we obtain

$$UV = \begin{bmatrix} U_1 V_1 & \cdots & U_1 V_p \\ \vdots & & \vdots \\ U_m V_1 & \cdots & U_m V_p \end{bmatrix}. \tag{6}$$

However, from (3),

$$U_i V_k = [U_{i1} \cdots U_{in}] \begin{bmatrix} V_{1k} \\ \vdots \\ V_{nk} \end{bmatrix} = U_{i1} V_{1k} + U_{i2} V_{2k} + \cdots + U_{in} V_{nk} = W_{ik} \,.$$

Substituting this in (6), we obtain (1).

* * *

It is often necessary to divide square matrices into blocks so that the diagonal blocks are also square. It is easy to see that if two square matrices are divided into blocks in such a way that their diagonal blocks are square and corresponding diagonal blocks have the same orders, then this division satisfies the conditions for addition and multiplication of block matrices.

14. Block-diagonal Matrices

A block matrix of the form

$$A = \begin{bmatrix} A_1 & 0 & \cdots & 0 \\ 0 & A_2 & \cdots & 0 \\ \vdots & \vdots & \ddots & \vdots \\ 0 & 0 & \cdots & A_s \end{bmatrix},$$

where $A_1, \cdots, A_s$ are square matrices and each zero is a zero-matrix of the proper dimensions, is called a ***block-diagonal matrix***. One also says that A is ***decomposed*** into parts $A_1, \cdots, A_s$, or that A is the ***direct sum of*** matrices $A_1, \cdots, A_s$; symbolically one writes

$$A = A_1 \dotplus A_2 \dotplus \cdots \dotplus A_s .$$

Operations with decomposable matrices reduce to operations with their diagonal blocks. From this, in turn, it follows that if $f(\lambda)$ is a polynomial and A is a block diagonal matrix with diagonal blocks $A_1, \cdots, A_s$, then

$$f(A) = \begin{bmatrix} f(A_1) & & & \\ & f(A_2) & & \\ & & \ddots & \\ & & & f(A_s) \end{bmatrix}. \tag{7}$$

We give further rules for finding the characteristic and minimal polynomials of decomposable matrices.

The characteristic polynomial of a decomposable matrix is the product of the characteristic polynomials of its diagonal blocks.

In fact, if A decomposes into blocks $A_1, \cdots, A_s$, then its characteristic matrix, as is easy to see, has the form

$$\lambda E - A = \begin{bmatrix} \lambda E_1 - A_1 & & & \\ & \lambda E_2 - A_2 & & \\ & & \ddots & \\ & & & \lambda E_s - A_s \end{bmatrix}$$

where $E_1, \cdots, E_s$ are identity matrices of suitable orders. From the theory of determinants it is known that the determinant of a decomposable matrix is the product of the determinants of its diagonal blocks. Consequently

$$|\lambda E - A| = |\lambda E_1 - A_1|\,|\lambda E_2 - A_2| \cdots |\lambda E_s - A_s| ,$$

which was to be proved.

The minimal polynomial of a decomposable matrix is the least common mul-

tiple of the minimal polynomials of its diagonal blocks.

Let the matrix A decompose into parts $A_1, \cdots, A_s$. Denote by $\psi_1(\lambda), \cdots, \psi_s(\lambda)$, respectively, their minimal polynomials. Consider an arbitrary polynomial $f(\lambda)$. If $f(A) = 0$, then by (7) it follows that $f(A_1) = \cdots = f(A_s) = 0$. But any polynomial which has A_i as a zero must be divisible by the minimal polynomial $\psi_i(\lambda)$ of A_i. Consequently $f(\lambda)$ is a common multiple of the polynomials $\psi_1(\lambda), \cdots, \psi_s(\lambda)$. Conversely, if some polynomial $f(\lambda)$ is a common multiple of $\psi_1(\lambda), \cdots, \psi_s(\lambda)$, then evidently $f(A) = 0$. Thus to obtain the minimal polynomial of the matrix A, it is necessary to take a common multiple of $\psi_1(\lambda), \cdots, \psi_s(\lambda)$ of least degree—that is, their least common multiple.

15. Semi-decomposable Matrices

A block matrix A is called ***semidecomposable*** or ***block-triangular*** if all its diagonal elements are square and the blocks on one side of the main diagonal are filled with zeros. In what follows we will always suppose that these zero blocks lie above the main diagonal. Thus, a semidecomposable block matrix has the form

$$A = \begin{bmatrix} A_{11} & & & \\ A_{21} & A_{22} & & \\ \cdot & \cdot & \cdot & \cdot \\ A_{s1} & A_{s2} & \cdots & A_{ss} \end{bmatrix}, \tag{8}$$

where $A_{11}, \cdots, A_{ss}$ are square and all blocks above them are filled with zeros.

Let B be a second semidecomposable matrix whose diagonal blocks have the same orders as the corresponding blocks of the matrix A. By the fundamental rules of operation with block matrices, we have

$$\begin{bmatrix} A_{11} & & & \\ A_{21} & A_{22} & & \\ \cdot & \cdot & \cdot & \cdot \\ A_{s1} & A_{s2} & \cdots & A_{ss} \end{bmatrix} + \begin{bmatrix} B_{11} & & & \\ B_{21} & B_{22} & & \\ \cdot & \cdot & \cdot & \cdot \\ B_{s1} & B_{s2} & \cdots & B_{ss} \end{bmatrix} = \begin{bmatrix} A_{11}+B_{11} & & & \\ A_{21}+B_{21} & A_{22}+B_{22} & & \\ \cdot & \cdot & \cdot & \cdot \\ A_{s1}+B_{s1} & A_{s2}+B_{s2} & \cdots & A_{ss}+B_{ss} \end{bmatrix},$$

$$\begin{bmatrix} A_{11} & & & \\ A_{21} & A_{22} & & \\ \cdot & \cdot & \cdot & \cdot \\ A_{s1} & A_{s2} & \cdots & A_{ss} \end{bmatrix} \begin{bmatrix} B_{11} & & & \\ B_{21} & B_{22} & & \\ \cdot & \cdot & \cdot & \cdot \\ B_{s1} & B_{s2} & \cdots & B_{ss} \end{bmatrix} = \begin{bmatrix} A_{11}B_{11} & & & \\ C_{21} & A_{22}B_{22} & & \\ \cdot & \cdot & \cdot & \cdot \\ C_{s1} & C_{s2} & \cdots & A_{ss}B_{ss} \end{bmatrix},$$

where

$$C_{ij} = A_{ij}B_{jj} + A_{i,j+1}B_{j+1,j} + \cdots + A_{ii}B_{ij}\,, \qquad i > j\,.$$

Consequently, *the sum and product of semidecomposable matrices are semidecomposable matrices, whose diagonal blocks are the sums and products of the corresponding blocks of the given matrices.* In particular, if $f(\lambda)$ is a polynomial in λ and A is a semidecomposable matrix of the form (8), then

$$f(A) = \begin{bmatrix} f(A_{11}) & & & \\ D_{21} & f(A_{22}) & & \\ \cdots & \cdots & \cdots & \cdots \\ D_{s1} & D_{s2} & \cdots & f(A_{ss}) \end{bmatrix}. \tag{9}$$

(The blocks D_{ij} have a more complicated structure.) From the theory of determinants it is known that the determinant of a semidecomposable matrix is the product of the determinants of its diagonal blocks.

From this it easily follows that *the characteristic polynomial of a semi-decomposable matrix is the product of the characteristic polynomials of the diagonal blocks of this matrix.*

If the semidecomposable matrix A is constructed from blocks of order 1, then A is also said to have ***triangular*** form, or is called simply a ***triangular matrix***. The proper values of a triangular matrix are its diagonal elements. From (9) it follows also that if $\zeta_1, \cdots, \zeta_n$ are the proper values of a triangular matrix, then $f(\zeta_1), \cdots, f(\zeta_n)$ are the proper values of the matrix $f(A)$.*

● EXAMPLES AND PROBLEMS

1. Compute A^2, ABA, B^3 if

$$A = \begin{bmatrix} \alpha & 1 & 0 & 0 \\ 0 & \alpha & 0 & 0 \\ 0 & 0 & \beta & 1 \\ 0 & 0 & 1 & \beta \end{bmatrix}, \quad B = \begin{bmatrix} \alpha & 0 & 0 & 0 \\ 1 & \alpha & 0 & 0 \\ 0 & 0 & \beta & 0 \\ 0 & 0 & 1 & \beta \end{bmatrix}.$$

2. Verify the following for finding the transpose of a block matrix: if

$$A = \begin{bmatrix} A_{11} & A_{12} & \cdots & A_{1n} \\ A_{21} & A_{22} & \cdots & A_{2n} \\ \vdots & \vdots & & \vdots \\ A_{n1} & A_{n2} & \cdots & A_{nn} \end{bmatrix},$$

then

$$A' = \begin{bmatrix} A'_{11} & A'_{21} & \cdots & A'_{n1} \\ A'_{12} & A'_{22} & \cdots & A'_{n2} \\ \vdots & \vdots & & \vdots \\ A'_{1n} & A'_{2n} & \cdots & A'_{nn} \end{bmatrix}.$$

3. A matrix is called ***nilpotent*** if some power of it is zero. Show that a semidecomposable matrix is nilpotent if and only if its diagonal blocks are nilpotent.

---

* The last assertion holds not only for triangular matrices, but also for arbitrary square matrices (compare Section 63).

4. Using the Cayley-Hamilton theorem, show that, over the field of complex numbers, if all the proper values of a matrix are zero, then the matrix is nilpotent.
5. Show that if the order of the summands in a *direct* sum of matrices is changed, then the new sum is *similar* to the old.

2 LINEAR SPACES

1. *Definitions and Simplest Properties*

16. Axioms

An arbitrary nonempty set $\mathfrak{L}$ is called a ***linear space*** over a field K if it has the following properties.

1) There is a rule that assigns to each pair of elements a, b in $\mathfrak{L}$ an element called the ***sum*** of a and b, denoted by $a + b$.

2) There is a rule that assigns to each pair consisting of a scalar α in K and an element a in $\mathfrak{L}$ an element in $\mathfrak{L}$ called the ***product*** of α and a and denoted by αa.

3) The operations of addition and multiplication by scalars satisfy the following requirements.

a) Addition is commutative:

$$a + b = b + a .$$

b) Addition is associative:

$$(a + b) + c = a + (b + c) .$$

c) Subtraction is possible—that is, for every two elements a, b in $\mathfrak{L}$ there exists an element x such that

$$a + x = b .$$

d) Multiplication by scalars is associative:

$$\alpha(\beta a) = (\alpha\beta)a .$$

e) Multiplication by scalars is distributive over addition in $\mathfrak{L}$:

$$\alpha(a + b) = \alpha a + \alpha b .$$

f) Multiplication by scalars is distributive over addition of scalars:

$$(\alpha + \beta)a = \alpha a + \beta a .$$

g) Multiplication by scalars satisfies the condition

$$1 \cdot a = a ,$$

where 1 is the unit element of K.

Besides *linear space* the term ***vector space*** is also used. The elements of a linear space are called ***vectors***, and in what follows will be denoted by small Latin letters $a, b, x, y, \cdots$. Linear spaces—that is, sets of vectors satisfying the above conditions—will be denoted by large German letters $\mathfrak{L}, \mathfrak{M}, \mathfrak{N}, \mathfrak{A}$.

If K is the field of complex numbers, then the linear space is called a ***complex linear space***; if K is the field of real numbers, a ***real linear space***. The most important examples of linear spaces will be examined later (Section 19), but for now we deduce a series of the simplest consequences of axioms (a) to (g).

First, it follows from (a) and (b) that the sum of several vectors does not depend upon their order, nor upon the way in which they are grouped. Further consequences are connected with the properties of what is called the zero vector.

17. The Zero Vector and Additive Inverses

Take an arbitrary linear space $\mathfrak{L}$ and choose in it some vector a. By axiom (c) there is a vector x in $\mathfrak{L}$ such that

$$a + x = a .$$

We show that x satisfies the relation

$$b + x = b , \tag{1}$$

for arbitrary b in $\mathfrak{L}$. By axiom (c) there is a vector y in $\mathfrak{L}$ such that

$$a + y = b ,$$

Using this we have

$$\begin{aligned} b + x &= (a + y) + x \\ &= (y + a) + x = y + (a + x) = y + a = b . \end{aligned}$$

Further, no other vector x' in $\mathfrak{L}$ has property (1). Suppose that for arbitrary b

$$b + x' = b ,$$

then setting $b = x$, we obtain

$$x + x' = x .$$

But if we replace b by x' in (1), we obtain

$$x' + x = x' ,$$

hence $x = x'$. Thus, *there exists a unique vector x with the property that for arbitrary b in $\mathfrak{L}$,*

$$b + x = b .$$

This vector is called the ***zero vector*** and is denoted by θ.

Consider the equation

$$a + y = \theta , \tag{2}$$

where a is any vector in $\mathfrak{L}$. By axiom (c) there is in $\mathfrak{L}$ at least one vector y that satisfies this equation. We show that there is only one such vector. Let

$$a + y' = \theta .$$

Adding y to both sides, we obtain

$$y + a + y' = y + \theta ; \quad y' = y .$$

The vector y satisfying equation (2) is called the ***additive inverse*** of a and is denoted by $-a$. Thus, by definition,

$$a + (-a) = \theta . \tag{3}$$

Substituting $-a$ for a, we obtain

$$-a + (-(-a)) = \theta .$$

Adding a to both sides and using (3), we have

$$-(-a) = a .$$

Similarly, we show that

$$-(a + b) = (-a) + (-b) .$$

Expressions of the form $(-a) + b + (-c)$ are commonly written $-a + b - c$.

Consider now the equation

$$a + x = b , \tag{4}$$

where a, b are vectors in $\mathfrak{L}$. Adding $-a$ to both sides, we obtain

$$x = (-a) + b = b + (-a) = b - a .$$

Thus equation (4) has a unique solution.

18. Linear Combinations

Up to now we have used only axioms (a), (b), and (c). If we take into consideration also the remaining axioms, it is easy to prove the following equalities:

$$0 \cdot a = \theta ,$$

$$ma = a + a + \cdots + a$$

(for m summands, where m is a positive integer),

$$(-\alpha)a = -(\alpha a) ,$$

$$\alpha\theta = \theta .$$

The first follows from

$$a = (1 + 0)a = 1 \cdot a + 0 \cdot a = a + 0 \cdot a ,$$

the second from

$$ma = (1 + 1 + \cdots + 1)a = a + a + \cdots + a .$$

Since

$$\alpha a + (-\alpha)a = (\alpha - \alpha)a = \theta ,$$

then $(-\alpha)a = -(\alpha a)$, the third equality. Finally, the fourth is a consequence of

$$\alpha\theta + \alpha a = \alpha(\theta + a) = \alpha a .$$

We remark also that *it follows from* $\alpha a = \theta$ *that either* $\alpha = 0$ *or* $a = \theta$. Indeed, if $\alpha \neq 0$, then, multiplying $\alpha a = \theta$ by α^{-1}, we obtain $a = \theta$.

An expression of the form

$$\alpha_1 a_1 + \alpha_2 a_2 + \cdots + \alpha_s a_s ,$$

is called a ***linear combination*** of the vectors $a_1, \cdots, a_s$. Our arguments show that linear combinations may be added, subtracted, multiplied by a scalar, and rearranged according to the usual rules.

19. Examples of Linear Spaces

The most common example of a linear space is the set of directed line segments emanating from some fixed point $\mathcal{O}$. To multiply a segment by a positive real number α means to multiply its length by α, without changing its direction. If α is negative, then to multiply a segment by α means to multiply its length by $|\alpha|$ and reverse its direction. To add two segments means to take the diagonal through $\mathcal{O}$ of the parallelogram constructed on them. The zero vector is the segment beginning and ending at the point $\mathcal{O}$. Inasmuch as the operation of multiplying a segment by a number is defined only for real numbers, the base field K is here the field of real numbers, and the space of directed segments is a *real* linear space. This space we will call the "ordinary space of line segment" and we denote it by $\mathfrak{R}$.

A more general example, and one which is fundamental in the whole theory of linear spaces, is the space of row matrices. Let us consider the set of all finite sequences of the form $[\alpha_1, \alpha_2, \cdots, \alpha_n]$, where $\alpha_1, \cdots, \alpha_n$ are elements of a field K, and n is a given whole number. We will call these sequences ***rows***, and will consider them as matrices consisting of one row. Two rows are *equal* if their corresponding elements are equal. The operations of row addition and multiplication by a scalar are defined by the corresponding matrix formulas:

$$[\alpha_1, \cdots, \alpha_n] + [\beta_1, \cdots, \beta_n] = [\alpha_1 + \beta_1, \cdots, \alpha_n + \beta_n] ,$$
$$\beta[\alpha_1, \cdots, \alpha_n] = [\beta\alpha_1, \cdots, \beta\alpha_n] .$$

It is clear that axioms (a) to (g) are satisfied, and that the set of all rows with n elements from a field K is a *linear space*.

Instead of rows it is possible to consider matrices having arbitrary fixed numbers of rows and of columns, with elements from a field K. Any such matrix, by the rules of matrix calculation, may be multiplied by a scalar from K, and any two may be added—the result is a matrix of the same form. Axioms (a) to (g) are evidently again satisfied, and we see that the matrices with m rows and n columns form a linear space with respect to the operations of addition and scalar multiplication.

We consider still another example. Let $\mathfrak{M}$ be an arbitrary set and K be a field. Suppose that we are given a law that places in correspondence to each element m of $\mathfrak{M}$ a definite element of K. Each such law is called a ***function***, defined on the set $\mathfrak{M}$, with values in K. If a function is denoted by a letter f, then $f(m)$ denotes the element of K which corresponds to the element m, and $f(m)$ is called the value of the function f for the element m. If functions f and g satisfy the equality $f(m) = g(m)$ for all m in $\mathfrak{M}$, then they are regarded as *equal*. For functions given on $\mathfrak{M}$, we define, in the customary way, the operations of multiplication by a scalar, addition of functions, and multiplication of functions. For example, for a given scalar α and function f, if we set in correspondence to each element m of $\mathfrak{M}$ the element $\alpha f(m)$ of K, we obtain a new function which is called the product of α and f. One defines the sum and product of two function similarly. If one considers only the first two of these operations—multiplication by a scalar and addition—then it is easy to see that axioms (a) to (g) of a linear space are satisfied. Consequently, the set of all functions defined on a given set $\mathfrak{M}$ with values in a field K form a linear space over K.

If $\mathfrak{M}$ has a finite number of elements, it is possible to introduce a more convenient notation for functions. Let $m_1, \cdots, m_s$ be the elements of $\mathfrak{M}$. Denote by $[m_i]$, for $i = 1, \cdots, s$, the function equal to 1 at m_i and equal to 0 at all the remaining elements of $\mathfrak{M}$. Then the product $\alpha[m_i]$ will be a function equal to α at m_i and 0 at all the remaining elements, and the expression

$$\alpha_1[m_1] + \alpha_2[m_2] + \cdots + \alpha_s[m_s] , \tag{5}$$

is evidently a function equal to α_1 at m_1, α_2 at $m_2, \cdots, \alpha_s$ at m_s. Consequently, every function defined on $\mathfrak{M}$ may be written in the form (5), and it is easy to see that this is possible in only one way. If there is no danger of confusion, (5) is written more briefly:

$$\alpha_1 m_1 + \alpha_2 m_2 + \cdots + \alpha_s m_s ,$$

moreover, the terms with zero coefficient are generally not written out. For example, if $\mathfrak{M}$ consists of the letters a, b, c, then $2a - c$ denotes the function equal to 2 at a, 0 at b, and -1 at c.

● EXAMPLES AND PROBLEMS

1. Let $a = [1, 3, 6]$, $b = [2, 1, 5]$, $c = [4, -3, 3]$. Show that

$$7a - 3b - 2c = [-7, 24, 21], \; 2a - 3b + c = \theta .$$

2. Show that the set of all polynomials in λ of degree not exceeding n and with coefficients from a field K is a linear space with respect to the usual operations of addition of polynomials and multiplication by scalars.
3. Is the set of polynomials of degree n, with respect to the same operations, a linear space?

2. *Dimension*

20. Linear Dependence

Let $\mathfrak{L}$ be a vector space over a field of coefficients K, and let $a_1, \cdots, a_m$ belong to $\mathfrak{L}$. A relation of the form

$$\alpha_1 a_1 + \alpha_2 a_2 + \cdots + \alpha_m a_m = \theta ,$$

where $\alpha_1, \cdots, \alpha_m$ are elements of K, is called a ***linear dependence relation*** among the vectors $a_1, \cdots, a_m$. If all the coefficients $\alpha_1, \cdots, \alpha_m$ are 0, the dependence relation is called ***trivial.*** Otherwise, i.e., when at least one coefficient is different from 0, the dependence relation is called ***nontrivial.*** It is clear that a trivial dependence relation exists among arbitrary vectors. The answer to the question—does there exist a nontrivial dependence relation?—depends on the vectors considered. In the space of rows of length 3, for example, the linear dependence relation

$$2a + 3b - 5c = \theta ,$$

exists among the vectors $a = [1, 4, 6]$, $b = [1, -1, 1]$, $c = [1, 1, 3]$. In the same space, however, there is no nontrivial linear dependence relation among the vectors $e_1 = [1, 0, 0]$, $e_2 = [0, 1, 0]$, $e_3 = [0, 0, 1]$, since the relation

$$\alpha_1 e_1 + \alpha_2 e_2 + \alpha_3 e_3 = \theta ,$$

means that

$$[\alpha_1, \alpha_2, \alpha_3] = [0, 0, 0] ,$$

or that

$$\alpha_1 = \alpha_2 = \alpha_3 = 0 .$$

A finite system of vectors $a_1, \cdots, a_m$ of a linear space is called linearly dependent if there exists a nontrivial linear dependence relation among them.

If such a relation does not exist—that is, if every relation of the form

$$\alpha_1 a_1 + \alpha_2 a_2 + \cdots + \alpha_m a_m = \theta ,$$

implies that $\alpha_1 = \alpha_2 = \cdots = \alpha_m = 0$—then the system $a_1, a_2, \cdots, a_m$ is called ***linearly independent.***

From this definition it is easy to see that *if vectors $b_1, \cdots, b_k$ are adjoined to a linearly dependent system of vectors $a_1, \cdots, a_m$, then the augmented system is still linearly dependent.* For if

$$\alpha_1 a_1 + \cdots + \alpha_m a_m = \theta ,$$

is a nontrivial relation among $a_1, \cdots, a_m$, then

$$\alpha_1 a_1 + \cdots + \alpha_m a_m + 0 \cdot b_1 + \cdots + 0 \cdot b_k = \theta ,$$

Is a nontrivial relation among $a_1, \cdots, a_m, b_1, \cdots, b_k$.

In questions connected with linear dependence, the zero vector θ occupies a special place, for *every system containing the zero vector is linearly dependent.* To prove this it is sufficient to note that the relation

$$1 \cdot \theta + 0 \cdot a_1 + \cdots + 0 \cdot a_m = \theta ,$$

is a nontrivial linear dependence relation which holds for arbitrary $a_1, \cdots, a_m$.

This definition of the linear dependence of a system presupposes that the system contains only a finite number of vectors. However, it is often necessary to consider infinite systems. We call an infinite system of vectors linearly dependent if some finite subsystem is linearly dependent. The following example shows that infinite linearly independent systems exist. Consider the set of all polynomials in λ with coefficients from a field K. These polynomials evidently form a linear space over K with respect to the operations of addition and multiplication by scalars. The polynomials

$$1, \lambda, \lambda^2, \cdots, \lambda^m, \cdots$$

constitute in this space a linearly independent system, for every finite subsystem

$$\lambda^{m_1}, \lambda^{m_2}, \cdots, \lambda^{m_k} \qquad (0 \leq m_1 < m_2 < \cdots < m_k)$$

is linearly independent, since from

$$\alpha_1 \lambda^{m_1} + \alpha_2 \lambda^{m_2} + \cdots + \alpha_k \lambda^{m_k} = 0 ,$$

it follows that $\alpha_1 = \alpha_2 = \cdots = \alpha_k = 0$.

We consider again an arbitrary linear space $\mathfrak{L}$. If a vector a can be represented in the form

$$a = \alpha_1 a_1 + \alpha_2 a_2 + \cdots + \alpha_m a_m ,$$

then we say that *a is linearly dependent on $a_1, \cdots, a_m$.*

If the vectors $a_1, \cdots, a_m$ are linearly dependent on $b_1, \cdots, b_n$, and $b_1, \cdots, b_n$

are linearly dependent on $c_1, \cdots, c_p$, *then* $a_1, \cdots, a_m$ *are linearly dependent on* $c_1, \cdots, c_p$.

To prove this, it is sufficient to replace, in the linear expressions of $a_1, \cdots, a_m$ in terms of $b_1, \cdots, b_n$, the vectors $b_1, \cdots, b_n$ by their expressions in terms of $c_1, \cdots, c_p$, and collect like terms.

THEOREM 1. *If the system of nonzero vectors* $a_1, \cdots, a_m$, *considered in a definite order, is linearly dependent, then at least one of its vectors is a linear combination of the preceding ones. Conversely, if one of the vectors of this sequence is a linear combination of the preceding ones, then the system is linearly dependent.*

Suppose the nontrivial dependence relation

$$\alpha_1 a_1 + \alpha_2 a_2 + \cdots + \alpha_m a_m = \theta , \tag{1}$$

holds. Denote by α_k the last nonzero coefficient. If $k = 1$, then relation (1) becomes

$$\alpha_1 a_1 = \theta ,$$

and hence $a_1 = \theta$, contrary to assumption. Consequently $k > 1$, and (1) may be written in the form

$$\alpha_1 a_1 + \cdots + \alpha_k a_k = \theta , \qquad \alpha_k \neq 0 ;$$

whence

$$a_k = \left(-\frac{\alpha_1}{\alpha_k}\right) a_1 + \cdots + \left(-\frac{\alpha_{k-1}}{\alpha_k}\right) a_{k-1} .$$

Thus the first part of the theorem is proved. The converse is obvious.

Let $\mathfrak{M}$ be a set of vectors of a linear space $\mathfrak{L}$. A system of vectors $a_1, a_2, \cdots$ of this set is called a ***system of generators*** of $\mathfrak{M}$ if every vector of $\mathfrak{M}$ is a linear combination of a finite number of the vectors $a_1, a_2, \cdots$. *A linearly independent system of generators of* $\mathfrak{M}$ *is called a* ***basis*** *of* $\mathfrak{M}$. For example, in the space of all polynomials in λ the polynomials

$$1, \lambda, \cdots, \lambda^m, \cdots \tag{2}$$

form a basis, since, as we have seen, these polynomials are linearly independent, and every polynomial has the form

$$\alpha_0 + \alpha_1 \lambda + \cdots + \alpha_m \lambda^m ,$$

that is, every polynomial is a linear combination of $1, \lambda, \cdots, \lambda^m, \cdots$.

LEMMA 1. *If a system of generators* $a_1, a_2, \cdots$ *of a set* $\mathfrak{M}$ *contains an element* a_i *which is a linear combination of a finite number of the remaining generators, then, removing* a_i *from the system of generators, we again obtain a system of generators of* $\mathfrak{M}$.

In fact, by assumption every vector in $\mathfrak{M}$ is a linear combination of a finite number of generators. If we replace in these combinations the vector

a_i by its expression in terms of the other generators, we obtain an expression for every element of $\mathfrak{M}$ in terms of the generators different from a_i, which was to be proved.

THEOREM 2. *It is possible to choose a basis of a space $\mathfrak{L}$ from any system of generators.*

Let $\mathfrak{L}$ have a finite system of generators $a_1, a_2, \cdots, a_s$. If we remove from this system all vectors which are linear combinations of the preceding ones, we obtain a system $a_{i_1}, a_{i_2}, \cdots, a_{i_n}$, which by the lemma is still a system of generators of $\mathfrak{L}$. By Theorem 1, since none of the vectors of this system are linear combinations of the preceding ones, this system is linearly independent, and consequently is a basis of $\mathfrak{L}$.

* * *

We have proved Theorem 2 under the assumption that there exists a finite system of generators. However, the theorem is true even when no finite system of generators exists. To prove this it is sufficient to arrange the generators in a transfinite sequence $a_1, a_2, \cdots, a_\omega, a_{\omega+1}, \cdots$, and to remove those elements which are linear combinations of a finite number of the preceding ones.

* * *

Let $a_1, a_2, \cdots$ be a basis of the space $\mathfrak{L}$. By the definition of a basis, each vector in $\mathfrak{L}$ is a linear combination of a finite number of the basis vectors. We show that this expression is unique. Indeed, let

$$a = \alpha_1 a_1 + \alpha_2 a_2 + \cdots + \alpha_s a_s ,$$
$$a = \beta_1 a_1 + \beta_2 a_2 + \cdots + \beta_s a_s .$$

Subtracting, we obtain

$$\theta = (\alpha_1 - \beta_1)a_1 + (\alpha_2 - \beta_2)a_2 + \cdots + (\alpha_s - \beta_s)a_s ,$$

and, since $a_1, a_2, \cdots$ are linearly independent, $\alpha_1 - \beta_1 = \alpha_2 - \beta_2 = \cdots = \alpha_s - \beta_s = 0$, or $\alpha_1 = \beta_1, \cdots, \alpha_s = \beta_s$.

21. Finite-dimensional Spaces

If a linear space $\mathfrak{L}$ has a finite basis, then $\mathfrak{L}$ is called ***finite-dimensional.*** In other words, $\mathfrak{L}$ is called finite-dimensional if there exists in $\mathfrak{L}$ a finite linearly independent system of vectors such that every vector in $\mathfrak{L}$ is a linear combination of the vectors of this system.

The notion of basis is not applicable to the zero space. However, we will also call the zero space finite-dimensional and assign to it dimension 0.

THEOREM 3. *Every basis of a finite-dimensional nonzero linear space $\mathfrak{L}$ has the same finite number of vectors. This number is called the dimension of $\mathfrak{L}$.*

By definition there is a finite basis of $\mathfrak{L}$. Let such a basis be

$$a_1, a_2, \cdots, a_n . \tag{3}$$

We show that the number of vectors in any other basis

$$x_1, x_2, \cdots, x_m, \cdots \tag{4}$$

cannot exceed n. Consider the system

$$x_1, a_1, a_2, \cdots, a_n . \tag{5}$$

Since system (3) is a generating system of $\mathfrak{L}$, so is system (5). However, system (5) is linearly dependent, since the vector x_1 is a linear combination of the others. Applying Theorem 1 to system (5), we see that one of the vectors of this sequence, say a_i, is a linear combination of the preceding ones. Removing a_i from (5), we obtain a new sequence

$$x_1, a_1', \cdots, a_{n-1}', \tag{6}$$

where $a_1', \cdots, a_{n-1}'$ denote the remaining vectors of $a_1, \cdots, a_n$. By Lemma 1, system (6) is still a generating system of $\mathfrak{L}$. Consider now the sequence

$$x_2, x_1, a_1', \cdots, a_{n-1}' . \tag{7}$$

This sequence is linearly dependent, since the vector x_2 is a linear combination of the others. Consequently, by Theorem 1, one of the vectors of this system is a linear combination of the *preceding* ones. This vector must be one of $a_1', \cdots, a_{n-1}'$, since x_2 and x_1 are linearly independent by assumption. Removing it from (7), we obtain a sequence

$$x_2, x_1, a_1'', \cdots, a_{n-2}'', \tag{8}$$

where $a_1'', \cdots, a_{n-2}''$ denote the remaining vectors of $a_1', \cdots, a_{n-1}'$. By Lemma 1, inasmuch as (7) is a system of generators of $\mathfrak{L}$, (8) is also a system of generators. If we now adjoin the vector x_3 to the sequence (8), we may remove from the new sequence another vector a_i'', which is a linear combination of the preceding ones, and so on. If the number of vectors x_i were greater than n, then after n steps we would obtain the sequence

$$x_n, x_{n-1}, \cdots, x_2, x_1, \tag{9}$$

entirely free of the vectors $a_1, \cdots, a_n$; moreover, this sequence would be a system of generators of $\mathfrak{L}$. This would mean that every vector of $\mathfrak{L}$ was a linear combination of the vectors (9). In particular, the vector x_{n+1} would be a linear combination of the vectors (9), which contradicts the linear independence of $x_1, x_2, \cdots$. Consequently the basis (4) cannot contain more vectors than the basis (3), and thus every basis of $\mathfrak{L}$ is *finite*. In place of (3), however, we could take an arbitrary finite basis. Therefore our argument shows that the number of vectors in one basis cannot be less than the number of vectors in any other—that is, every basis of $\mathfrak{L}$ has the same number of elements.

THEOREM 4. *For every linearly independent system of vectors $a_1, \cdots, a_m$ of a finite-dimensional space $\mathfrak{L}$ it is possible to find, in $\mathfrak{L}$, vectors $a_{m+1}, \cdots, a_n$ such that the system $a_1, \cdots, a_m, a_{m+1}, \cdots, a_n$ is a basis of $\mathfrak{L}$.*

We choose in $\mathfrak{L}$ some basis $x_1, \cdots, x_n$ and construct the sequence

$$a_1, a_2, \cdots, a_m, \qquad x_1, x_2, \cdots, x_n. \tag{10}$$

We now remove from this sequence all those vectors which are linear combinations of the preceding ones. Since $a_1, \cdots, a_m$ are linearly independent, no a_i will be removed, and the remaining system has the form

$$a_1, \cdots, a_m, \qquad x_{i_1}, \cdots, x_{i_k}, \tag{11}$$

By Theorem 1, this system is linearly independent. But (10) is a generating system; hence, by Lemma 1, (11) is also. Consequently the system (11) is a basis, and $x_{i_1}, \cdots, x_{i_k}$ are the desired vectors.

Theorem 4 may also be formulated as follows: *every linearly independent system of vectors of a space $\mathfrak{L}$ is itself a basis, or else is part of a basis, of $\mathfrak{L}$.*

Let $\mathfrak{L}$ have dimension n. Then every basis of $\mathfrak{L}$ contains n vectors, and therefore the number of vectors in any linearly independent system is less than or equal to n. In the latter case the system must be a basis of $\mathfrak{L}$. In particular, n is the maximal number of linearly independent vectors in $\mathfrak{L}$, and designates the dimension of $\mathfrak{L}$.

We have already proved the following theorem.

THEOREM 5. *Every system of $n+1$ vectors in an n-dimensional linear space $\mathfrak{L}$ is linearly dependent. Any n linearly independent vectors form a basis. The maximal number of linearly independent vectors of a space $\mathfrak{L}$ is the dimension of $\mathfrak{L}$.*

Although we have formulated Theorems 3 and 4 for finite-dimensional spaces, they remain true for arbitrary vector spaces. To prove this it is only necessary to consider, instead of the number of vectors in a basis, the cardinality of the set of vectors in a basis, and to take this cardinality as the dimension of the space. So far as Theorem 5 is concerned, only the last of its assertions carries over to the infinite-dimensional case. However, in the present book we study only finite-dimensional spaces and therefore, in what follows, *except where otherwise stated, a linear space will denote a finite-dimensional linear space.*

22. The Dimension of the Space of Rows

We determine the dimensions of the spaces considered in Section 19. Let $\mathfrak{R}$ be the usual space of directed line segments with origin $\mathcal{O}$. These segments, as usual, will be called vectors. We show that *any three vectors a_1, a_2, a_3 of $\mathfrak{R}$ not lying in one plane constitute a basis of $\mathfrak{R}$.* The vectors a_1, a_2, a_3 are linearly independent, since otherwise one of them, say a_3, would be a linear combination of the other two. However, the relation

$a_3 = \alpha_1 a_1 + \alpha_2 a_2$ means that a_3 is the diagonal of the parallelogram constructed on the vectors $\alpha_1 a_1$ and $\alpha_2 a_2$. Since $\alpha_1 a_1$ and $\alpha_2 a_2$ lie in the plane $a_1 \mathcal{O} a_2$, then so does a_3, which is contrary to our assumption. On the other hand, every vector $\overrightarrow{\mathcal{O}A}$ of $\mathfrak{R}$ is a linear combination of a_1, a_2, a_3 (Fig. 1):

$$\overrightarrow{\mathcal{O}A} = \overrightarrow{\mathcal{O}P_1} + \overrightarrow{P_1P_2} + \overrightarrow{P_2A} = \alpha_1 a_1 + \alpha_2 a_2 + \alpha_3 a_3 ,$$

where α_i is the ratio of the length of the segment $P_{i-1}P_i$ ($P_0 = \mathcal{O}, P_3 = A$) to the lenght of a_i, taken with the proper sign. Thus the system a_1, a_2, a_3 is a basis of $\mathfrak{R}$; consequently $\mathfrak{R}$ has dimension 3.

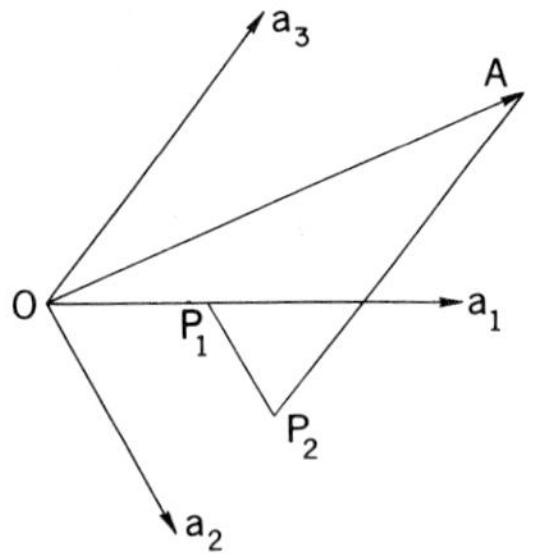

Figure 1

In a similar way, we show that the set of vectors with origin $\mathcal{O}$, lying in some plane through $\mathcal{O}$, is a space with dimension 2, and also that the set of vectors with origin $\mathcal{O}$, lying in some line through $\mathcal{O}$, is a one-dimensional space.

Let us consider the space of rows of length n with elements from some field K. Let

$$e_1 = [1, 0, \cdots, 0] ,$$
$$e_2 = [0, 1, \cdots, 0] ,$$
$$\vdots$$
$$e_n = [0, 0, \cdots, 1] .$$

Multiplying these rows successively by arbitrary scalars $\alpha_1, \cdots, \alpha_n$ and adding, we obtain

$$\alpha_1 e_1 + \alpha_2 e_2 + \cdots + \alpha_n a_n = [\alpha_1, \alpha_2, \cdots, \alpha_n] .$$

Thus an arbitrary row $[\alpha_1, \cdots, \alpha_n]$ is a linear combination of $e_1, \cdots, e_n$. However, the system $e_1, \cdots, e_n$ is linearly independent, since the relation

$$\alpha_1 e_1 + \alpha_2 e_2 + \cdots + \alpha_n e_n = \theta ,$$

yields

$$[\alpha_1, \alpha_2, \cdots, \alpha_n] = [0, 0, \cdots, 0] ,$$

and hence $\alpha_1 = \alpha_2 = \cdots = \alpha_n = 0$. Therefore the system $e_1, \cdots, e_n$ is a basis of the row space whose dimension is n.

Finally, let $\mathfrak{L}$ be the space of functions defined on a finite set $\mathfrak{M}$ with values in a field K. We denote the elements of $\mathfrak{M}$ by $m_1, \cdots, m_s$. By Section 19, every function f of $\mathfrak{M}$ can be represented in the form

$$f = \alpha_1[m_1] + \alpha_2[m_2] + \cdots + \alpha_s[m_s] ,$$

where $[m_i]$ is the function equal to 1 at m_i and 0 elsewhere. Consequently, f is a linear combination of $[m_1], \cdots, [m_s]$. But the equation

$$\alpha_1[m_1] + \cdots + \alpha_s[m_s] = \theta ,$$

means that every value of the function on the left is 0, and hence that $\alpha_1 = \cdots = \alpha_s = 0$. Thus the system $[m_1], \cdots, [m_s]$ is a basis of $\mathfrak{L}$, so that $\mathfrak{L}$ has dimension s.

23. Isomorphism

The notion of linear space has two essentially different parts. First, a linear space is a set of some kind of objects, called vectors; second, these objects are subjected to the operations of addition and multiplication by a scalar. We may be interested in the nature and properties of the vectors, or, oppositely, be interested in the properties of the operations, independently of the nature of the elements on which they are performed. In what follows we are interested only in properties of the second kind. Therefore if two spaces are constructed in the same way with respect to addition and multiplication by a scalar, we consider them as having identical properties, or as being ***isomorphic***. The concept of isomorphism may be more precisely formulated in the following way.

Two linear spaces over the same field of coefficients are called isomorphic if their elements can be put into one-to-one correspondence in such a way that the sum of vectors in the first space corresponds to the sum of the corresponding vectors in the second, and a scalar times a vector in the first space corresponds to the same scalar times the corresponding vector in the second.

A one-to-one correspondence possessing the indicated properties is called an ***isomorphism***. We consider the simplest properties of isomorphisms.

Under an isomorphism the zero vector is carried into the zero vector. Suppose that under an isomorphic mapping of one linear space $\mathfrak{L}$ onto another space $\mathfrak{L}_1$ the vector a of $\mathfrak{L}$ is carried into a_1 of $\mathfrak{L}_1$. Then by the definition of isomorphism, the product $0 \cdot a$ must be carried into $0 \cdot a_1$; that is, the zero vector of the first space must be carried into the zero vector of the second.

Under an isomorphism a system of generators of the first space is carried into a system of generators of the second.

Let $a_1, a_2, \cdots, a_s$ be generators of the first space and $b_1, b_2, \cdots, b_s$ be the corresponding vectors in the second. Take an arbitrary vector b in the second space and consider the corresponding vector a in the first space. By assumption, a may be represented in the form

$$a = \alpha_1 a_1 + \alpha_2 a_2 + \cdots + \alpha_s a_s ,$$

and by the definition of isomorphism, the sum $\alpha_1 a_1 + \cdots + \alpha_s a_s$ must be carried into the sum $\alpha_1 b_1 + \cdots + \alpha_s b_s$; consequently, $b = \alpha_1 b_1 + \cdots + \alpha_s b_s$, and $b_1, \cdots, b_s$ constitutes a system of generators of the second space.

Under an isomorphism linearly independent vectors are carried into linearly independent vectors.

To prove this, let the linearly independent vectors $a_1, \cdots, a_m$ of the first space be carried into the vectors $b_1, \cdots, b_m$ of the second, and suppose that among the latter vectors there exists a relation

$$\beta_1 b_1 + \cdots + \beta_m b_m = \theta_1 .$$

By the definition of isomorphism, the left side of this equation corresponds to $\beta_1 a_1 + \cdots + \beta_m a_m$ in the first space, and the zero vector θ_1 corresponds to the zero vector θ in the first space. Consequently,

$$\beta_1 a_1 + \cdots + \beta_m a_m = \theta .$$

Since $a_1, \cdots, a_m$ are linearly independent,

$$\beta_1 = \cdots = \beta_m = 0 ,$$

that is, $b_1, \cdots, b_m$ are linearly independent.

From the last two properties it is easy to show that *a basis of a linear space is carried, under an isomorphism, into a basis; thus isomorphic linear spaces have the same dimension.*

The converse is also true: *if two linear spaces over the same field of coefficients have the same dimension, they are isomorphic.*

To prove this, let $a_1, \cdots, a_n$ and $b_1, \cdots, b_n$ be bases of the two spaces respectively. Call the vectors

$$a = \alpha_1 a_1 + \cdots + \alpha_n a_n ,$$
$$b = \beta_1 b_1 + \cdots + \beta_n b_n ,$$

correspondents if $\alpha_1 = \beta_1, \cdots, \alpha_n = \beta_n$. Since each vector has a unique expression in terms of the proper basis, this correspondence is *one-to-one.* Now let

$$a = \alpha_1 a_1 + \cdots + \alpha_n a_n ,$$
$$b = \alpha_1 b_1 + \cdots + \alpha_n b_n ,$$

be two corresponding vectors. Then

$$\alpha a = \alpha\alpha_1 a_1 + \cdots + \alpha\alpha_n a_n ,$$
$$\alpha b = \alpha\alpha_1 b_1 + \cdots + \alpha\alpha_n b_n .$$

Since the corresponding coefficients in these expressions are equal, then αa and αb are corresponding vectors; that is, under our correspondence a scalar times a vector is carried into the same scalar times the corresponding vector. In a similar way we see that the sum of vectors is carried into the sum of the corresponding vectors. Therefore our correspondence is an isomorphism.

The properties of an isomorphism enumerated above show that for a given base field K, each linear space is determined up to isomorphism by its dimension. Therefore the spaces of rows of length n with elements from a field K, for $n = 1, 2, \cdots$, exhaust, up to isomorphism, all spaces of finite dimension. In particular, the usual space of directed line segments is isomorphic to the space of rows of length 3 over the field of real numbers; the space of functions defined on a set $\mathfrak{M}$ containing s elements, with values in a field K, is isomorphic to the space of rows of length s with elements from K; and so on.

● EXAMPLES AND PROBLEMS

1. Show that the space of all polynomials in one indeterminate of degree not higher than n has dimension $n+1$.
2. The homogeneous polynomials of degree n in two indeterminates (together with the zero polynomial) form a linear space of dimension $n+1$.
3. What is the dimension of the space of homogeneous polynomials of degree n in K indeterminates (together with the zero polynomial)?
4. The set of matrices with m rows and n columns, with elements from a given field K, is a linear space with respect to the ordinary matrix operations of addition and multiplication by scalars. Show that this space has dimension mn and that the matrices in which one element is 1 and the remaining elements are 0 form a basis.
5. The sets of symmetric and of skew-symmetric matrices of order n with elements from some field K are linear spaces over K. Show that the dimensions of these spaces are respectively $n(n+1)/2$ and $n(n-1)/2$.

3. *Coordinates*

24. Coordinate Rows

The simplest general properties of linear spaces have just been considered. In applications, however, besides a knowledge of general properties it is important to be able to give vectors in terms of numbers and to reduce vector operations to operations with numbers. This problem is solved by introducing coordinates for the vectors of a vector space.

We call every basis of a linear space $\mathfrak{L}$, whose vectors are taken in a definite order, a ***coordinate basis,*** or ***coordinate system*** in $\mathfrak{L}$. Thus, if

$$a_1, \cdots, a_n, \tag{1}$$

is a coordinate system in $\mathfrak{L}$, then the same vectors, taken in another order, will be another coordinate system in $\mathfrak{L}$. We have seen that every vector a of $\mathfrak{L}$ may be expressed uniquely in the form

$$a = \alpha_1 a_1 + \alpha_2 a_2 + \cdots + \alpha_n a_n . \tag{2}$$

The numbers $\alpha_1, \cdots, \alpha_n$ are called the ***coordinate of the vector*** a in the coordinate system (1). The row $[\alpha_1, \cdots, \alpha_n]$, consisting of the coordinates of a taken in the proper order, is called a ***coordinate row,*** and is denoted by $[a]$. Consequently, if a definite coordinate system is selected in a space $\mathfrak{L}$, then to each vector there corresponds a coordinate row, and, conversely, to each row of n elements there corresponds, by formula (2), a definite vector a which has this as its coordinate row.

Let a and b have coordinate rows $[\alpha_1, \cdots, \alpha_n]$ and $[\beta_1, \cdots, \beta_n]$:

$$a = \alpha_1 a_1 + \cdots + \alpha_n a_n ,$$
$$b = \beta_1 a_1 + \cdots + \beta_n a_n .$$

Then evidently

$$\alpha a = (\alpha\alpha_1)a_1 + \cdots + (\alpha\alpha_n)a_n ,$$
$$a + b = (\alpha_1 + \beta_1)a_1 + \cdots + (\alpha_n + \beta_n)a_n .$$

Using operations with rows, these equations may be written in the form

$$[\alpha a] = \alpha[a] , \qquad [a + b] = [a] + [b] .$$

Consequently, *the coordinate row of a sum is the sum of the coordinate rows of the summands, and the coordinate row of a scalar times a vector is the same scalar times the coordinate row of the vector.*

This result may be further interpreted. Suppose that we have some linear space $\mathfrak{L}$ of dimension n over a field K. Denote by $\mathfrak{L}_n$ the space of rows of length n with elements from K. We choose a definite coordinate system in $\mathfrak{L}$ and place in correspondence with each vector its coordinate row. Our result shows that this correspondence is an isomorphism between $\mathfrak{L}$ and $\mathfrak{L}_n$. In particular, it follows that linearly independent vectors have linearly independent coordinate rows, and that every linear dependence relation among given vectors holds also among their coordinate rows.

Using these definitions, it is easy to decide the question of linear dependence, given the coordinates of the vectors involved. Let $x_1, \cdots, x_m$ have coordinate rows

$$[x_1] = [\alpha_{11}, \alpha_{12}, \cdots, \alpha_{1n}] ,$$
$$[x_2] = [\alpha_{21}, \alpha_{22}, \cdots, \alpha_{2n}] ,$$
$$\vdots$$
$$[x_m] = [\alpha_{m1}, \alpha_{m2}, \cdots, \alpha_{mn}] .$$

We construct from these rows the matrix

$$A = \begin{bmatrix} \alpha_{11} & \alpha_{12} & \cdots & \alpha_{1n} \\ \alpha_{21} & \alpha_{22} & \cdots & \alpha_{2n} \\ \vdots & \vdots & & \vdots \\ \alpha_{m1} & \alpha_{m2} & \cdots & \alpha_{mn} \end{bmatrix} .$$

We already know that the maximal number of linearly independent vectors among $x_1, \cdots, x_m$ is the maximal number of their coordinate rows which are linearly independent, or the maximal number of linearly independent rows of A. In the theory of determinants this number is called the ***rank*** of A. It is shown there that the rank of a matrix is the order of the largest non-zero determinant belonging to the matrix. Consequently, *the maximal number of linearly independent vectors among $x_1, \cdots, x_m$ is the rank of the matrix constructed from the coordinate rows of these vectors.*

We now consider the conditions under which a system of n vectors $x_1, \cdots, x_n$ in an n-dimensional space $\mathfrak{L}$ will be a basis. We know that a necessary and sufficient condition for this is the linear independence of $x_1, \cdots, x_n$. The matrix A constructed from the coordinate rows of $x_1, \cdots, x_n$ is square, and the condition that its rank be n is that its determinant is different from zero. Hence, *a system of n vectors in an n-dimensional linear space is a basis if and only if the determinant constructed from the coordinate rows of these vectors is different from zero.*

25. Transformation of Coordinates

In any vector space $\mathfrak{L}$ there are many different coordinate systems. Therefore the question arises: how do we change the coordinates of a vector if we pass from one coordinate system to another? To find the answer to this question, consider two coordinate systems $a_1, a_2, \cdots, a_n$ and $a'_1, a'_2, \cdots, a'_n$ in $\mathfrak{L}$. Since the set $a_1, \cdots, a_n$ is a basis, each of the vectors $a'_1, \cdots, a'_n$ is a linear combination of these elements. Let

$$\begin{aligned} a'_1 &= \tau_{11}a_1 + \tau_{12}a_2 + \cdots + \tau_{1n}a_n , \\ a'_2 &= \tau_{21}a_1 + \tau_{22}a_2 + \cdots + \tau_{2n}a_n , \\ &\vdots \\ a'_n &= \tau_{n1}a_1 + \tau_{n2}a_2 + \cdots + \tau_{nn}a_n . \end{aligned}$$

The matrix

$$T = \begin{bmatrix} \tau_{11}\tau_{12} & \cdots & \tau_{1n} \\ \tau_{21}\tau_{22} & \cdots & \tau_{2n} \\ \vdots \;\; \vdots & & \vdots \\ \tau_{n1}\tau_{n2} & \cdots & \tau_{nn} \end{bmatrix}$$

is called the ***matrix of the transformation*** from the (old) coordinate system $a_1, \cdots, a_n$ to the (new) system $a'_1, \cdots, a'_n$. Take an arbitrary vector a and let $[\alpha_1, \cdots, \alpha_n]$ and $[\alpha'_1, \cdots, \alpha'_n]$ be its coordinate rows in the old and new coordinate systems. We have

$$\begin{aligned} a &= \alpha_1 a_1 + \cdots + \alpha_n a_n , \\ a &= \alpha'_1 a'_1 + \cdots + \alpha'_n a'_n . \end{aligned}$$

Replacing $a'_1, \cdots, a'_n$ in the second equation by their expressions in terms of $a_1, \cdots, a_n$, we obtain

$$\begin{aligned} a = (&\alpha'_1\tau_{11} + \alpha'_2\tau_{21} + \cdots + \alpha'_n\tau_{n1})a_1 \\ &+ (\alpha'_1\tau_{12} + \alpha'_2\tau_{22} + \cdots + \alpha'_n\tau_{n2})a_2 + \cdots , \end{aligned}$$

or

$$\begin{aligned} \alpha_1 &= \alpha'_1\tau_{11} + \alpha'_2\tau_{21} + \cdots + \alpha'_n\tau_{n1} , \\ \alpha_2 &= \alpha'_1\tau_{12} + \alpha'_2\tau_{22} + \cdots + \alpha'_n\tau_{n2} , \\ &\vdots \\ \alpha_n &= \alpha'_1\tau_{1n} + \alpha'_2\tau_{2n} + \cdots + \alpha'_n\tau_{nn} . \end{aligned}$$

These equations are the desired formulas of the transformation of coordinates.

Observe that the expression for α_i,

$$\alpha_i = \alpha'_1\tau_{1i} + \alpha'_2\tau_{2i} + \cdots + \alpha'_n\tau_{ni} ,$$

represents the product of the coordinate row $[\alpha'_1, \cdots, \alpha'_n]$ by the ith column of T. Thus the entire system of formulas above may be written in the shorter matrix form

$$[\alpha_1, \cdots, \alpha_n] = [\alpha'_1, \cdots, \alpha'_n]T .$$

Rule for the transformation of coordinates. *The old coordinate row of a vector equals the new multiplied by the matrix of the transformation.*

26. The Inverse Transformation

First we prove the following very useful lemma.

LEMMA. *Let A and B be square matrices of order n with elements from a field K. If*

$$[\xi_1, \cdots, \xi_n]A = [\xi_1, \cdots, \xi_n]B \tag{3}$$

for arbitrary rows $[\xi_1, \cdots, \xi_n]$, then $A = B$.

If the elements of A are denoted by α_{ij}, and those of B by β_{ij}, for $i, j = 1, \cdots, n$, then for each i, where $i = 1, \cdots, n$, the values $\xi_i = 1$, $\xi_j = 0$, for $j \neq i$ in equation (3) give $\alpha_{ik} = \beta_{ik}$, where $k = 1, \cdots, n$.

Now consider two coordinate systems $a_1, \cdots, a_n$ and $a'_1, \cdots, a'_n$ in an n-dimensional space $\mathfrak{L}$. We may either express $a'_1, \cdots, a'_n$ in terms of $a_1, \cdots, a_n$:

$$\begin{aligned} a'_1 &= \tau_{11}a_1 + \cdots + \tau_{1n}a_n , \\ &\vdots \\ a'_n &= \tau_{n1}a_1 + \cdots + \tau_{nn}a_n , \end{aligned}$$

or $a_1, \cdots, a_n$ in terms of $a'_1, \cdots, a'_n$:

$$\begin{aligned} a_1 &= \sigma_{11}a'_1 + \cdots + \sigma_{1n}a'_n , \\ &\vdots \\ a_n &= \sigma_{n1}a'_1 + \cdots + \sigma_{nn}a'_n . \end{aligned}$$

The matrix T, consisting of the coefficients τ_{ij}, is the matrix of the transformation from $a_1, \cdots, a_n$ to $a'_1, \cdots, a'_n$, and the matrix s, consisting of the coefficients σ_{ij}, is the matrix of the inverse transformation from $a'_1, \cdots, a'_n$ to $a_1, \cdots, a_n$. Let $[x]$ be the coordinate row of an arbitrary vector x in the coordinate system $a_1, \cdots, a_n$, and let $[x]_1$ be the coordinate row of x in system $a'_1, \cdots, a'_n$. If we take $a_1, \cdots, a_n$ as the old system, we obtain, by the rule of transformation of coordinates,

$$[x] = [x]_1 T . \tag{4}$$

If, instead, we take $a'_1, \cdots, a'_n$ as the old system, we obtain

$$[x]_1 = [x]S .$$

Substituting for $[x]$ its expression from (4), we have

$$[x]_1 = [x]_1 TS .$$

The vector x, and consequently its coordinate row $[x]'$, is arbitrary. By the lemma just proved, this gives

$$E = TS\,, \qquad S = T^{-1}\,.$$

Thus, *the matrix of a transformation of coordinates always has an inverse—namely, the matrix of the inverse transformation.*

We now show that *every non-singular matrix T is the matrix of some transformation of coordinates.* Let $a_1, \cdots, a_n$ be a given coordinate system in a space $\mathfrak{L}$. Consider the vectors $a_1', \cdots, a_n'$, defined by

$$\begin{aligned} a_1' &= \tau_{11}a_1 + \tau_{12}a_2 + \cdots + \tau_{1n}a_n\,, \\ a_2' &= \tau_{21}a_1 + \tau_{22}a_2 + \cdots + \tau_{2n}a_n\,, \\ &\vdots \\ a_n' &= \tau_{n1}a_1 + \tau_{n2}a_2 + \cdots + \tau_{nn}a_n\,. \end{aligned} \qquad (5)$$

These vectors are chosen so that the matrix consisting of their coordinate rows is the matrix T. By assumption the determinant of T is not zero. Therefore, by the last result in Section 24, we may assert that $a_1', \cdots, a_n'$ is a basis, and hence may be taken as a new coordinate system in $\mathfrak{L}$. Relations (5) show that T is the matrix of the transformation from $a_1, \cdots, a_n$ to $a_1', \cdots, a_n'$.

● EXAMPLES AND PROBLEMS

1. In the space of rows length 3, take as a coordinate system $a_1 = [1, 3, 5]$, $a_2 = [6, 3, 2]$, $a_3 = [3, 1, 0]$. In this system, what are the coordinates of the vectors $[3, 7, 1]$, $[0, 0, 1]$, $[2, 3, 5]$?
2. In the space of rows of length n, take as a coordinate system
$$e_1 = [1, 0, \cdots, 0], e_2 = [0, 1, \cdots, 0], \cdots, e_n = [0, 0, \cdots, 1]\,.$$
Compute the coordinate row of the vector $[\alpha_1, \alpha_2, \cdots, \alpha_n]$.
3. Let the space $\mathfrak{L}$ consist of the polynomials in λ of degree not higher than n. Show that the system of polynomials $1, \lambda - 1, (\lambda - 1)^2, \cdots, (\lambda - 1)^n$ is a basis of this space. Find in this basis the coordinate row of the polynomial $f(\lambda) = \beta_0 + \beta_1\lambda + \cdots + \beta_5\lambda^5$.
4. In the plane take two perpendicular vectors a, b of length 1 as a coordinate system, and perform a transformation of coordinates with the matrix $\left[\begin{smallmatrix}\alpha & \beta \\ \delta & \gamma\end{smallmatrix}\right]$. What conditions must $\alpha, \beta, \gamma, \delta$ satisfy in order that the new coordinate vectors be perpendicular and have length 1?

4. *Linear Subspaces*

27. The Construction of Subspaces

A nonempty subset $\mathfrak{A}$ of a linear space $\mathfrak{L}$ is called a ***linear subspace*** of $\mathfrak{L}$ if the following two conditions are fulfilled.

1. When $\mathfrak{A}$ contains the vector a, then $\mathfrak{A}$ also contains all scalar multiples αa.
2. When $\mathfrak{A}$ contains a and b, then $\mathfrak{A}$ also contains the sum $a + b$.

It is easily seen that *every linear subspace $\mathfrak{A}$ contains the zero vector and also contains all linear combinations of any two vectors that are in the subspace.* Thus a linear subspace of $\mathfrak{L}$ is itself a linear space with respect to the operations of addition and multiplication by scalars given in $\mathfrak{L}$.

The set consisting only of the zero vector has properties 1 and 2, and consequently is a linear subspace of $\mathfrak{L}$. It is called the ***zero subspace***. On the other hand, $\mathfrak{L}$ itself is considered a subspaces. The zero subspace and $\mathfrak{L}$ are sometimes called ***trivial* subspaces** of $\mathfrak{L}$. All others are called ***nontrivial***.

The simplest method of constructing a linear subspace is the following. Let us take, in a given space $\mathfrak{L}$, arbitrary vectors $a_1, \cdots, a_m$, and consider the set of all linear combinations

$$\alpha_1 a_1 + \alpha_2 a_2 + \cdots + \alpha_m a_m .$$

Denote this set by $\mathfrak{A}$. Since the sum of linear combinations of $a_1, \cdots, a_m$ and a scalar times a linear combination are again linear combinations of $a_1, \cdots, a_m$, $\mathfrak{A}$ is a linear subspace. The vectors $a_1, \cdots, a_m$ are called generators of this subspace. If we remove those which are linearly dependent upon the preceding ones, we obtain a linearly independent system of generators of $\mathfrak{A}$, or a basis of $\mathfrak{A}$. The number of vectors in a basis is the dimension of the space. Hence, *the dimension of the subspace $\mathfrak{A}$ is the maximal number of linearly independent vectors contained in the system $a_1, \cdots, a_m$.* Sometimes one says that $\mathfrak{A}$ is the subspace *spanned* by $a_1, \cdots, a_m$. Consequently the dimension of the subspace spanned by $a_1, \cdots, a_m$ is the maximal number of linearly independent vectors contained in the system.

The method of spanning a subspace by a given system of vectors is completely general: *every linear subspace $\mathfrak{A}$ of $\mathfrak{L}$ is spanned by its basis.*

Inasmuch as the number of linearly independent vectors in $\mathfrak{L}$ cannot be larger than the dimension of $\mathfrak{L}$, it follows that the dimension of a linear subspace cannot exceed the dimension of the containing space. Further, if the dimension of $\mathfrak{L}$ equals the dimension of a subspace $\mathfrak{A}$, then any basis of $\mathfrak{A}$ will be a basis of $\mathfrak{L}$. Therefore every vector of $\mathfrak{L}$ will be expressible in terms of the basis of $\mathfrak{A}$, and $\mathfrak{A}$ will coincide with $\mathfrak{L}$. Consequently the dimension of a proper subspace is less than the dimension of the containing space.

As an example, consider the usual space $\mathfrak{R}$ of directed segments with origin $\mathcal{O}$. The dimension of $\mathfrak{R}$ is 3, and hence a proper subspace has dimension either 1 or 2. A subspace of dimension 1 must be spanned by some single nonzero vector a; that is, it must be the set of multiples αa of the segment a. But all segments of the form αa lie on the line containing a. Thus every one-dimensional subspace of $\mathfrak{R}$ coincides with some line passing through the point $\mathcal{O}$.

A two-dimensional subspace must be spanned by two linearly independent vectors—two vectors a, b not lying on one line. Let $\mathfrak{A}$ be the plane determined by the segments a, b. Then every linear combination $\alpha a + \beta b$ will lie in the plane $\mathfrak{A}$, and, conversely, every vector in $\mathfrak{A}$ will be some linear combination of a and b. Consequently, the subspace spanned by a, b is the set of vectors lying in the plane $\mathfrak{A}$. Thus *every two-dimensional subspace of* $\mathfrak{R}$ *coincides with some plane through* $\mathcal{O}$.

Spaces of dimension greater than 3 do not have such an intuitive geometric interpretation. However, we still apply a geometric terminology, calling a one-dimensional subspace a ***line***, a two-dimensional subspace a ***plane***, a k-dimensional subspace, for $k \geqq 3$, a ***k-plane***. A subspace of dimension one less than the dimension of the space is given the special name ***hyperplane***.

28. Intersection and Sum of Subspaces

It is possible to perform certain operations on the subspaces of a given linear space $\mathfrak{L}$, the most important of which are sum and intersection. The ***intersection*** of subspaces $\mathfrak{A}, \mathfrak{B}, \cdots$ of $\mathfrak{L}$ is the set $\mathfrak{P}$ of vectors belonging simultaneously to all of these subspaces. The operation of intersection is denoted by the symbol $\cap$:

$$\mathfrak{P} = \mathfrak{A} \cap \mathfrak{B} \cap \cdots .$$

The intersection of an arbitrary number of linear subspaces of $\mathfrak{L}$ *is again a linear subspace of* $\mathfrak{L}$.

The zero vector is contained in each of the subspaces $\mathfrak{A}, \mathfrak{B}, \cdots$; hence it is contained in their intersection $\mathfrak{P}$, which is therefore nonempty. On the other hand, if a, b belong to $\mathfrak{P}$, then they, and every linear combination $\alpha a + \beta b$, belong to each subspace $\mathfrak{A}, \mathfrak{B}, \cdots$. Consequently, $\alpha a + \beta b$ belongs to $\mathfrak{P}$, and $\mathfrak{P}$ is a linear subspace.

The ***sum*** of a finite number of subspaces $\mathfrak{A}_1, \cdots, \mathfrak{A}_s$ of $\mathfrak{L}$ is the set of vectors of the form

$$a = a_1 + \cdots + a_s , \tag{1}$$

where a_i is taken from $\mathfrak{A}_i$, where $i = 1, \cdots, s$. The operation of addition of subspaces is denoted by the symbol $+$.

The sum of a finite number of linear subspaces of $\mathfrak{L}$ *is again a linear subspace of* $\mathfrak{L}$, which contains all the vectors of the given subspaces and all of their linear combinations.

To prove this, let $\mathfrak{A} = \mathfrak{A}_1 + \mathfrak{A}_2 + \cdots + \mathfrak{A}_s$, and suppose that a, b belong to $\mathfrak{A}$; that is, a and b have representations of the form

$$a = a_1 + a_2 + \cdots + a_s , \qquad b = b_1 + b_2 + \cdots + b_s ,$$

where a_i, b_i belong to $\mathfrak{A}_i$, where $i = 1, \cdots, s$. But then, for arbitrary α, β,

$$\alpha a + \beta b = (\alpha a_1 + \beta b_1) + (\alpha a_2 + \beta b_2) + \cdots + (\alpha a_s + \beta b_s) ,$$

is an expression of type (1), since $\alpha a_i + \beta b_i$ belongs to $\mathfrak{A}_i$. Consequently,

$\alpha a + \beta b$ belongs to $\mathfrak{A}$, and $\mathfrak{A}$ is a linear subspace. Now setting $a_j = \theta$ for $j \neq i$ in (1), we see that a_i is contained in $\mathfrak{A}$—that is, $\mathfrak{A}$ contains all the vectors of $\mathfrak{A}_i$.

Finally, we note without proof the following properties of sums of subspaces, which follow easily from the definition.

1) $\mathfrak{A} + \mathfrak{B} = \mathfrak{B} + \mathfrak{A}$.
2) $\mathfrak{A} + (\mathfrak{B} + \mathfrak{C}) = (\mathfrak{A} + \mathfrak{B}) + \mathfrak{C}$.
3) *If $\mathfrak{A}$ is contained in $\mathfrak{B}$, then $\mathfrak{A} + \mathfrak{B} = \mathfrak{B}$.*

The dimension of the sum of two linear subspaces $\mathfrak{A}, \mathfrak{B}$ depends not only upon the dimensions of $\mathfrak{A}$ and $\mathfrak{B}$, but also upon the dimension of their intersection. The exact value of the dimension of a sum is given in the following theorem.

THEOREM 1. *The dimension of the sum of two linear subspaces is the sum of their dimensions minus the dimension of their intersection.*

Let $\mathfrak{A}$ and $\mathfrak{B}$ be subspaces with dimensions r_1 and r_2. Let their intersection $\mathfrak{C}$ have dimension m, and take in $\mathfrak{C}$ a basis $c_1, c_2, \cdots, c_m$. The vectors $c_1, \cdots, c_m$ are linearly independent and lie in $\mathfrak{A}$. Therefore, there exist vectors $a_1, \cdots, a_k$ in $\mathfrak{A}$ such that $c_1, \cdots, c_m, a_1, \cdots, a_k$ is a basis of $\mathfrak{A}$ (compare Section 21). Similarly, in $\mathfrak{B}$, let $b_1, \cdots, b_p, c_1, \cdots, c_m$ be a basis. Inasmuch as the number of vectors in a basis is the same as the dimension, we have the relations

$$k + m = r_1 , \qquad p + m = r_2 .$$

If we show that the system

$$a_1, \cdots, a_k , \qquad c_1, \cdots, c_m , \qquad b_1, \cdots, b_p . \tag{2}$$

is a basis of $\mathfrak{A} + \mathfrak{B}$, then Theorem 1 will be proved, for then the dimension of $\mathfrak{A} + \mathfrak{B}$ is

$$k + m + p = r_1 + r_2 - m .$$

Now every vector a in $\mathfrak{A}$ is a linear combination of $a_1, \cdots, a_k, c_1, \cdots, c_m$, which is a basis of $\mathfrak{A}$, and is certainly, therefore, a linear combination of the vectors (2). Analogously, every vector b in $\mathfrak{B}$ is a linear combination of the vectors (2). But then the sum $a + b$—that is, an arbitrary vector of $\mathfrak{A} + \mathfrak{B}$—is also a linear combination of the vectors (2). It remain to show that the system (2) is linearly independent.

Let

$$\alpha_1 a_1 + \cdots + \alpha_k a_k + \gamma_1 c_1 + \cdots + \gamma_m c_m + \beta_1 b_1 + \cdots + \beta_p b_p = \theta \tag{3}$$

be some linear relation among these vectors. Set

$$b = \beta_1 b_1 + \cdots + \beta_p b_p .$$

The vector b belongs to $\mathfrak{B}$, since it is a linear combination of $b_1, \cdots, b_p$, which are in $\mathfrak{B}$. On the other hand, from (3),

$$b = -\alpha_1 a_1 - \cdots - \alpha_k a_k - \gamma_1 c_1 - \cdots - \gamma_m c_m . \tag{4}$$

Since $a_1, \cdots, a_k, c_1, \cdots, c_m$ are contained in $\mathfrak{A}$, then b is also contained in $\mathfrak{A}$. Consequently b belongs to the intersection of $\mathfrak{A}$ and $\mathfrak{B}$, and this means, in the expression (4) of b in terms of the basis of $\mathfrak{A}$, that the terms in $a_1, \cdots, a_k$ are absent:

$$\alpha_1 = \cdots = \alpha_k = 0 .$$

From (3) we obtain

$$\gamma_1 c_1 + \cdots + \gamma_m c_m + \beta_1 b_1 + \cdots + \beta_p b_p = \theta .$$

But the system $c_1, \cdots, c_m, b_1, \cdots, b_p$ is a basis of $\mathfrak{B}$, hence is linearly independent, and

$$\gamma_1 = \cdots = \gamma_m = \beta_1 = \cdots = \beta_p = 0 .$$

This completes the proof.

From Theorem 1 we may deduce a lower bound for the dimension of the intersection of subspaces. Let us consider arbitrary linear subspaces $\mathfrak{A}, \mathfrak{B}$ of $\mathfrak{L}$, with dimensions r_1, r_2; let the dimension of $\mathfrak{L}$ be n and the dimension of $\mathfrak{A} \cap \mathfrak{B}$ be m. By Theorem 1 the dimension of $\mathfrak{A} + \mathfrak{B}$ is $r_1 + r_2 - m$. However, this cannot be larger than the dimension of $\mathfrak{L}$, and consequently, $r_1 + r_2 - m \leqq n$, or $m \geqq r_1 + r_2 - n$. Hence, *the dimension of the intersection of two linear subspaces of a space* $\mathfrak{L}$ *is not less than the sum of the dimensions of these subspaces minus the dimension of* $\mathfrak{L}$.

As examples, the intersection of two planes in a three-dimensional space always contains a line, the intersection of a two-dimensional and a three-dimensional subspace of a four-dimensional space contains a line, the intersection of two three-dimensional subspaces of a four-dimensional space contains a plane, and so on.

29. Direct Sums

By definition, every vector a belonging to a sum of linear subspaces

$$\mathfrak{A} = \mathfrak{A}_1 + \cdots + \mathfrak{A}_s ,$$

has a representation of the form

$$a = a_1 + \cdots + a_s , \tag{5}$$

where $a_i \in \mathfrak{A}$ and $i = 1, \cdots, s$. In general, this representation is not unique. However, when each vector a of $\mathfrak{A}$ admits only one representation of form (5)—that is, from (5) and

$$a = a_1' + \cdots + a_s' \qquad (a_i' \in \mathfrak{A}_i, i = 1, \cdots, s) \tag{6}$$

it follows that $a_1 = a_1', \cdots, a_s = a_s'$—then the sum is called a ***direct sum*** and is written

$$\mathfrak{A} = \mathfrak{A}_1 \dotplus \cdots \dotplus \mathfrak{A}_s .$$

Direct sums have many special properties, a few of which we will consider. First of all, the requirement of a unique representation for each vector of the sum may be replaced, in the definition of direct sum, by the weaker requirement of a unique representation for the zero vector: if the zero vector admits only one representation of form (5)—that is, *if from*

$$a_1 + \cdots + a_s = \theta \qquad (a_i \in \mathfrak{A}_i,\ i = 1, \cdots, s)$$

it follows that $a_1 = \cdots = a_s = \theta$, *then the sum is direct.*

To prove this, suppose that a vector a has the two representations (5) and (6). Subtracting, we obtain

$$(a_1 - a_1') + \cdots + (a_s - a_s') = \theta .$$

Since $(a_i - a_i') \in \mathfrak{A}_i$, $i = 1, \cdots, s$, then by assumption

$$a_1 - a_1' = \cdots = a_s - a_s' = \theta ,$$

or

$$a_1 = a_1', \cdots, a_s = a_s' .$$

The following theorem refers to the use of parentheses in direct sums.

THEOREM 2. *If the decompositions into linear subspaces*

$$\mathfrak{A} = \mathfrak{A}_1 + \mathfrak{A}_2 + \cdots + \mathfrak{A}_s , \tag{7}$$

$$\left.\begin{aligned} \mathfrak{A}_1 &= \mathfrak{A}_{11} + \mathfrak{A}_{12} + \cdots + \mathfrak{A}_{1m_1} , \\ &\vdots \\ \mathfrak{A}_s &= \mathfrak{A}_{s1} + \mathfrak{A}_{s2} + \cdots + \mathfrak{A}_{sm_s} , \end{aligned}\right\} \tag{8}$$

are direct, then the decomposition

$$\mathfrak{A} = \mathfrak{A}_{11} + \cdots + \mathfrak{A}_{1m_1} + \cdots + \mathfrak{A}_{s1} + \cdots + \mathfrak{A}_{sm_s} \tag{9}$$

is also direct. In other words, if each summand in a direct sum is replaced by a direct decomposition, then a new direct decomposition is obtained. Conversely, if decomposition (9) is direct, then decompositions (8) and (7) are also direct.

We prove the first assertion first. Let

$$a_{11} + a_{12} + \cdots + a_{1m_1} + \cdots + a_{s1} + a_{s2} + \cdots + a_{sm_s} = \theta .$$

Rewrite this equation in the form

$$a_1 + a_2 + \cdots + a_s = \theta , \tag{10}$$

where

$$a_i = a_{i1} + a_{i2} + \cdots + a_{im_i} . \tag{11}$$

Since $a_i \in \mathfrak{A}_i$ and the sum (7) is direct, (10) implies that $a_1 = \cdots = a_s = \theta$, and therefore

$$a_{i1} + a_{i2} + \cdots + a_{im_i} = \theta \tag{12}$$

for $i = 1, \cdots, s$. But by assumption the decomposition

$$\mathfrak{A}_i = \mathfrak{A}_{i1} + \mathfrak{A}_{i2} + \cdots + \mathfrak{A}_{im_i}$$

is also direct, and hence (12) implies that $a_{i1} = \cdots = a_{im_i} = \theta$. Hence (9) is a direct sum. Repeating the argument backward, we obtain a proof of the second assertion.

Theorem 2 permits us to consider the direct sum of several subspaces as the result of a sequence of direct sums with two summands. The conditions under which a sum of two subspaces is direct may be given in the following convenient form.

THEOREM 3. *The sum of two subspaces is direct if and only if the intersection of these subspaces is zero.*

If the intersection of two subspaces $\mathfrak{A}$ and $\mathfrak{B}$ contains a nonzero vector a, then for θ it is possible to write the decomposition

$$a + (-a) = \theta ,$$

where $a \neq \theta$, $a \in \mathfrak{A}$, $-a \in \mathfrak{B}$, and hence the sum $\mathfrak{A} + \mathfrak{B}$ is not direct. Conversely, if the sum $\mathfrak{A} + \mathfrak{B}$ is not direct, the zero vector has a decomposition

$$a + b = \theta , \qquad (a \neq \theta,\ a \in \mathfrak{A},\ b \in \mathfrak{B}).$$

Since $b = -a$, then b also belongs to $\mathfrak{A}$. Consequently the intersection of $\mathfrak{A}$ and $\mathfrak{B}$ contains the nonzero vector b.

THEOREM 4. *The dimension of a direct sum of subspaces is the sum of their dimensions.*

If there are two summands, then by Theorem 1 the dimension of the sum is the sum of the dimensions minus the dimension of the intersection. But by Theorem 3 the intersection is the zero space and has dimension zero. Therefore *the dimension of the direct sum of two subspaces is the sum of their dimensions*. If the number of summands is greater than 2, the proof is easily carried out by induction.

From Theorem 4 we have the following.

COROLLARY: *if a subspace $\mathfrak{A}$ is the direct sum of subspaces $\mathfrak{A}_1, \cdots, \mathfrak{A}_s$, then, taking a basis $a_{i1}, \cdots, a_{im_i}$ of each subspace $\mathfrak{A}_i$ for $i = 1, \cdots, s$ and combining these bases into one system,*

$$a_{11}, \cdots, a_{1m_1}, \cdots, a_{s1}, \cdots, a_{sm_s}, \tag{13}$$

we obtain a basis of the subspace $\mathfrak{A}$.

Every vector of $\mathfrak{A}_i$ is a linear combination of the vectors (13), and therefore an arbitrary vector of $\mathfrak{A}$ is also. The number of vectors in the system (13) is, by Theorem 4, the dimension of the subspace $\mathfrak{A}$. Hence (13) is a basis of $\mathfrak{A}$.

Theorem 4 permits the converse: *if the dimension of a sum of linear subspaces is the sum of their dimensions, then the sum is direct.*

To prove this, let $\mathfrak{A} = \mathfrak{A}_1 + \mathfrak{A}_2$ and

$$\dim \mathfrak{A} = \dim \mathfrak{A}_1 + \dim \mathfrak{A}_2 .$$

By Theorem 1, the dimension of $\mathfrak{A}_1 \cap \mathfrak{A}_2$ is zero, and hence $\mathfrak{A}_1 \cap \mathfrak{A}_2$ is the zero space. Thus, by Theorem 3, the sum $\mathfrak{A}_1 + \mathfrak{A}_2$ is direct. If the number of summands is greater than 2, the result is proved by induction.

● EXAMPLES AND PROBLEMS

1. Find the dimension of the linear subspace spanned by the vectors

$$a = [1, 3, 2, 1] , \qquad b = [4, 9, 5, 4] , \qquad c = [3, 7, 4, 3] .$$

2. If $e_1, \cdots, e_n$ is a basis of the linear space $\mathfrak{L}$ and $\mathfrak{A}_i$ is the subspace spanned by e_i, then $\mathfrak{L} = \mathfrak{A}_1 \dotplus \cdots \dotplus \mathfrak{A}_n$.

3. For each subspace $\mathfrak{A}$ of a space $\mathfrak{L}$ there exists a subspace $\mathfrak{B}$ such that

$$\mathfrak{L} = \mathfrak{A} \dotplus \mathfrak{B} .$$

4. Prove the following generalization of Theorem 3: a sum of several given linear subspaces is direct if and only if each of the given subspaces has zero intersection with the sum of all the remaining subspaces.

5. Show that the intersection of all the linear subspaces of a space $\mathfrak{L}$ whicn contain given linear subspaces equals the sum of the given subspaces.

6. Show that for arbitrary subspaces $\mathfrak{A}, \mathfrak{B}, \mathfrak{C}$ of a linear space,

$$\mathfrak{A}(\mathfrak{A}\mathfrak{B} + \mathfrak{C}) = \mathfrak{A}\mathfrak{B} + \mathfrak{A}\mathfrak{C} ,$$

$$(\mathfrak{A} + \mathfrak{B})(\mathfrak{A} + \mathfrak{C}) = \mathfrak{A} + (\mathfrak{A} + \mathfrak{B})\mathfrak{C} ,$$

where for brevity the intersection of subspaces is denoted by juxtaposition.

7. Every infinite dimensional linear space $\mathfrak{L}$ contains a proper subspace whose dimension coincides with that of $\mathfrak{L}$.

3 LINEAR TRANSFORMATIONS

The chief aim of this chapter is to study the properties of transformations of linear spaces. We need first, however, some notions concerning transformations of completely arbitrary sets.

1. *Transformations of Arbitrary Sets*

30. The Product of Transformations

Consider an arbitrary set $\mathfrak{M}$, either finite or infinite. A law which permits us to find, for each element of $\mathfrak{M}$, another element of $\mathfrak{M}$, is called a transformation of $\mathfrak{M}$. Let us agree to denote transformations by letters $\mathscr{A}, \mathscr{B}, \mathscr{C}, \cdots$. If m is an element of $\mathfrak{M}$, then $m\mathscr{A}$ denotes that element of $\mathfrak{M}$ which is obtained from m by the transformation $\mathscr{A}$. The element $m\mathscr{A}$ is called the *image* of the element m under the transformation $\mathscr{A}$, and m is called the *pre-image* of the element $m\mathscr{A}$.

Let us consider as an example the set of all points in the plane and denote by $\mathscr{U}$ the transformation consisting of a counterclockwise rotation of 90° about some point $\mathscr{O}$ (Fig. 2).

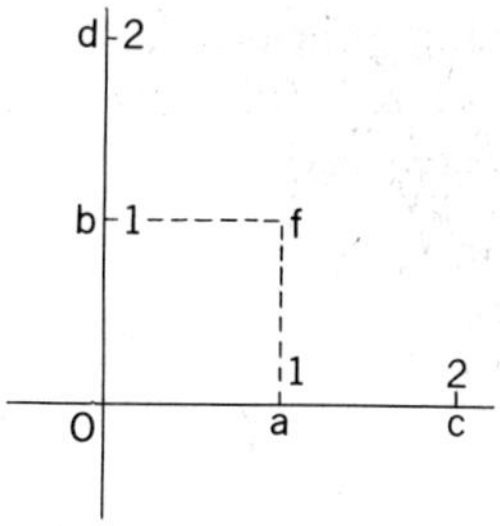

Figure 2

In the figure, we see that

$$a\mathscr{U} = b\,, \quad c\mathscr{U} = d\,.$$

Analogously, if $\mathscr{D}$ denotes a displacement

by 1 parallel to the axis $\mathscr{O}a$, then

$$a\mathscr{D} = c\,, \quad b\mathscr{D} = f\,,$$

Two transformations $\mathscr{A}$, $\mathscr{B}$ of a set $\mathfrak{M}$ are called equal if for each ele ment m of $\mathfrak{M}$,

$$m\mathscr{A} = m\mathscr{B}\,.$$

One of the fundamental notions of the theory of transformations is that of the product of transformations, which is introduced in the following way. Let $\mathscr{A}$, $\mathscr{B}$ be given transformations on a set $\mathfrak{M}$. The first carries an arbitrary element m of $\mathfrak{M}$ into $m\mathscr{A}$. If to the new element we apply the transformation $\mathscr{B}$, then we obtain the element $(m\mathscr{A})\mathscr{B}$. The transformation which carries m immediately into $(m\mathscr{A})\mathscr{B}$ is called the ***product*** of $\mathscr{A}$ and $\mathscr{B}$, and is denoted by $\mathscr{A}\mathscr{B}$. Thus by definition,

$$m(\mathscr{A}\mathscr{B}) = (m\mathscr{A})\mathscr{B}\,.$$

But if we apply to the element m first $\mathscr{B}$ and then $\mathscr{A}$, we obtain $(m\mathscr{B})\mathscr{A}$, and this may not coincide with $(m\mathscr{A})\mathscr{B}$. Indeed, in the example above we have

$$a(\mathscr{U}\mathscr{D}) = (a\mathscr{U})\mathscr{D} = b\mathscr{D} = f\,,$$
$$a(\mathscr{D}\mathscr{U}) = (a\mathscr{D})\mathscr{U} = c\mathscr{U} = d\,,$$

which means that $\mathscr{U}\mathscr{D} \neq \mathscr{D}\mathscr{U}$. Thus, *the product of transformations depends in general on the order of the factors.* We see that one of the fundamental laws of the multiplication of numbers fails for transformations. However, another fundamental law—the ***associativity of multiplication***—does hold for transformations. Let $\mathscr{A}$, $\mathscr{B}$, $\mathscr{C}$ be arbitrary transformations of a set $\mathfrak{M}$, and let $m \in \mathfrak{M}$. By definition, we have

$$m((\mathscr{A}\mathscr{B})\mathscr{C}) = (m(\mathscr{A}\mathscr{B}))\mathscr{C} = ((m\mathscr{A})\mathscr{B})\mathscr{C}\,,$$
$$m(\mathscr{A}(\mathscr{B}\mathscr{C})) = (m\mathscr{A})(\mathscr{B}\mathscr{C}) = ((m\mathscr{A})\mathscr{B})\mathscr{C}\,,$$

so

$$(\mathscr{A}\mathscr{B})\mathscr{C} = \mathscr{A}(\mathscr{B}\mathscr{C})\,.$$

Using this law it is easy to deduce that *the product of an arbitrary finite number of transformations, written in a definite order, does not depend on the arrangement of parentheses.* Thus, for example,

$$(\mathscr{A}\mathscr{B})(\mathscr{C}\mathscr{D}) = ((\mathscr{A}\mathscr{B})\mathscr{C})\mathscr{D} = (\mathscr{A}(\mathscr{B}\mathscr{C}))\mathscr{D} = \mathscr{A}((\mathscr{B}\mathscr{C})\mathscr{D})\,.$$

Therefore, in products containing a number of factors, it is possible to omit parentheses, and to speak simply of the product of two, three, or more transformations. The product of n factors each equal to $\mathscr{A}$ is called the nth power of $\mathscr{A}$ and is denoted by $\mathscr{A}^n$. Operations with powers are subject to the usual rules

$$\mathscr{A}^m \mathscr{A}^n = \mathscr{A}^{m+n}, \tag{1}$$

$$(\mathscr{A}^m)^n = \mathscr{A}^{mn}. \tag{2}$$

If the product of two transformations $\mathscr{A}$, $\mathscr{B}$ does not depend on the order of the factors, then $\mathscr{A}$ and $\mathscr{B}$ are called ***permutable*** or ***commutable.*** (1) shows that *powers of a transformation permute with each other.*

If $\mathscr{A}$, $\mathscr{B}$ are permutable, then

$$(\mathscr{A}\mathscr{B})^2 = \mathscr{A}\mathscr{B}\mathscr{A}\mathscr{B} = \mathscr{A}\mathscr{A}\mathscr{B}\mathscr{B} = \mathscr{A}^2\mathscr{B}^2,$$

and, in general,

$$(\mathscr{A}\mathscr{B})^n = \mathscr{A}^n\mathscr{B}^n. \tag{3}$$

If $\mathscr{A}$ and $\mathscr{B}$ are not permutable, then formula (3) may be false.

31. The Identity and Inverse Transformation

Among all transformations of a set $\mathfrak{M}$, a special place is occupied by the transformation which places in correspondence with each element m of $\mathfrak{M}$ this same element m. It is called the ***identity*** transformation, and we denote it by $\mathscr{E}$. Thus, for arbitrary m,

$$m\mathscr{E} = m.$$

Let $\mathscr{A}$ be an arbitrary transformation of a set $\mathfrak{M}$. Since

$$m(\mathscr{E}\mathscr{A}) = (m\mathscr{E})\mathscr{A} = m\mathscr{A},$$

$$m(\mathscr{A}\mathscr{E}) = (m\mathscr{A})\mathscr{E} = m\mathscr{A},$$

we see that

$$\mathscr{E}\mathscr{A} = \mathscr{A}\mathscr{E} = \mathscr{A}.$$

If for a transformation $\mathscr{A}$ it is possible to find a transformation $\mathscr{B}$ such that

$$\mathscr{A}\mathscr{B} = \mathscr{B}\mathscr{A} = \mathscr{E}, \tag{4}$$

then $\mathscr{B}$ is called the ***inverse*** of $\mathscr{A}$, and $\mathscr{A}$ is called ***invertible.*** It is easy to see that *every invertible transformation has only one inverse.* Indeed, if $\mathscr{A}$ had two inverses $\mathscr{B}$, $\mathscr{C}$, then, multiplying

$$\mathscr{A}\mathscr{C} = \mathscr{E}$$

on the left by $\mathscr{B}$ and using (4) and the associative law, we obtain $\mathscr{E}\mathscr{C} = \mathscr{B}\mathscr{E}$, or $\mathscr{C} = \mathscr{B}$.

The inverse transformation of $\mathscr{A}$ is denoted by $\mathscr{A}^{-1}$. Relation (4) is symmetric in $\mathscr{A}$ and $\mathscr{B}$; therefore, if $\mathscr{A}$ is the inverse of $\mathscr{B}$, then $\mathscr{B}$ is the inverse of $\mathscr{A}$; that is,

$$(\mathscr{A}^{-1})^{-1} = \mathscr{A}. \tag{5}$$

Let us, by definition, set

$$\mathscr{A}^0 = \mathscr{E}, \quad \mathscr{A}^{-n} = (\mathscr{A}^{-1})^n, \qquad n = 1, 2, \cdots.$$

From (4) and (5) it follows that (1) and (2) are valid not only for positive integral exponents, but for all integral exponents. In particular,

$$(\mathscr{A}^n)^{-1} = (\mathscr{A}^{-1})^n = \mathscr{A}^{-n} .$$

Further, the relation

$$\mathscr{A}\mathscr{B}\mathscr{B}^{-1}\mathscr{A}^{-1} = \mathscr{E}$$

shows that

$$(\mathscr{A}\mathscr{B})^{-1} = \mathscr{B}^{-1}\mathscr{A}^{-1} .$$

32. One-to-one Transformations

Not every transformation is invertible. The following theorem indicates the intuitive criterion for invertible transformations.

THEOREM. *A transformation $\mathscr{A}$ of a set $\mathfrak{M}$ is invertible if and only if $\mathscr{A}$ is a one-to-one mapping of $\mathfrak{M}$ onto itself—that is, if and only if distinct elements of $\mathfrak{M}$ are carried into distinct elements and each element of $\mathfrak{M}$ has a pre-image in $\mathfrak{M}$.*

We first prove the necessity. Let $\mathscr{A}$ have an inverse transformation $\mathscr{B}$, so

$$\mathscr{A}\mathscr{B} = \mathscr{B}\mathscr{A} = \mathscr{E} .$$

Take an arbitrary element m in $\mathfrak{M}$ and let $m\mathscr{B} = n$. Taking the image under $\mathscr{A}$ and replacing $\mathscr{B}\mathscr{A}$ by $\mathscr{E}$, we obtain $m = n\mathscr{A}$; that is, each element m of $\mathfrak{M}$ is the image of some element n of $\mathfrak{M}$. But if two elements m_1, m_2 are carried by $\mathscr{A}$ into the same element

$$m_1\mathscr{A} = m_2\mathscr{A} ,$$

then, taking the image under $\mathscr{B}$, we obtain $m_1 = m_2$. Consequently, each element of $\mathfrak{M}$ has only one pre-image in $\mathfrak{M}$.

We prove now the sufficiency of the conditions. By assumption, for each element m of $\mathfrak{M}$ there is one and only one element n for which

$$n\mathscr{A} = m . \tag{6}$$

We denote the transformation which carries m into n by $\mathscr{B}$. Thus,

$$m\mathscr{B} = n . \tag{7}$$

Operating on (7) by $\mathscr{A}$ and using (6), we obtain

$$m(\mathscr{B}\mathscr{A}) = n\mathscr{A} = m .$$

Since m is arbitrary, $\mathscr{B}\mathscr{A} = \mathscr{E}$. Analogously, operating on (6) by $\mathscr{B}$ and using (7), we obtain $\mathscr{A}\mathscr{B} = \mathscr{E}$. Consequently, $\mathscr{B}$ is the desired inverse transformation.

33. Permutations

Several other properties of transformations of finite sets that will be needed in Chapter VIII are presented now.

A transformation of a finite set is usually given by means of a table, in which the elements of the given set, in some order, are written in the first row, while beneath these elements are the ***corresponding image elements.*** For example,

$$\sigma = \begin{pmatrix} 1 & 2 & 3 \\ 3 & 1 & 2 \end{pmatrix}$$

is a transformation of the set {1, 2, 3}, under which 1 is carried into 3, 2 into 1, and 3 into 2; using the notation given above,

$$1\sigma = 3 , \quad 2\sigma = 1 , \quad 3\sigma = 2 .$$

Invertible transformations of finite sets are called ***permutations.*** In order that a transformation, written in a table, be a permutation, it is necessary and sufficient that each element of the set be found exactly once in each row. To write the inverse transformation σ^{-1}, it is evidently sufficient to interchange the two rows of the table.

Let $F(x_1, \cdots, x_n)$ be a function in the indeterminates $x_1, \cdots, x_n$, and σ be a permutation of the numbers $1, \cdots, n$. The effect on the function F of performing σ on the indeterminates $x_1, \cdots, x_n$ is, by definition,

$$F\sigma = F(x_{1\sigma}, \cdots, x_{n\sigma}) .$$

From this definition it follows immediately that for arbitrary permutations σ, ρ and arbitrary functions F, G in $x_1, \cdots, x_n$ we have

$$F(\rho\sigma) = (F\rho)\sigma , \tag{8}$$

$$(FG)\sigma = F\sigma \cdot G\sigma , \quad (F + G)\sigma = F\sigma + G\sigma . \tag{9}$$

Let us take now for the function F the expression

$$\Delta = \prod_{i<j} (x_i - x_j) = (x_1 - x_2)(x_1 - x_3)\cdots(x_1 - x_n)(x_2 - x_3)\cdots(x_{n-1} - x_n) . \tag{10}$$

It is clear that for any permutation σ we have $\Delta\sigma = \pm \Delta$. If $\Delta\sigma = \Delta$, then σ is called an ***even*** permutation, while if $\Delta\sigma = - \Delta$, σ is called an ***odd*** permutation. For noninvertible transformations σ we have $\Delta\sigma = 0$. Therefore for any transformation σ of $1, \cdots, n$ we have

$$\Delta\sigma = \varepsilon_\sigma \Delta ,$$

where $\varepsilon_\sigma = +1$ if σ is an even permutation, $\varepsilon_\sigma = -1$ if σ is an odd permutation, and $\varepsilon_\sigma = 0$ if σ is a noninvertible transformation. The symbol ε_σ is also called the ***sign*** of the transformation σ.

From (8), (9) we have, for arbitrary transformations ρ, σ,

$$\varepsilon_{\rho\sigma}\Delta = \Delta(\rho\sigma) = (\Delta\rho)\sigma = \varepsilon_\sigma\varepsilon_\rho\Delta ,$$

or

$$\varepsilon_{\rho\sigma} = \varepsilon_\rho\varepsilon_\sigma .$$

That is, *the sign of the product of transformations is the product of the signs of the factors.* Since the sign of the identity transformation is $+1$, *the sign of the inverse of a permutation always coincides with the sign of the given permutation.*

A ***cyclical permutation***, or a ***cycle*** $(i_1 i_2 \cdots i_m)$, is a permutation σ under which $i_1\sigma = i_2$, $i_2\sigma = i_3$, $\cdots$, $i_{m-1}\sigma = i_m$, $i_m\sigma = i_1$, and $i\sigma = i$ for the remaining elements i of the set, if there are any. In particular, a permutation which interchanges i and j and leaves the remaining elements fixed is called a ***transposition***. Interchanging the indices 1 and 2 in expression (10) for Δ, it is easy to see that $\Delta(12) = -\Delta$; that is, the transposition is an odd permutation. On the other hand, immediate computations show that

$$(1i)(12)(1i) = (i2)\ , \quad (2j)(i2)(2j) = (ij)\ ,$$

and sincc $\varepsilon_{\rho\sigma\rho} = \varepsilon_\sigma$ for all ρ, σ, we have

$$\varepsilon_{(ij)} = \varepsilon_{(2j)\,(i2)\,(2j)} = \varepsilon_{(i2)} = \varepsilon_{(1i)\,(12)\,(1i)} = \varepsilon_{(12)}\ .$$

That is, *every transposition is an odd permutation.*

It follows further that the product of an odd number of transpositions is an odd permutation, and the product of an even number of transpositions is an even permutation. In particular, from the easily verified formula

$$(123\cdots m) = (12)(13)\cdots(1m)\ ,$$

it follows that a cycle $(i_1 i_2 \cdots i_m)$ of even length m is an odd permutation, and a cycle of odd length is an even permutation.

It is clear that cycles without common elements are permutable (commutable). At the same time, a completely arbitrary permutation is easily decomposed into a product of cycles without common elements. For this we take an arbitrary element i_1 of the set and consider its image i_2 under the permutation. If $i_1 = i_2$, then we obtain the cycle (i_1), or the identity transformation, as the first factor. If $i_1 \neq i_2$, then we take the image i_3 of i_2. For $i_3 = i_1$ we obtain the cycle $(i_1 i_2)$ as a factor; for $i_3 \neq i_1$, we consider the image i_4 of i_3. If $i_4 = i_1$, the cycle is closed, and we obtain the factor $(i_1 i_2 i_3)$, and so on; finally, examining all the elements of the set, we obtain a decomposition of the permutation into cycles without common elements. For example, we have

$$\rho = \begin{pmatrix} 1 & 2 & 3 & 4 & 5 \\ 3 & 4 & 5 & 2 & 1 \end{pmatrix} = (135)(24)$$

Multiplying the signs of the cycles, we obtain $\varepsilon_\rho = -1$.

There is another method of determining the sign of a permutation, by counting the number of so-called inversions. In the table for a permutation the upper row may contain the elements of the set in an arbitrary order. But where the set under consideration is a set of integers, we may agree to write them in the first row in increasing order. Then the permutation will be fully known if we are given only the lower row of the table, the *permuted* numbers. Thus we have the possibility of writing a permutation in a one-rowed table instead of a two-rowed table. Let σ be a permutation $i_1, i_2, \cdots, i_n$, given in this way, of the numbers $1, 2, \cdots, n$. We consider all possible pairs i_k, i_l, where $k < l$, and say that the pair i_k, i_l gives an ***inversion*** if $i_k > i_l$. From

$$\Delta\sigma = \prod_{k<l}(x_{k\sigma} - x_{l\sigma}) = \prod_{k<l}(x_{i_k} - x_{i_l}),$$

it is evident that $\varepsilon_\sigma = 1$ if the number of factors $x_{i_k} - x_{i_l}$ for which $i_k > i_l$ is even, and $\varepsilon_\sigma = -1$ if the number of such factors is odd. Consequently, evenness of the permutation σ is equivalent to evenness of the number of inversions is $i_1, i_2, \cdots, i_n$.

● EXAMPLES AND PROBLEMS

1. In the usual space $\mathfrak{R}$ take an orthogonal system of coordinates $\mathscr{O}xyz$. Denote by $\mathscr{A}$ a rotation of the space by 90° about the axis $\mathscr{O}x$ in the direction from $\mathscr{O}y$ to $\mathscr{O}z$, by $\mathscr{B}$ a rotation about $\mathscr{O}y$ of 90° from $\mathscr{O}z$ to $\mathscr{O}x$, and by $\mathscr{C}$ a rotation about $\mathscr{O}z$ of 90° from $\mathscr{O}x$ to $\mathscr{O}y$. Let m be the point with coordinates, (1, 0, 1). Find the coordinates of the point $m\mathscr{A}$, $m(\mathscr{B}\mathscr{C})$, $m(\mathscr{C}\mathscr{B})$, and show that
$$\mathscr{A}^4 = \mathscr{B}^4 = \mathscr{C}^4 = \mathscr{E}, \quad \mathscr{A}\mathscr{B} \neq \mathscr{B}\mathscr{A}, \quad \mathscr{A}^2\mathscr{B}^2 = \mathscr{B}^2\mathscr{A}^2.$$
2. Consider two transformations $\mathscr{A}, \mathscr{C}$ of an arbitrary set $\mathfrak{M}$, where $\mathscr{C}$ is invertible. Take an arbitrary element u of $\mathfrak{M}$ and let $v = u\mathscr{A}$. The transformation $\mathscr{C}$ takes u, v into some elements x, y. Show that then the transformation $\mathscr{C}^{-1}\mathscr{A}\mathscr{C}$ takes x into y (Fig. 3).
3. Let $\mathscr{O}$ be an arbitrary point in the plane and let $\mathscr{A}$ denote a rotation of the plane about $\mathscr{O}$ through some angle α. Let $\mathscr{B}$ be a translation of the plane by a distance a in some definite direction. Show that $\mathscr{B}^{-1}\mathscr{A}\mathscr{B}$ is a rotation through α about the point $\mathscr{O}\mathscr{B}$, and that $\mathscr{A}^{-1}\mathscr{B}\mathscr{A}$ is a translation by the distance a in a direction differing by α from the original direction.

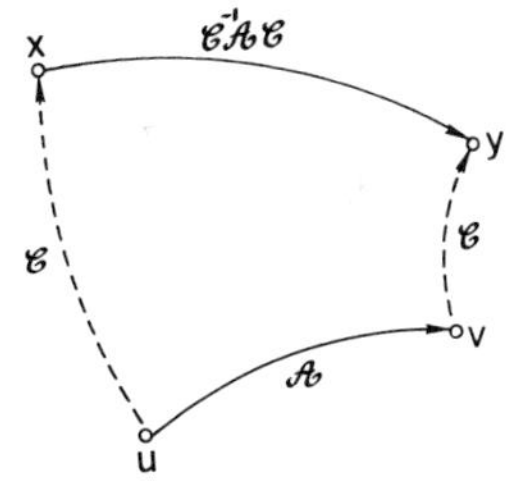

Figure 3

2. *Linear Transformations and Their Matrices*

34. Simplest Properties

A ***transformation*** of a linear space $\mathfrak{L}$ is a mapping that places in correspondence with each vector in $\mathfrak{L}$ a uniquely determined vector in $\mathfrak{L}$. A transformation is called ***linear*** if it carries a scalar times a vector into the same scalar times the corresponding vector, and carries the sum of vectors into the sum of the corresponding vectors. More briefly, a transformation $\mathscr{A}$ is called linear if for arbitrary vectors x, y in $\mathfrak{L}$ and an arbitrary scalar α from the field of coefficients we have

$$(\alpha x)\mathscr{A} = \alpha(x\mathscr{A}) , \tag{1}$$

$$(x + y)\mathscr{A} = x\mathscr{A} + y\mathscr{A} . \tag{2}$$

In (1), for $\alpha = 0$, we obtain

$$\theta\mathscr{A} = \theta .$$

That is, *every linear transformation takes the zero vector into the zero vector.*

From (1) and (2) the following fundamental property of linear transformations is immediate: if $\mathscr{A}$ is a linear transformation, then

$$(\alpha_1 x_1 + \cdots + \alpha_m x_m)\mathscr{A} = \alpha_1(x_1\mathscr{A}) + \cdots + \alpha_m(x_m\mathscr{A}) , \tag{3}$$

where $x_1, \cdots, x_m$ are arbitrary vectors in $\mathfrak{L}$, and $\alpha_1, \cdots, \alpha_m$ are arbitrary scalars from the base field.

To prove this, we use induction on m. For $m = 1$, (3) coincides with (1). Suppose now that (3) holds for $m - 1$ summands. Then

$$\begin{aligned}(\alpha_1 x_1 + \cdots + \alpha_m x_m)\mathscr{A} &= (\alpha_1 x_1 + (\alpha_2 x_2 + \cdots + \alpha_m x_m))\mathscr{A} \\ &= (\alpha_1 x_1)\mathscr{A} + (\alpha_2 x_2 + \cdots + \alpha_m x_m)\mathscr{A} \\ &= \alpha_1(x_1\mathscr{A}) + \alpha_2(x_2\mathscr{A}) + \cdots + \alpha_m(x_m\mathscr{A}) .\end{aligned}$$

For $m = 2$, (3) becomes

$$(\alpha x + \beta y)\mathscr{A} = \alpha(x\mathscr{A}) + \beta(y\mathscr{A}) , \tag{4}$$

which for $\beta = 0$ and for $\alpha = \beta = 1$ again yields (1) and (2). Thus, property (4) fully characterizes linear transformations and may serve as their definition.

We agreed above to call the transformation which carries each element into itself the identity transformation $\mathscr{E}$. Therefore, if the set under consideration is the set of vectors of a linear space,

$$(\alpha x + \beta y)\mathscr{E} = \alpha x + \beta y = \alpha(x\mathscr{E}) + \beta(y\mathscr{E}) ,$$

Consequently, *the identity transformation of a vector space is linear.* The transformation which carries each vector into the zero vector is called the ***zero transformation*** and is denoted by $\mathscr{O}$. It is clear that the zero transformation is also linear.

Let us consider two concrete examples. Let $\mathfrak{R}$ be the usual vector space of directed segments with origin $\mathscr{O}$. Choose a plane through $\mathscr{O}$ and denote by $x\mathscr{A}$ the projection of the segment x on this plane. Then these properties of projections are known: 1) the projection of the sum of segments is the sum of their projections, 2) if a segment is multiplied by α, then its projection is multiplied by α; these may be written

$$(x + y)\mathscr{A} = x\mathscr{A} + y\mathscr{A} , \quad (\alpha x)\mathscr{A} = \alpha(x\mathscr{A}) ,$$

which shows that the operation of projection is a linear transformation.

As the second example, we consider the set of all polynomials in an indeterminate λ of degree not higher than n. With respect to the usual operations of addition and multiplication by a scalar, these polynomials constitute a linear space of dimension $n + 1$. We set in correspondence to each polynomial its derivative. Since the derivative of a sum is the sum of the derivatives of the summands, and a constant factor is carried directly into the derivative, the operation of differentiation is a linear transformation of the space of polynomials.

We now consider a method of specifying a linear transformation in terms of basis vectors.

THEOREM 1. *Let $a_1, \cdots, a_n$ be a basis of the linear space $\mathfrak{L}$, and let $b_1, \cdots, b_n$ be any set of n vectors of $\mathfrak{L}$. Then there exists one and only one linear transformation of the space $\mathfrak{L}$ which takes $a_1, \cdots, a_n$ into $b_1, \cdots, b_n$ respectively.*

To construct the desired transformation, we take an arbitrary vector x and express it as a linear combination of the basis $a_1, \cdots, a_n$. Let

$$x = \xi_1 a_1 + \cdots + \xi_n a_n , \tag{5}$$

and let

$$x' = \xi_1 b_1 + \cdots + \xi_n b_n ,$$

Denote by $\mathscr{A}$ the transformation which takes x into x'. Thus, if x has the expression (5)

$$x\mathscr{A} = \xi_1 b_1 + \cdots + \xi_n b_n . \tag{6}$$

Substituting $\xi_i = 1$, $\xi_j = 0$, where ($j \neq i$ and $i = 1, \cdots, n$), we obtain $a_i\mathscr{A} = b_i$ for $i = 1, \cdots, n$, so that $\mathscr{A}$ takes $a_1, \cdots, a_n$ into $b_1, \cdots, b_n$. We now show that $\mathscr{A}$ is linear. Multiplying (5) by an arbitrary scalar α, we have

$$\alpha x = (\alpha\xi_1)a_1 + \cdots + (\alpha\xi_n)a_n ,$$

Comparing this with (6), we obtain

$$(\alpha x)\mathscr{A} = (\alpha\xi_1)b_1 + \cdots + (\alpha\xi_n)b_n ,$$

or

$$(\alpha x)\mathscr{A} = \alpha(x\mathscr{A}) . \tag{7}$$

Let

$$y = \eta_1 a_1 + \cdots + \eta_n a_n$$

be any other vector in $\mathfrak{L}$. Then

$$x + y = (\xi_1 + \eta_1)a_1 + \cdots + (\xi_n + \eta_n)a_n ,$$

and, consequently,

$$y\mathscr{A} = \eta_1 b_1 + \cdots + \eta_n b_n ,$$
$$(x + y)\mathscr{A} = (\xi_1 + \eta_1)b_1 + \cdots + (\xi_n + \eta_n)b_n .$$

The last equation gives

$$(x + y)\mathscr{A} = \xi_1 b_1 + \cdots + \xi_n b_n + \eta_1 b_1 + \cdots + \eta_n b_n = x\mathscr{A} + y\mathscr{A} . \tag{8}$$

Equations (7) and (8) together show that $\mathscr{A}$ is linear.

It is still necessary to show that every linear transformation $\mathscr{B}$ which takes $a_1, \cdots, a_n$ into $b_1, \cdots, b_n$ coincides with $\mathscr{A}$. By assumption, $a_i\mathscr{B} = b_i$ for $i = 1, \cdots, n$. Consequently, if x is as in (5), then

$$x\mathscr{B} = \xi_1(a_1\mathscr{B}) + \cdots + \xi_n(a_n\mathscr{B}) = \xi_1 b_1 + \cdots + \xi_n b_n = x\mathscr{A} ,$$

or $\mathscr{B} = \mathscr{A}$.

35. The Matrix of a Linear Transformation

We will now show how to specify a linear transformation by means of scalars. Let $a_1, \cdots, a_n$ be a coordinate system in the space $\mathfrak{L}$, and suppose we are given some linear transformation $\mathscr{A}$ of $\mathfrak{L}$. The transformation $\mathscr{A}$ takes $a_1, \cdots, a_n$ into some vectors $a_1\mathscr{A}, \cdots, a_n\mathscr{A}$, which may be expressed in terms of $a_1, \cdots, a_n$. Let these expressions be

$$\begin{aligned} a_1\mathscr{A} &= \alpha_{11}a_1 + \alpha_{12}a_2 + \cdots + \alpha_{1n}a_n , \\ a_2\mathscr{A} &= \alpha_{21}a_1 + \alpha_{22}a_2 + \cdots + \alpha_{2n}a_n , \\ &\vdots \\ a_n\mathscr{A} &= \alpha_{n1}a_1 + \alpha_{n2}a_2 + \cdots + \alpha_{nn}a_n . \end{aligned}$$

The matrix

$$A = \begin{bmatrix} \alpha_{11} & \alpha_{12} \cdots & \alpha_{1n} \\ \alpha_{21} & \alpha_{22} \cdots & \alpha_{2n} \\ \vdots & \vdots & \vdots \\ \alpha_{n1} & \alpha_{n2} \cdots & \alpha_{nn} \end{bmatrix} ,$$

consisting of the coordinate rows of the vectors $a_1\mathscr{A}, \cdots, a_n\mathscr{A}$, is called the ***matrix of the transformation*** $\mathscr{A}$ in the coordinate system $a_1, \cdots, a_n$. Thus, for a given coordinate system, a definite matrix corresponds to each linear transformation. The question arises as to whether this correspondence is one-to-one. The answer is in the affirmative, since, given a matrix A, we may first find the vectors

$$\begin{aligned} b_1 &= \alpha_{11}a_1 + \cdots + \alpha_{1n}a_n , \\ &\vdots \\ b_n &= \alpha_{n1}a_1 + \cdots + \alpha_{nn}a_n , \end{aligned}$$

and then construct, by Theorem 1, the linear transformation $\mathscr{A}$ which takes $a_1, \cdots, a_n$ into $b_1, \cdots, b_n$, This transformation is unique, and its matrix evidently coincides with A.

We now construct the matrices that correspond to the identity and zero transformations of $\mathfrak{L}$. Let $a_1, \cdots, a_n$ be any system of coordinates in $\mathfrak{L}$. Then

$$\begin{aligned} a_1\mathscr{O} &= 0\cdot a_1 + \cdots + 0\cdot a_n , & a_1\mathscr{E} &= 1\cdot a_1 + \cdots + 0\cdot a_n , \\ &\vdots \\ a_n\mathscr{O} &= 0\cdot a_1 + \cdots + 0\cdot a_n , & a_n\mathscr{E} &= 0\cdot a_1 + \cdots + 1\cdot a_n . \end{aligned}$$

Consequently, *in any coordinate system, the zero transformation has the zero matrix, and the identity transformation has the identity matrix.*

We now pose the problem: how, given the matrix of a linear transformation, $\mathscr{A}$, and the coordinates of a vector x, are the coordinates of $x\mathscr{A}$ found?

Let the chosen coordinate system be $a_1, \cdots, a_n$, and let the coordinates of x in this system be $\xi_1, \cdots, \xi_n$. Denote the elements of the matrix A of $\mathscr{A}$, in the same coordinate system, by α_{ij} where $i, j = 1, \cdots, n$. Then

$$x = \xi_1 a_1 + \cdots + \xi_n a_n$$

and

$$x\mathscr{A} = \xi_1(a_1\mathscr{A}) + \cdots + \xi_n(a_n\mathscr{A}) .$$

By the definition of A,

$$a_i\mathscr{A} = \alpha_{i1}a_1 + \cdots + \alpha_{in}a_n .$$

Putting these values into the preceding equation, we obtain

$$x\mathscr{A} = (\xi_1\alpha_{11} + \xi_2\alpha_{21} + \cdots + \xi_n\alpha_{n1})a_1 + \cdots + (\xi_1\alpha_{1n} + \xi_2\alpha_{2n} + \cdots + \xi_n\alpha_{nn})a_n .$$

Consequently the coordinate row of the new vector $x\mathscr{A}$ is

$$[x\mathscr{A}] = [\xi_1\alpha_{11} + \cdots + \xi_n\alpha_{n1}, \cdots, \xi_1\alpha_{1n} + \cdots + \xi_n\alpha_{nn}] = [x]A .$$

That is *the coordinate row of the new vector is the coordinate row of the old vector multiplied by the matrix of the transformation*:

$$[x\mathscr{A}] = [x]A .$$

36. Transformation of Coordinates

In the preceding section it was shown that there exist one-to-one correspondences between linear transformations of an n-dimensional vector space and square matrices of order n. However, to determine such a correspondence it was necessary to choose a definite coordinate system in $\mathfrak{L}$. If this coordinate system is changed, then the correspondence is changed. Hence a single linear transformation $\mathscr{A}$ will correspond to different matrices in different coordinate systems. We seek the connection between these matrices.

Let $a_1, \cdots, a_n$ be the old, and $a'_1, \cdots, a'_n$ be the new, coordinate system, and let T be the matrix of the transformation from the old system to the new (compare Section 25). Let $[x]$, $[x]_1$ denote the coordinate rows of x in the old and new systems. In the old system we have

$$[x\mathscr{A}] = [x]A .$$

In the new system we have

$$[x\mathscr{A}]_1 = [x]_1 A_1 .$$

However, in Section 25 it was shown that

$$[x] = [x]_1 T , \quad [x\mathscr{A}] = [x\mathscr{A}]_1 T .$$

If we combine these with the preceding equalities, we obtain

$$[x]_1 TA = [x]_1 A_1 T .$$

Since x is arbitrary, then, by the lemma of Section 26, we have $TA = A_1 T$, or

$$A_1 = TAT^{-1} .$$

Thus, *the matrix of a linear transformation in the new coordinate system is the matrix of the same linear transformation in the old system transformed by the inverse of the matrix of the transformation from the old system to the new.*

We consider one further question: from the point of view of the theory of linear transformations, how should the matrix of the transformation from one coordinate system to another be interpreted? Let $a_1, \cdots, a_n$ and $a'_1, \cdots, a'_n$ be two coordinate systems in a space $\mathfrak{L}$. By Theorem 1 there exists a unique linear transformation $\mathscr{T}$ which carries the old system of coordinates into the new; that is, it has the property

$$a_i \mathscr{T} = a'_i , \qquad i = 1, \cdots, n .$$

To write the matrix of the transformation $\mathscr{T}$ in the old system, we must, by Section 35, express all the vectors a'_i as linear combinations of $a_1, \cdots, a_n$. But this is the same way in which the matrix of the transformation of coordinates is obtained. Thus, *the matrix of the transformation of coordinates is the matrix of the linear transformation which carries the old coordinate system into the new*, computed in the old coordinate system. The last part of the statement, however, is superfluous, since if we computed the matrix of the transformation $\mathscr{T}$ in the new coordinate system we would obtain the same matrix T of the transformation of coordinates. In fact, if the matrix of the transformation $\mathscr{T}$ in the old coordinate system is T, then the matrix of the transformation of coordinates is also T. This means that the matrix of $\mathscr{T}$ in the new system equals $TTT^{-1} = T$, which was to be proved.

● EXAMPLES AND PROBLEMS

1. Consider the space of vectors in the plane with origin $\mathscr{O}$. Show that the transformation which rotates all vectors through an angle α about $\mathscr{O}$ is linear, and that in a coordinate system of perpendicular vectors of unit length the matrix of this transformation is $\begin{bmatrix} \cos\alpha & \sin\alpha \\ -\sin\alpha & \cos\alpha \end{bmatrix}$.

2. Let $\mathfrak{R}$ be the usual space of directed line segments with origin $\mathscr{O}$. In $\mathfrak{R}$ let e_1, e_2, e_3 be a coordinate system of orthogonal vectors of unit length. Let $\mathscr{P}$ denote the projection onto the e_1 axis, and show that the matrix of the linear transformation $\mathscr{P}$ is $\begin{vmatrix} 1 & 0 & 0 \\ 0 & 0 & 0 \\ 0 & 0 & 0 \end{vmatrix}$; show also that the matrix of the projection onto the plane $e_1 \mathscr{O} e_2$ is

$$\begin{bmatrix} 1 & 0 & 0 \\ 0 & 1 & 0 \\ 0 & 0 & 0 \end{bmatrix}.$$

3. How is the matrix of a transformation $\mathscr{A}$ changed if some two vectors of the coordinate system are interchanged?
4. Prove that a linear transformation of a one-dimensional space multiplies each vector by a fixed scalar.
5. Let $\mathfrak{L}$ be the space of square matrices of order 2 (over, say, the real field). Show that the transformation $\mathscr{A}$, which multiplies, on the right, every matrix in $\mathfrak{L}$ by the matrix $\begin{bmatrix} 1 & 2 \\ 3 & -1 \end{bmatrix}$, is linear. Find the matrix of the transformation $\mathscr{A}$ in the coordinate system

$$\begin{bmatrix} 1 & 0 \\ 0 & 0 \end{bmatrix}, \begin{bmatrix} 0 & 1 \\ 0 & 0 \end{bmatrix}, \begin{bmatrix} 0 & 0 \\ 1 & 0 \end{bmatrix}, \begin{bmatrix} 0 & 0 \\ 0 & 1 \end{bmatrix}.$$

3. *Operations with Linear Transformations*

37. Multiplication of Linear Transformations

Let two linear transformations $\mathscr{A}$ and $\mathscr{B}$ be given in a linear space $\mathfrak{L}$. Apply first the transformation $\mathscr{A}$ and then the transformation $\mathscr{B}$ to the vector x in $\mathfrak{L}$, and obtain the vector

$$y = (x\mathscr{A})\mathscr{B}.$$

The transformation which carries x immediately into y is called the product of $\mathscr{A}$ and $\mathscr{B}$ (compare Section 30). Consequently,

$$x(\mathscr{A}\mathscr{B}) = (x\mathscr{A})\mathscr{B}. \tag{1}$$

We show that *the product of linear transformations is a linear transformation*, By Section 34, it is sufficient to show that

$$(\alpha x + \beta y)(\mathscr{A}\mathscr{B}) = \alpha \cdot x(\mathscr{A}\mathscr{B}) + \beta \cdot y(\mathscr{A}\mathscr{B}).$$

From (1),

$$(\alpha x + \beta y)(\mathscr{A}\mathscr{B}) = ((\alpha x + \beta y)\mathscr{A})\mathscr{B}.$$

Since $\mathscr{A}$ and $\mathscr{B}$ are linear, then

$$((\alpha x + \beta y)\mathscr{A})\mathscr{B} = (\alpha(x\mathscr{A}) + \beta(y\mathscr{A}))\mathscr{B} = \alpha \cdot (x\mathscr{A})\mathscr{B} + \beta \cdot (y\mathscr{A})\mathscr{B},$$

or

$$(\alpha x + \beta y)(\mathscr{A}\mathscr{B}) = \alpha \cdot x(\mathscr{A}\mathscr{B}) + \beta \cdot y(\mathscr{A}\mathscr{B}),$$

which was to be proved.

Now take a coordinate system in $\mathfrak{L}$ and let A, B be the matrices of the transformations $\mathscr{A}$, $\mathscr{B}$ relative to this coordinate system. How does one find the matrix of the transformation $\mathscr{A}\mathscr{B}$ relative to this coordinate system? Denote this unknown matrix by C and let x be an arbitrary vector of $\mathfrak{L}$ with coordinate row $[x]$. Then

$$[x(\mathscr{A}\mathscr{B})] = [x]C .$$

On the other hand,

$$[x(\mathscr{A}\mathscr{B})] = [(x\mathscr{A})\mathscr{B}] = [x\mathscr{A}]B = [x]AB .$$

Comparing the two results, we have

$$[x]C = [x]AB$$

for arbitrary x. By the lemma of Section 26,

$$C = AB .$$

That is, *the matrix of the product of linear transformations equals the product of the matrices of these transformations.*

Consider a one-to-one linear transformation $\mathscr{A}$. If $\mathscr{A}$ carries x into y, then the transformation which carries y into x will be the inverse transformation $\mathscr{A}^{-1}$ (compare Section 32). We show that *if $\mathscr{A}$ is linear, then $\mathscr{A}^{-1}$ is also linear.* Let

$$u\mathscr{A}^{-1} = x , \quad v\mathscr{A}^{-1} = y ,$$

where u, v are arbitrary vectors in $\mathfrak{L}$. Since $\mathscr{A}$ is linear,

$$(\alpha x + \beta y)\mathscr{A} = \alpha \cdot x\mathscr{A} + \beta \cdot y\mathscr{A} = \alpha u + \beta v .$$

Hence

$$(\alpha u + \beta v)\mathscr{A}^{-1} = \alpha x + \beta y = \alpha \cdot u\mathscr{A}^{-1} + \beta \cdot v\mathscr{A}^{-1} ,$$

which was to be proved.

If A is the matrix of the transformation $\mathscr{A}$ and X is the matrix of $\mathscr{A}^{-1}$, then as a consequence of

$$\mathscr{A}\mathscr{A}^{-1} = \mathscr{A}^{-1}\mathscr{A} = \mathscr{E}$$

we have

$$AX = XA = E .$$

Thus, *an invertible transformation has an invertible matrix.* In particular, *in order that a linear transformation be invertible, it is necessary and sufficient that its matrix be invertible.*

An immediate consequence of our results is the following rule: *the matrix of the transformation $\mathscr{A}^n$ equals A^n, where A is the matrix of the transformation $\mathscr{A}$.*

38. Addition and Multiplication by a Scalar

The transformation obtained by first applying a transformation $\mathscr{A}$ and then multiplying the result by a scalar α, is called the ***product*** of $\mathscr{A}$ and

α, written $\alpha\mathscr{A}$.* This may be expressed by the formula

$$x(\alpha\mathscr{A}) = \alpha(x\mathscr{A}) .$$

Arguing as in the case of a product of linear transformations, it is easy to see that *if $\mathscr{A}$ is a linear transformation, then $\alpha\mathscr{A}$ is again a linear transformation.* We now find its matrix. Let the transformation $\mathscr{A}$ have the matrix A in some fixed coordinate system, and let $\alpha\mathscr{A}$ have the matrix B. Then

$$[x(\alpha\mathscr{A})] = [x]B ,$$
$$[x(\alpha\mathscr{A})] = [\alpha(x\mathscr{A})] = \alpha[x\mathscr{A}] = \alpha[x]A = [x](\alpha A) ,$$

and thus $[x]B = [x](\alpha A)$, or

$$B = \alpha A .$$

Therefore, *the matrix of the product of a scalar and a linear transformation equals the product of this scalar and the matrix of the linear transformation.*

We note finally the formulas

$$\alpha(\beta\mathscr{A}) = (\alpha\beta)\mathscr{A} ,$$
$$0\cdot\mathscr{A} = \mathscr{O} ,$$
$$1\cdot\mathscr{A} = \mathscr{A} ,$$
$$\alpha(\mathscr{A}\mathscr{B}) = (\alpha\mathscr{A})\mathscr{B} = \mathscr{A}(\alpha\mathscr{B}) ,$$

which are completely analogous to the corresponding formulas of the matrix calculus. Their proofs are left to the reader.

Take now transformations $\mathscr{A}$, $\mathscr{B}$ of a linear space $\mathfrak{L}$ and place in correspondence to each vector x in $\mathfrak{L}$ the vector $x\mathscr{A} + x\mathscr{B}$. The transformation which carries x into $x\mathscr{A} + x\mathscr{B}$ is called the ***sum*** $\mathscr{A} + \mathscr{B}$ of $\mathscr{A}$ and $\mathscr{B}$. Thus, by definition,

$$x(\mathscr{A} + \mathscr{B}) = x\mathscr{A} + x\mathscr{B} .$$

If the transformations $\mathscr{A}$, $\mathscr{B}$ are linear, then

$$\begin{aligned}(\alpha x + \beta y)(\mathscr{A} + \mathscr{B}) &= (\alpha x + \beta y)\mathscr{A} + (\alpha x + \beta y)\mathscr{B} \\ &= \alpha\cdot x\mathscr{A} + \beta\cdot y\mathscr{A} + \alpha\cdot x\mathscr{B} + \beta\cdot y\mathscr{B} \\ &= \alpha\cdot(x\mathscr{A} + x\mathscr{B}) + \beta\cdot(y\mathscr{A} + y\mathscr{B}) \\ &= \alpha\cdot x(\mathscr{A} + \mathscr{B}) + \beta\cdot y(\mathscr{A} + \mathscr{B}) .\end{aligned}$$

Consequently, *the sum of two linear transformations is a linear transformation.* We find its matrix. Let the transformations $\mathscr{A}$, $\mathscr{B}$ have matrices A, B in some coordinate system. Let C denote the matrix of the transformation $\mathscr{A} + \mathscr{B}$. Then

* We shall also agree that $\alpha\mathscr{A} = \mathscr{A}\alpha$.

$$[x(\mathscr{A} + \mathscr{B})] = [x]C ,$$

$$[x(\mathscr{A} + \mathscr{B})] = [x\mathscr{A} + x\mathscr{B}] = [x\mathscr{A}] + [x\mathscr{B}]$$
$$= [x]A + [x]B = [x](A + B) .$$

Consequently,

$$[x]C = [x](A + B) , \quad C = A + B .$$

That is, *the matrix of the sum of transformations equals the sum of their matrices.*

Operations with linear transformations are subject to the same fundamental laws as are operations with matrices. We have already indicated those dealing with multiplication only. We now write out those which deal with addition and with the connection between addition and multiplication.

$$\mathscr{A} + \mathscr{B} = \mathscr{B} + \mathscr{A} ;$$
$$(\mathscr{A} + \mathscr{B}) + \mathscr{C} = \mathscr{A} + (\mathscr{B} + \mathscr{C}) ;$$
$$\mathscr{A} + \mathscr{O} = \mathscr{A} ;$$
$$\alpha(\mathscr{A} + \mathscr{B}) = \alpha\mathscr{A} + \alpha\mathscr{B} ;$$
$$(\alpha + \beta)\mathscr{A} = \alpha\mathscr{A} + \beta\mathscr{A} ;$$
$$\mathscr{A}(\mathscr{B} + \mathscr{C}) = \mathscr{A}\mathscr{B} + \mathscr{A}\mathscr{C} ;$$
$$(\mathscr{A} + \mathscr{B})\mathscr{C} = \mathscr{A}\mathscr{C} + \mathscr{B}\mathscr{C} .$$

The proofs of all of these are carried out in the same way: take an arbitrary vector x and show that the transformations on the right and left carry x into the same vector. For example,

$$x\mathscr{A}(\mathscr{B} + \mathscr{C}) = (x\mathscr{A})(\mathscr{B} + \mathscr{C}) = (x\mathscr{A})\mathscr{B} + (x\mathscr{A})\mathscr{C} ,$$
$$x(\mathscr{A}\mathscr{B} + \mathscr{A}\mathscr{C}) = x(\mathscr{A}\mathscr{B}) + x(\mathscr{A}\mathscr{C}) = (x\mathscr{A})\mathscr{B} + (x\mathscr{A})\mathscr{C} ,$$

hence

$$\mathscr{A}(\mathscr{B} + \mathscr{C}) = \mathscr{A}\mathscr{B} + \mathscr{A}\mathscr{C} .$$

It is also possible to deduce all these laws immediately from the corresponding laws of the matrix calculus. Indeed, between square matrices of order n and linear transformations of an n-dimensional linear space there exist one-to-one correspondences that preserve sums and products; therefore every identity among matrices gives an analogous identity among linear transformations.

39. Polynomials in Linear Transformations

Let

$$f(\lambda) = \alpha_0 + \alpha_1\lambda + \cdots + \alpha_m\lambda^m$$

be a polynomial in the indeterminate λ. The expression

$$f(\mathscr{A}) = \alpha_0\mathscr{E} + \alpha_1\mathscr{A} + \cdots + \alpha_m\mathscr{A}^m ,$$

where $\mathscr{E}$ is the identity transformation and $\mathscr{A}$ is an arbitrary linear transformation, is called the value of the polynomial $f(\lambda)$ at $\lambda = \mathscr{A}$, or simply a ***polynomial in*** $\mathscr{A}$. If the matrix of the transformation $\mathscr{A}$ in some coordinate system is A, then the matrix of the transformation $f(\mathscr{A})$ in the same coordinate system is

$$f(A) = \alpha_0 E + \alpha_1 A + \cdots + \alpha_m A^m ,$$

Indeed, $f(\mathscr{A})$ is obtained from $\mathscr{A}$ by the operations of multiplication, multiplication by a scalar, and addition. From the results indicated above, it is evident that we obtain the matrix of the transformation $f(\mathscr{A})$ by performing the same operations on the matrix A.

All the rules for operating with polynomials in one indeterminate hold also for polynomials in a linear transformation. Therefore, if in a polynomial identity one replaces λ by a linear transformation, a valid relation results. For example, as a consequence of the identities

$$\lambda^2 - 1 = (\lambda - 1)(\lambda + 1) , \quad (\lambda + 1)^2 + (\lambda - 1)^2 - 2\lambda^2 = 2 ,$$

we have

$$\mathscr{A}^2 - \mathscr{E} = (\mathscr{A} - \mathscr{E})(\mathscr{A} + \mathscr{E}) ,$$
$$(\mathscr{A} + \mathscr{E})^2 + (\mathscr{A} - \mathscr{E})^2 - 2\mathscr{A}^2 = 2\mathscr{E} .$$

In particular, as a consequence of

$$f(\lambda)g(\lambda) = g(\lambda)f(\lambda) ,$$

we have

$$f(\mathscr{A})g(\mathscr{A}) = g(\mathscr{A})f(\mathscr{A}) ,$$

which shows that polynomials in a given linear transformation always commute with each other.

The situation is different for polynomials in several variables. Common simplifications such as $\lambda\mu\lambda = \lambda^2\mu$, $\lambda\mu^2\lambda\mu = \lambda^2\mu^3$, and so on, rest upon the assumption that the indeterminates commute with each other.

Substituting linear transformations $\mathscr{A}$, $\mathscr{B}$ for the indeterminates in these equalities gives the relations

$$\mathscr{A}\mathscr{B}\mathscr{A} = \mathscr{A}^2\mathscr{B} , \quad \mathscr{A}\mathscr{B}^2\mathscr{A}\mathscr{B} = \mathscr{A}^2\mathscr{B}^3 ,$$

which may not be valid for all linear transformations but which surely do hold for transformations that commute with each other. Thus, in every identity between polynomials in several indeterminates, it is possible to replace the indeterminates by arbitrary linear transformations that commute among themselves; the result is a valid relationship among linear transformations.

We have agreed that all linear spaces considered in this book are to be finite-dimensional. However, some of the definitions and theorems remain valid also for infinite-dimensional spaces. As examples, we may cite the definition of linear transformations, the operations with them, and those properties of linear transformations presented in this paragraph* that are not connected with matrices.

● EXAMPLE AND PROBLEMS

1. Let $\mathfrak{L}$ be the space of polynomials in λ of degree $\leq n$. Denote by $\mathscr{D}$ the transformation which carries each polynomial $f(\lambda)$ into its derivative $f'(\lambda)$. Show that $\mathscr{D}^{n+1} = \mathscr{O}$, and find the matrix of $\mathscr{D}$ in the coordinate system $1, \lambda, \cdots, \lambda^n$.
2. Let $\mathfrak{L}$ be the infinite-dimensional space of all polynomials in λ. Let $\mathscr{D}$ denote the operation of differentiation, and $\mathscr{C}$ denote the operation of multiplication by λ. Show that both operations are linear and that

$$\mathscr{C}^n\mathscr{D} - \mathscr{D}\mathscr{C}^n = n\mathscr{C}^{n-1}, \qquad (n = 1, 2, \cdots).$$

3. Why is it impossible to consider the transformation $\mathscr{C}$, indicated in the last problem, in the space of polynomials of degree not exceeding n?
4. The linear transformations of a space $\mathfrak{L}$, with respect to the operations of addition and multiplication by scalars, form a linear space. What is the dimension of this space, if the dimension of $\mathfrak{L}$ is n?

4. *Rank and Nullity† of a Linear Transformation*

The properties of linear transformations considered above were primarily algebraic. We now consider some properties of a more geometric nature.

40. Range and Kernel

Let $\mathfrak{M}$ be a given set of vectors in a linear space $\mathfrak{L}$, and let $\mathscr{A}$ be an arbitrary linear transformation of $\mathfrak{L}$. Each vector a of $\mathfrak{M}$ is carried by $\mathscr{A}$ into some new vector $a\mathscr{A}$, the image of a. In general this image will not belong to $\mathfrak{M}$. The set of images of all the vectors of $\mathfrak{M}$ is called the image of $\mathfrak{M}$ under $\mathscr{A}$, and is denoted by $\mathfrak{M}\mathscr{A}$. The pre-image of $\mathfrak{M}$ is the set of all vectors in $\mathfrak{L}$ whose images lie in $\mathfrak{M}$.

THEOREM 1. *The image and pre-image of a linear subspace of a space $\mathfrak{L}$ under an arbitrary linear transformation are again linear subspaces of $\mathfrak{L}$.*

To prove this, let $\mathfrak{A}$ be a linear subspace of $\mathfrak{L}$. We show that $\mathfrak{A}\mathscr{A}$ is also a linear subspace. Take vectors a, b in $\mathfrak{A}\mathscr{A}$. These vectors are the images of some vectors x, y in $\mathfrak{A}$; that is $a = x\mathscr{A}$, $b = y\mathscr{A}$. Since $\mathfrak{A}$ is a linear subspace, $\alpha x + \beta y$ belongs to $\mathfrak{A}$ for arbitrary α, β, and therefore $(\alpha x + \beta y)\mathscr{A}$ belongs to $\mathfrak{A}\mathscr{A}$, But

$$(\alpha x + \beta y)\mathscr{A} = \alpha \cdot x\mathscr{A} + \beta \cdot y\mathscr{A} = \alpha a + \beta b .$$

* "Paragraph," as used in this book, always refers to the numbered parts (1, ···) of a chapter.

† The Russian original uses the word "defect" instead of "nullity." (*Ed.*)

That is, $\mathfrak{A}\mathscr{A}$ contains $\alpha a + \beta b$, and consequently is a linear subspace. A completely similar argument proves the remainder of the theorem.

The ***kernel*** of a linear transformation $\mathscr{A}$ is the pre-image of θ, or the set of all vectors in $\mathfrak{L}$ which are carried by $\mathscr{A}$ into the zero vector. The ***range*** of $\mathscr{A}$ is the image of $\mathfrak{L}$, or the set of all images of vectors in $\mathfrak{L}$. The dimension of the range is the ***rank*** of the transformation, and the dimension of the kernel is the ***nullity*** of the transformation.

THEOREM 2. *The sum of the rank and the nullity of a linear transformation $\mathscr{A}$ of a space $\mathfrak{L}$ equals the dimension of $\mathfrak{L}$.*

Let $\mathfrak{N}$ be the kernel of the transformation $\mathscr{A}$, and suppose that it has dimension d. Let r be the dimension of the range $\mathfrak{L}\mathscr{A}$. By definition, d and r are the nullity and rank of the transformation $\mathscr{A}$. Choose a basis $a_1, \cdots, a_r$ of $\mathfrak{L}\mathscr{A}$ and let $b_1, \cdots, b_r$ be a set of pre-images of these vectors. The vectors $b_1, \cdots, b_r$ are linearly independent, since from

$$\alpha_1 b_1 + \cdots + \alpha_r b_r = \theta$$

it follows that

$$(\alpha_1 b_1 + \cdots + \alpha_r b_r)\mathscr{A} = \alpha_1 a_1 + \cdots + \alpha_r a_r = \theta ,$$

and hence that

$$\alpha_1 = \cdots = \alpha_r = 0 ,$$

since $a_1, \cdots, a_r$ are linearly independent.

Consider the space $\mathfrak{M}$ spanned by $b_1, \cdots, b_r$. The system $b_1, \cdots, b_r$ is a ***basis*** of $\mathfrak{M}$, and therefore $\mathfrak{M}$ has dimension r, the rank of the transformation $\mathscr{A}$. We show that $\mathfrak{L}$ is the direct sum of the subspaces $\mathfrak{M}$ and $\mathfrak{N}$. To do this it is sufficient to show that $\mathfrak{M} \cap \mathfrak{N} = \{\theta\}$ and $\mathfrak{L} = \mathfrak{M} + \mathfrak{N}$ (compare Section 29). First, every vector in $\mathfrak{M}$ has the form

$$b = \alpha_1 b_1 + \cdots + \alpha_r b_r .$$

If b belongs to $\mathfrak{N}$, then $b\mathscr{A} = \theta$; that is,

$$(\alpha_1 b_1 + \cdots + \alpha_r b_r)\mathscr{A} = \alpha_1 a_1 + \cdots + \alpha_r a_r = \theta .$$

But since $a_1, \cdots, a_r$ are linearly independent, then $\alpha_1 = \cdots = \alpha_r = 0$, and hence $b = \theta$. Thus $\mathfrak{M} \cap \mathfrak{N} = \{\theta\}$. Now we need only show that $\mathfrak{L} = \mathfrak{M} + \mathfrak{N}$. Take an arbitrary vector a in $\mathfrak{L}$. Its image lies in $\mathfrak{L}\mathscr{A}$, and is a linear combination of $a_1, \cdots, a_r$:

$$a\mathscr{A} = \alpha_1 a_1 + \cdots + \alpha_r a_r .$$

Let

$$b = \alpha_1 b_1 + \cdots + \alpha_r b_r , \quad a - b = c .$$

Since

$$b\mathscr{A} = \alpha_1 a_1 + \cdots + \alpha_r a_r = a\mathscr{A} ,$$

then

$$c\mathscr{A} = (a - b)\mathscr{A} = a\mathscr{A} - b\mathscr{A} = \theta \ .$$

Consequently, c belongs to $\mathfrak{N}$. Hence

$$a = b + c \ , \qquad (b \in \mathfrak{M},\ c \in \mathfrak{N}) \ .$$

This means that

$$\mathfrak{L} = \mathfrak{M} + \mathfrak{N} \ .$$

Since the sum is direct, the dimension of $\mathfrak{L}$ equals the sum of the dimensions of $\mathfrak{M}$ and $\mathfrak{N}$; that is, it equals the sum of the rank and the nullity of the transformation $\mathscr{A}$.

We consider an example. Let $\mathfrak{R}$ be the usual space of line segments with origin $\mathscr{O}$. Take an arbitrary plane $\mathfrak{B}$ passing through $\mathscr{O}$ and denote by $\mathscr{P}$ the operation of orthogonal projection onto the plane $\mathfrak{B}$. The transformation $\mathscr{P}$ takes the whole space $\mathfrak{R}$ onto $\mathfrak{B}$. Thus $\mathfrak{B}$ is the range of $\mathscr{P}$, and $\mathscr{P}$ has rank 2. The kernel of $\mathscr{P}$ consists of those vectors which lie on the line through $\mathscr{O}$ perpendicular to the plane $\mathfrak{B}$, since only these vectors are carried onto the zero vector by $\mathscr{P}$. Consequently, the nullity of $\mathscr{P}$ is 1. The sum of the rank and the nullity of $\mathscr{P}$ is 3, as it must be by Theorem 2.

41. Singular and Nonsingular Transformations

It was mentioned above (compare Section 37) that not every transformation is invertible. Invertible linear transformations are called ***nonsingular***; noninvertible linear transformations are called ***singular***. We obtained in Section 37, in matrix form, conditions under which a linear transformation is nonsingular. We wish now to give a more geometrical character to these conditions.

THEOREM 3. *A linear transformation $\mathscr{A}$ of a space $\mathfrak{L}$ is nonsingular if and only if the kernel of this transformation is the zero space; that is, the nullity of $\mathscr{A}$ is zero.*

If the given transformation $\mathscr{A}$ is nonsingular, then each vector has exactly one pre-image; in particular the zero vector θ has exactly one pre-image. Since θ is always a pre-image of itself, the kernel, in this case, consists of only one vector: the kernel is the zero space.

Conversely, let $\mathscr{A}$ have nullity zero. By Theorem 2, the rank of $\mathscr{A}$ is the dimension of $\mathfrak{L}$; that is, the dimension of the range $\mathfrak{L}\mathscr{A}$ is the dimension of $\mathfrak{L}$. Consequently, $\mathfrak{L}\mathscr{A} = \mathfrak{L}$, and we see that every vector in $\mathfrak{L}$ is the image of some vector in $\mathfrak{L}$. It is now only necessary to show that $\mathscr{A}$ carries distinct vectors into distinct vectors (Section 32). But from $a\mathscr{A} = b\mathscr{A}$ it follows that $(a - b)\mathscr{A} = \theta$. Since by assumption the kernel of $\mathscr{A}$ is zero, then $(a - b) = \theta$ and $a = b$. This completes the proof.

The nullity of $\mathscr{A}$ is zero if and only if the rank of $\mathscr{A}$ equals the dimension of $\mathfrak{L}$. Therefore Theorem 3 may also be written in the following form.

THEOREM 4. *A linear transformation $\mathscr{A}$ of a space $\mathfrak{L}$ is nonsingular if and only if the range of $\mathscr{A}$ coincides with $\mathfrak{L}$; that is, the rank of $\mathscr{A}$ equals the dimension of $\mathfrak{L}$.*

A one-to-one mapping of one linear space onto another is called an ***isomorphism*** if it carries each sum of vectors in the first space into the sum of the corresponding vectors in the second, and carries a scalar times a vector in the first space into the same scalar times the corresponding vector in the second (see Section 23). If the two linear spaces are identical, we obtain an isomorphic mapping of the linear space onto itself. Such a mapping is called an ***automorphism*** of the linear space. The definition of automorphism evidently coincides with the definition of nonsingular linear transformation. Consequently, nonsingular linear transformations of the space $\mathfrak{L}$ may be considered as automorphisms of $\mathfrak{L}$. From the very definition of automorphism, it is obvious that the automorphisms of a space $\mathfrak{L}$ are those superpositions of $\mathfrak{L}$ on itself which preserve all of its geometric properties—the properties which can be expressed by addition and scalar multiplication.

Consider two arbitrary linear transformations $\mathscr{A}$, $\mathscr{B}$ of a space $\mathfrak{L}$. These transformations are called ***similar*** if there exists an automorphism $\mathscr{C}$ of $\mathfrak{L}$ that carries one transformation into the other.

Let u be a vector in $\mathfrak{L}$ and $v = u\mathscr{A}$. The automorphism $\mathscr{C}$ carries u, v into some vectors x, y. If $x\mathscr{B} = y$, then we say that $\mathscr{C}$ carries the transformation $\mathscr{A}$ into the transformation $\mathscr{B}$ (compare Fig. 3, p. 61). Since $x = u\mathscr{C}$ and $y = v\mathscr{C}$, the equality $x\mathscr{B} = y$ gives

$$u\mathscr{C}\mathscr{B} = v\mathscr{C}\,, \quad u\mathscr{C}\mathscr{B}\mathscr{C}^{-1} = v = u\mathscr{A}\,,$$

and hence

$$\mathscr{C}\mathscr{B}\mathscr{C}^{-1} = \mathscr{A}\,, \quad \mathscr{B} = \mathscr{C}^{-1}\mathscr{A}\mathscr{C}\,. \tag{1}$$

Consequently *the linear transformation $\mathscr{B}$ is similar to the linear transformation $\mathscr{A}$ if and only if $\mathscr{B}$ is the transform of $\mathscr{A}$ by an automorphism of $\mathfrak{L}$—that is, by a nonsingular linear transformation of $\mathfrak{L}$.*

If a coordinate system is given in $\mathfrak{L}$ and the matrices of the transformations $\mathscr{A}$, $\mathscr{B}$, $\mathscr{C}$ relative to this coordinate system are A, B, C respectively, then (1) is equivalent to the matrix equation

$$B = C^{-1}AC\,.$$

We have thus proved the following assertion: *in order that two linear transformations of a space $\mathfrak{L}$ be similar, it is necessary and sufficient that their matrices be similar.*

Similar transformations may properly be considered as transformations having identical geometrical properties. The importance of the classification of all linear transformations up to similarity is now evident. Algebraically, the problem is equivalent to the classification (up to similarity) of all square matrices of order n. While the classification of all linear spaces over a given field presents no difficulty (compare Section 23), the classification of linear transformations requires a deeper study of their properties. This problem will be solved completely only in the following chapter.

We observe one further property of similar linear transformations: *in order that the linear transformations $\mathscr{A}$, $\mathscr{B}$ be similar, it is necessary and sufficient that there exist coordinate systems in which these transformations are expressed by the same matrix.*

Indeed, if $\mathscr{A}$ and $\mathscr{B}$ are similar, then their matrices satisfy a relation $A = CBC^{-1}$. But this relation shows that if we proceed from the given coordinate system to another in such a way that C is the matrix of the transformation of coordinates, then the matrix of the transformation $\mathscr{B}$ in the new system will be A; that is, it will be identical with the matrix of the transformation $\mathscr{A}$, computed in the old coordinate system. Conversely, if the matrix A of the transformation $\mathscr{A}$ in the coordinate system $a_1, \cdots, a_n$ coincides with the matrix of the transformation $\mathscr{B}$, computed in the coordinate system $a'_1, \cdots, a'_n$, then, denoting the matrix of the transformation from the first coordinate system to the second by C, we note that in the second system of coordinates the matrices of the transformations $\mathscr{A}$, $\mathscr{B}$ are respectively CAC^{-1} and A, or $\mathscr{A}$ and $\mathscr{B}$ are similar.

42. Rank of the Matrix of a Transformation

In Section 40 we introduced the notion of the rank of a linear transformation. But the notion of the rank of a matrix (the maximal number of linearly independent rows) is also familiar in the theory of determinants. The question arises as to the connection between these notions. The answer is given in the following theorem.

THEOREM 5. *The rank of an arbitrary linear transformation $\mathscr{A}$ of a space $\mathfrak{L}$ equals the rank of the matrix of this transformation.*

Let $a_1, \cdots, a_n$ be a coordinate system in $\mathfrak{L}$. The range of $\mathscr{A}$ consists of the images of vectors in $\mathfrak{L}$—vectors of the form

$$(\alpha_1 a_1 + \cdots + \alpha_n a_n)\mathscr{A} = \alpha_1(a_1\mathscr{A}) + \cdots + \alpha_n(a_n\mathscr{A}) .$$

This shows that the range of $\mathscr{A}$ is a subspace spanned by the vectors $a_1\mathscr{A}, \cdots, a_n\mathscr{A}$. The rank of $\mathscr{A}$ is the dimension of the range, and consequently equals the maximal number of linearly independent vectors among $a_1\mathscr{A}, \cdots, a_n\mathscr{A}$ (see Section 27). Let

$$\begin{aligned} a_1\mathscr{A} &= \alpha_{11}a_1 + \alpha_{12}a_2 + \cdots + \alpha_{1n}a_n , \\ a_2\mathscr{A} &= \alpha_{21}a_1 + \alpha_{22}a_2 + \cdots + \alpha_{2n}a_n , \\ &\vdots \\ a_n\mathscr{A} &= \alpha_{n1}a_1 + \alpha_{n2}a_2 + \cdots + \alpha_{nn}a_n . \end{aligned}$$

The matrix

$$A = \begin{bmatrix} \alpha_{11} & \cdots & \alpha_{1n} \\ \vdots & & \vdots \\ \alpha_{n1} & \cdots & \alpha_{nn} \end{bmatrix}$$

is the matrix of the transformation $\mathscr{A}$. The rows of this matrix are the coordinate rows of the vectors $a_1\mathscr{A}, \cdots, a_n\mathscr{A}$. Therefore the maximal number of linearly independent vectors among $a_1\mathscr{A}, \cdots, a_n\mathscr{A}$ equals the maximal number of linearly independent rows of the matrix A, or the rank of $\mathscr{A}$ equals the rank of A.

We define the ***nullity*** of a square matrix as the difference between its order and its rank. It is an immediate consequence of Theorems 2 and 5 that *the nullity of a linear transformation equals the nullity of its matrix.*

* * *

As an example we investigate the solution of a system of n homogeneous linear equations in n unknowns $\xi_1, \cdots, \xi_n$:

$$\begin{aligned} \alpha_{11}\xi_1 + \alpha_{12}\xi_2 + \cdots + \alpha_{1n}\xi_n &= 0\,, \\ \alpha_{21}\xi_1 + \alpha_{22}\xi_2 + \cdots + \alpha_{2n}\xi_n &= 0\,, \\ &\vdots \\ \alpha_{n1}\xi_1 + \alpha_{n2}\xi_2 + \cdots + \alpha_{nn}\xi_n &= 0\,. \end{aligned} \tag{2}$$

This problem can be interpreted geometrically in the following way. Take an arbitrary n-dimensional linear space $\mathfrak{L}$ with a coordinate system $a_1, \cdots, a_n$, and consider $\xi_1, \cdots, \xi_n$ to be the coordinates of some vector x in $\mathfrak{L}$. Let $\mathscr{A}$ be the linear transformation of $\mathfrak{L}$ which has (in the coordinate system $a_1, \cdots, a_n$) the matrix A with elements α_{ij}, for $i, j = 1, \cdots, n$. Then the system of equations (2) may be written in the form

$$[x]A = 0$$

or in the vector form

$$x\mathscr{A} = \theta\,.$$

It is now evident that the solutions of (2) are the coordinate rows of vectors belonging to the kernel of the transformation $\mathscr{A}$. Since the dimension of the kernel is the nullity of the transformation, and the nullity of the transformation equals the nullity of its matrix, we arrive at the familiar theorem in the theory of determinants: *the maximal number of linearly independent solutions of a system of n homogeneous linear equations in n unknowns equals the nullity of the matrix of this system.*

* * *

● EXAMPLES AND PROBLEMS

1. In the space of rows of length 4 take the coordinate system

$$e_1 = [1, 0, 0, 0]\,, \quad e_2 = [0, 1, 0, 0]\,, \quad e_3 = [0, 0, 1, 0]\,, \quad e_4 = [0, 0, 0, 1]\,.$$

Find the kernel and range of the linear transformations given by the matrices

$$\begin{bmatrix} 2 & & & \\ & 0 & & \\ & & 3 & \\ & & & 0 \end{bmatrix}, \quad \begin{bmatrix} 2 & 1 & 0 & 0 \\ & 2 & 1 & 0 \\ & & 2 & 0 \\ & & & 2 \end{bmatrix}, \quad \begin{bmatrix} 3 & 1 & & \\ 2 & 1 & & \\ & & 0 & 0 \\ & & 0 & 0 \end{bmatrix}, \quad \begin{bmatrix} 1 & 3 & 5 & 1 \\ 2 & 1 & 3 & 1 \\ 4 & 7 & 13 & 3 \\ 3 & -1 & 1 & 1 \end{bmatrix}.$$

2. Let $\mathscr{A}$ be a linear transformation of a space $\mathfrak{L}$, and let $\mathfrak{M}$ be a linear subspace. Show that the dimension of the image of $\mathfrak{M}$ statisfies the inequalities

$$\dim \mathfrak{M} - \text{nullity}\, \mathscr{A} \leqq \dim \mathfrak{M}\mathscr{A} \leqq \dim \mathfrak{M}\,.$$

3. If $\mathscr{A}_1$, $\mathscr{A}_2$ are arbitrary linear transformations, with $\mathscr{A}_2$ nonsingular, then

$$\text{rank}\,(\mathscr{A}_1\mathscr{A}_2) = \text{rank}\,(\mathscr{A}_2\mathscr{A}_1) = \text{rank}\,\mathscr{A}_1\,.$$

4. Let $\mathscr{A}_1$, $\mathscr{A}_2$ be arbitrary linear transformations of a linear space $\mathfrak{L}$. Then

$$\text{rank}\,(\mathscr{A}_1 + \mathscr{A}_2) \leqq \text{rank}\,\mathscr{A}_1 + \text{rank}\,\mathscr{A}_2\,,$$
$$\text{nullity}\,(\mathscr{A}_1\mathscr{A}_2) \leqq \text{nullity}\,\mathscr{A}_1 + \text{nullity}\,\mathscr{A}_2\,,$$
$$\text{rank}\,(\mathscr{A}_1\mathscr{A}_2) \leqq \min\,\{\text{rank}\,\mathscr{A}_1,\ \text{rank}\,\mathscr{A}_2\}\,.$$

5. Every linear transformation of rank m can be represented as the sum of transformations of rank 1.
6. The matrix A of order n has rank not higher than 1 if and only if

$$A = \begin{bmatrix} \alpha_1 \\ \alpha_2 \\ \vdots \\ \alpha_n \end{bmatrix} [\beta_1\beta_2\cdots\beta_n] = \|\,\alpha_i\beta_j\,\|$$

for suitable α_i, β_j.

5. *Invariant Subspaces*

43. Induced Transformations

We say that a linear subspace $\mathfrak{A}$ of a linear space $\mathfrak{L}$ is ***invariant*** under a transformation $\mathscr{A}$ if $\mathscr{A}$ takes each vector of $\mathfrak{A}$ into a vector of $\mathfrak{A}$; that is, if

$$\mathfrak{A}\mathscr{A} \subset \mathfrak{A}\,,$$

It is an immediate consequence of this definition that the zero space and $\mathfrak{L}$ itself are invariant under an arbitrary linear transformation. It is also clear that *the sum and intersection of invariant subspaces are again invariant subspaces.*

We observe further that *if a subspace $\mathfrak{A}$ is invariant under a linear transformation $\mathscr{A}$, then $\mathfrak{A}$ is also invariant under the transformation $f(\mathscr{A})$, where*

$f(\mathscr{A}) = \alpha_0\mathscr{E} + \alpha_1\mathscr{A} + \cdots + \alpha_m\mathscr{A}^m$ is an arbitrary polynomial in $\mathscr{A}$.

If a is a vector in $\mathfrak{A}$, then by assumption $a\mathscr{A}$ is contained in $\mathfrak{A}$. From this it follows that $(a\mathscr{A})\mathscr{A} = a\mathscr{A}^2$ is contained in $\mathfrak{A}$, and so on. Consequently, for $k \geqq 0$, the vector $a\mathscr{A}^k$ is contained in $\mathfrak{A}$. But then $\mathfrak{A}$ contains also all linear combinations of these vectors, and in particular contains

$$af(\mathscr{A}) = \alpha_0 a + \alpha_1 \cdot a\mathscr{A} + \cdots + \alpha_m \cdot a\mathscr{A}^m ,$$

which was to be proved.

Methods for finding invariant subspaces will be considered in the last paragraph of this chapter; here we wish to show how the matrix of a transformation can be simplified by a knowledge of the invariant subspaces of the transformation.

Let the linear transformation $\mathscr{A}$ have a nontrivial invariant subspace $\mathfrak{A}$. Take a basis $a_1, \cdots, a_m$ of $\mathfrak{A}$ and supplement it with linearly independent vectors $a_{m+1}, \cdots, a_n$ to form a basis of $\mathfrak{L}$. To find the matrix of $\mathscr{A}$ in the coordinate system $a_1, \cdots, a_m, a_{m+1}, \cdots, a_n$, we must express the vectors $a_1\mathscr{A}, \cdots, a_n\mathscr{A}$ as linear combinations of $a_1, \cdots, a_n$. However, the subspace $\mathfrak{A}$ is invariant, and hence the vectors $a_1\mathscr{A}, \cdots, a_m\mathscr{A}$ are contained in $\mathscr{A}$, and can be written as linear combinations of $a_1, \cdots, a_m$. Consequently,

$$\begin{aligned} a_1\mathscr{A} &= \alpha_{11}a_1 + \cdots + \alpha_{1m}a_m , \\ &\vdots \\ a_m\mathscr{A} &= \alpha_{m1}a_1 + \cdots + \alpha_{mm}a_m , \\ a_{m+1}\mathscr{A} &= \alpha_{m+1,1}a_1 + \cdots + \alpha_{m+1,m}a_m + \cdots + \alpha_{m+1,n}a_n , \\ &\vdots \\ a_n\mathscr{A} &= \alpha_{n1}a_1 + \cdots + \alpha_{nm}a_m + \cdots + \alpha_{nn}a_n , \end{aligned} \tag{1}$$

and the matrix of the transformation $\mathscr{A}$ is

$$A = \begin{bmatrix} \alpha_{11} & \cdots & \alpha_{1m} & 0 & \cdots & 0 \\ \vdots & & \vdots & \vdots & & \vdots \\ \alpha_{m1} & \cdots & \alpha_{mm} & 0 & \cdots & 0 \\ \alpha_{m+1,1} & \cdots & \alpha_{m+1,m} & \alpha_{m+1,m+1} & \cdots & \alpha_{m+1,n} \\ \vdots & & \vdots & \vdots & & \vdots \\ \alpha_{n1} & \cdots & \alpha_{nm} & \alpha_{n,m+1} & \cdots & \alpha_{nn} \end{bmatrix} = \begin{bmatrix} A_1 & 0 \\ B & A_2 \end{bmatrix} . \tag{2}$$

Thus, *if a linear transformation has an invariant linear subspace, then in a suitable coordinate system its matrix decomposes into four blocks: the diagonal blocks are square, and the upper right block is filled with zeros.* A matrix of this form is called ***semidecomposable*** (compare Section 15). Conversely, if, in some coordinate system, the matrix of a linear transformation $\mathscr{A}$ has the semidecomposable form (2), then equalities (1) show that the subspace $\mathscr{A}$, spanned by the first m coordinate vectors, is invariant under $\mathscr{A}$.

The geometric meaning of the matrix A_1 may be interpreted in the following way. We know that $\mathscr{A}$ carries each vector in $\mathfrak{A}$ into a vector in $\mathfrak{A}$. Therefore it is possible to consider $\mathscr{A}$ as a transformation of the space $\mathfrak{A}$. We denote this transformation by $\mathscr{A}_1$, and agree to call it the transformation ***induced*** in $\mathfrak{A}$ by $\mathscr{A}$. The transformations $\mathscr{A}$ and $\mathscr{A}_1$ act identically on the vectors of the subspace $\mathfrak{A}$: if a is a vector in $\mathfrak{A}$, then $a\mathscr{A} = a\mathscr{A}_1$. Their difference is in their domains of definition: if a belongs to $\mathfrak{L}$ but not to $\mathfrak{A}$, then $a\mathscr{A}$ has a meaning, but $a\mathscr{A}_1$ does not.

The first m equalities of (1) show that A_1 is the matrix of the induced transformation $\mathscr{A}_1$, in the coordinate system $a_1, \cdots, a_m$.

44. Direct Sum of Invariant Subspaces

We have considered the case when a linear transformation $\mathscr{A}$ has one invariant subspace. We assume now that $\mathscr{A}$ has two invariant subspaces $\mathfrak{A}_1, \mathfrak{A}_2$, and further that $\mathfrak{L} = \mathfrak{A}_1 \dotplus \mathfrak{A}_2$. Let $a_1, \cdots, a_m$ and $a_{m+1}, \cdots, a_n$ be coordinate systems in $\mathfrak{A}_1$ and $\mathfrak{A}_2$ respectively. In Section 29 it was shown that $a_1, \cdots, a_m, a_{m+1}, \cdots, a_n$ is a coordinate system in $\mathfrak{L}$. We consider the form of the matrix of $\mathscr{A}$ in this system. By assumption, the vectors $a_1\mathscr{A}, \cdots, a_m\mathscr{A}$ lie in $\mathfrak{A}_1$, and $a_{m+1}\mathscr{A}, \cdots, a_n\mathscr{A}$ lie in $\mathfrak{A}_2$. Thus,

$$
\begin{aligned}
a_1\mathscr{A} &= \alpha_{11}a_1 + \cdots + \alpha_{1m}a_m, \\
&\ \vdots \\
a_m\mathscr{A} &= \alpha_{m1}a_1 + \cdots + \alpha_{mm}a_m, \\
a_{m+1}\mathscr{A} &= \qquad\qquad\qquad\qquad \alpha_{m+1,m+1}a_{m+1} + \cdots + \alpha_{m+1,n}a_n, \\
&\ \vdots \\
a_n\mathscr{A} &= \qquad\qquad\qquad\qquad \alpha_{n,m+1}a_{m+1} + \cdots + \alpha_{nn}a_n.
\end{aligned}
\tag{3}
$$

Consequently, the matrix of the transformation $\mathscr{A}$ is

$$
A = \begin{bmatrix}
\alpha_{11} & \cdots & \alpha_{1m} & 0 & \cdots & 0 \\
\vdots & & \vdots & \vdots & & \vdots \\
\alpha_{m1} & \cdots & \alpha_{mm} & 0 & \cdots & 0 \\
0 & \cdots & 0 & \alpha_{m+1,}\alpha_{m+1} & \cdots & \alpha_{m+1,n} \\
\vdots & & \vdots & \vdots & & \vdots \\
0 & \cdots & 0 & \alpha_{n,m+1} & \cdots & \alpha_{nn}
\end{bmatrix}
= \begin{bmatrix} A_1 & 0 \\ 0 & A_2 \end{bmatrix}. \tag{4}
$$

That is, the matrix is decomposable. Let the transformations induced by $\mathscr{A}$ in the subspaces $\mathfrak{A}_1, \mathfrak{A}_2$ be denoted by $\mathscr{A}_1$, $\mathscr{A}_2$, respectively. Then, as a consequence of (3), A_1 and A_2 are the matrices of the transformations $\mathscr{A}_1$ and $\mathscr{A}_2$ in the corresponding coordinate systems.

Thus, *if a space $\mathfrak{L}$ decomposes into the direct sum of subspaces which are invariant under the linear transformation $\mathscr{A}$, then the matrix of $\mathscr{A}$ in a suitable coordinate system is block diagonal, and the diagonal blocks are the matrices of the transformations induced by $\mathscr{A}$ in the invariant subspaces.*

We have proved this proposition only for the case of two direct summands. However, the entire argument carries over without change to the case of an arbitrary number of summands.

Assume now the converse, that in some coordinate system the matrix of the transformation $\mathscr{A}$ has the decomposable form (4). Then from (3) we see that the subspace $\mathfrak{A}_1$, spanned by the first m coordinate vectors, and the subspace $\mathfrak{A}_2$, spanned by the remaining coordinate vectors, are invariant under $\mathscr{A}$. The sum is evidently direct, and coincides with $\mathfrak{L}$. Consequently, the condition of the reducibility of the matrix of the linear transformation $\mathscr{A}$ to block diagonal form is not only necessary but is also sufficient for the decomposition of $\mathfrak{L}$ into the direct sum of subspaces invariant under $\mathscr{A}$.

Consider the following problem. Let the space $\mathfrak{L}$ decompose into the direct sum of several subspaces:

$$\mathfrak{L} = \mathfrak{A}_1 \dotplus \cdots \dotplus \mathfrak{A}_s ,$$

and for each i let $\mathscr{A}_i$ be a linear transformation of $\mathfrak{A}_i$. Does there exist a linear transformation $\mathscr{A}$ of $\mathfrak{L}$ under which each subspace $\mathfrak{A}_i$ is invariant, and which induces in each $\mathfrak{A}_i$ the transformation $\mathscr{A}_i$; and if so, is it unique? The answer is evidently in the affirmative. Take in each $\mathfrak{A}_i$ a basis $a_{i1}, a_{i2}, \cdots, a_{im_i}$, and denote by A_i the matrix of the transformation $\mathscr{A}_i$ in this coordinate system. Consider the block diagonal matrix

$$A = A_1 \dotplus \cdots \dotplus A_s .$$

Now the system $a_{11}, \cdots, a_{1m_1}, \cdots, a_{s1}, \cdots, a_{sm_s}$ is a basis of the space $\mathfrak{L}$. In this basis the matrix A corresponds to some linear transformation $\mathscr{A}$ of $\mathfrak{L}$. From what has been stated, the transformation $\mathscr{A}$ satisfies all the requirements of our problem. Since, in the indicated coordinate system, the matrix A is uniquely determined by the conditions of the problem, this transformation is unique.

45. The Characteristic Polynomial of a Transformation

Let $\mathscr{A}$ be a linear transformation of an n-dimensional linear space $\mathfrak{L}$ and let A be its matrix in the coordinate system $a_1, \cdots, a_n$. The characteristic polynomial $\varphi(\lambda) = |\lambda E - A|$ of the matrix A is called the ***characteristic polynomial of the transformation*** $\mathscr{A}$. If we take some other coordinate system $a'_1, \cdots, a'_n$ and denote the matrix of the transformation of coordinates by T, then the matrix of $\mathscr{A}$ in the new coordinate system (see Section 36) is

$$A_1 = TAT^{-1} ,$$

or is a matrix similar to A. It was shown in Section 10 that similar matrices have identical characteristic polynomials. Thus, *the characteristic polynomial of a transformation* $\mathscr{A}$ *does not depend on the coordinate system in which it is computed.*

The degree of the characteristic polynomial equals the order of the matrix A, and the order of A equals the dimension of the space $\mathfrak{L}$. Therefore *the* *degree of the characteristic polynomial of a transformation $\mathscr{A}$ equals the dimension of the space in which the transformation operates.*

The sum of the zeros of the characteristic polynomial equals the trace of the matrix A and the product of the zeros equals its determinant. Since the characteristic polynomial of A is independent of the coordinate system, so are its zeros; hence the trace and determinant of A are independent of the coordinate system, and are called the ***trace*** and ***determinant*** of the transformation $\mathscr{A}$.

If the space $\mathfrak{L}$ breaks into the direct sum of subspaces $\mathfrak{A}_1, \mathfrak{A}_2$, which are invariant under $\mathscr{A}$, then in the proper coordinate system the matrix of $\mathscr{A}$ has the blockdiagonal form

$$A = \begin{bmatrix} A_1 & 0 \\ 0 & A_2 \end{bmatrix}.$$

From this (compare Section 14), the characteristic polynomial of the matrix A equals the product of the characteristic polynomials of the matrices A_1, A_2. But A_1, A_2 are the matrices of the linear transformations induced by $\mathscr{A}$ in the invariant subspaces $\mathfrak{A}_1, \mathfrak{A}_2$. Consequently, *if the space $\mathfrak{L}$ is the direct sum of subspaces invariant under the linear transformation $\mathscr{A}$, then the characteristic polynomial of $\mathscr{A}$ is the product of the characteristic polynomials of the transformations induced by $\mathscr{A}$ in the invariant subspaces.*

By the Cayley-Hamilton theorem (see Section 11), every square matrix A is a zero of its characteristic polynomial $\varphi(\lambda)$—that is, $\varphi(A) = 0$. Let $\mathscr{A}$ be a linear transformation with matrix A. The transformation $\varphi(\mathscr{A})$, by Section 39, has matrix $\varphi(A)$. Since this is the zero matrix, $\varphi(\mathscr{A}) = \mathscr{O}$. Consequently, *every linear transformation is a zero of its characteristic polynomial.*

The monic polynomial of least degree which has the transformation $\mathscr{A}$ as a zero is called the ***minimal polynomial*** *of the linear transformation* $\mathscr{A}$. Let A be the matrix of $\mathscr{A}$, computed in some coordinate system. Since the relations $f(A) = 0$ and $f(\mathscr{A}) = \mathscr{O}$ are equivalent, where $f(\lambda)$ is an arbitrary polynomial *the minimal polynomial of a transformation is identical with the minimal polynomial of the matrix of the transformation.*

If a space $\mathfrak{L}$ decomposes into the direct sum of subspaces invariant under the transformation $\mathscr{A}$, then the matrix of $\mathscr{A}$, in the proper coordinate system, also decomposes. The minimal polynomial of a decomposable matrix (compare Section 14) is the least common multiple of the minimal polynomials of its diagonal blocks. Therefore, the minimal polynomial of the transformation $\mathscr{A}$ equals the least common multiple of the minimal polynomials of the transformations induced by $\mathscr{A}$ in the invariant subspaces.

46. Proper Vectors and Proper Values

We wish now to make a more detailed study of one-dimensional invariant subspaces. We first introduce the following definition. The scalar ζ is called a ***proper value*** of the linear transformation $\mathscr{A}$ if there exists a nonzero vector a in the space $\mathfrak{L}$ for which

$$a\mathscr{A} = \zeta a \ . \tag{5}$$

Every vector which satisfies this relation is called a ***proper vector*** of the transformation $\mathscr{A}$, belonging to the proper value ζ.

Finding the proper vectors and finding the one-dimensional invariant subspaces are equivalent problems. Let a be a nonzero proper vector of $\mathscr{A}$, with ζ the corresponding proper value. Consider the one-dimensional subspace $\mathfrak{A}$, spanned by the vector a, that is, the set of all vectors of the form αa. The relation

$$(\alpha a)\mathscr{A} = \alpha(a\mathscr{A}) = \zeta\alpha a \tag{6}$$

shows that $\mathfrak{A}$ is invariant under $\mathscr{A}$. Conversely, let some one-dimensional subspace $\mathfrak{A}$ be invariant under $\mathscr{A}$. Take in $\mathfrak{A}$ an arbitrary nonzero vector a. Since $\mathfrak{A}$ is one-dimensional, all vectors in $\mathfrak{A}$ have the form αa. By assumption, $a\mathscr{A}$ belongs to $\mathfrak{A}$; consequently

$$a\mathscr{A} = \zeta a \ ,$$

so, a is a proper vector of $\mathscr{A}$, belonging to the proper value ζ. Equality (6) shows that all the remaining vectors of $\mathfrak{A}$ are also proper vectors belonging to ζ.

Choose a system of coordinates $a_1, \cdots, a_n$ in $\mathfrak{L}$, and let the linear transformation $\mathscr{A}$ have the matrix $A = \| \alpha_{ij} \|$ in this system. Let a be a nonzero proper vector of $\mathscr{A}$ corresponding to ζ, and let its coordinate row be $[\xi_1, \cdots, \xi_n]$. Equality (5) in coordinate form is

$$[a]A = \zeta[a] \ , \tag{7}$$

or

$$\begin{aligned} \xi_1\alpha_{11} + \xi_2\alpha_{21} + \cdots + \xi_n\alpha_{n1} &= \zeta\xi_1 \ , \\ \xi_1\alpha_{12} + \xi_2\alpha_{22} + \cdots + \xi_n\alpha_{n2} &= \zeta\xi_2 \ , \\ &\vdots \\ \xi_1\alpha_{1n} + \xi_2\alpha_{2n} + \cdots + \xi_n\alpha_{nn} &= \zeta\xi_n \ . \end{aligned} \tag{8}$$

Transferring all terms to one side, we obtain

$$\begin{aligned} \xi_1(\zeta - \alpha_{11}) - \xi_2\alpha_{21} - \cdots - \xi_n\alpha_{n1} &= 0 \ , \\ -\xi_1\alpha_{12} + \xi_2(\zeta - \alpha_{22}) - \cdots - \xi_n\alpha_{n2} &= 0 \ , \\ &\vdots \\ -\xi_1\alpha_{1n} - \xi_2\alpha_{2n} - \cdots + \xi_n(\zeta - \alpha_{nn}) &= 0 \ . \end{aligned} \tag{9}$$

This may be considered as a system of n homogeneous linear equations in n unknowns $\xi_1, \cdots, \xi_n$. Since the coordinates of the nonzero proper vector α satisfy system (9), then (compare Section 42)

$$\begin{vmatrix} \zeta - \alpha_{11} & -\alpha_{12} & \cdots & -\alpha_{1n} \\ -\alpha_{21} & \zeta - \alpha_{22} & \cdots & -\alpha_{2n} \\ \cdots & \cdots & \cdots & \cdots \\ -\alpha_{n1} & -\alpha_{n2} & \cdots & \zeta - \alpha_{nn} \end{vmatrix} = |\zeta E - A| = 0 \ , \tag{10}$$

where E is the identity matrix. But $|\lambda E - A|$ is the characteristic polynomial of A, and hence (10) shows that *every proper value of a linear transformation is a zero of its characteristic polynomial.* Conversely, *if ζ is a zero of the characteristic polynomial of the transformation $\mathscr{A}$, and belongs to the field of coefficients of the linear space, then ζ is a proper value of $\mathscr{A}$.* In fact, (10) shows that the rank of the matrix of system (9) is less than n. Consequently, this system has at least one nonzero solution. Denoting this solution by $[\xi_1, \cdots, \xi_n]$, it follows immediately from (8) and (7) that the vector a with coordinates $\xi_1, \cdots, \xi_n$ is the desired nonzero proper vector.*

The ***multiplicity*** of a proper value ζ of a linear transformation $\mathscr{A}$ is the multiplicity with which ζ occurs as a zero of the characteristic polynomial of $\mathscr{A}$.

We consider an example. Let $\mathscr{A}$ be the linear transformation in a three-dimensional real linear space with matrix

$$A = \begin{bmatrix} 3 & 3 & 2 \\ 1 & 1 & -2 \\ -3 & -1 & 0 \end{bmatrix}$$

in the coordinate system a_1, a_2, a_3. We seek the proper values and proper vectors of $\mathscr{A}$. First of all we compute the characteristic polynomial of $\mathscr{A}$:

$$\begin{vmatrix} \lambda-3 & -3 & -2 \\ -1 & \lambda-1 & 2 \\ 3 & 1 & \lambda \end{vmatrix} = (\lambda - 4)(\lambda^2 + 4) .$$

It has zeros $\lambda_1 = 4$, $\lambda_2 = 2i$, $\lambda_3 = -2i$. Since the base field is real, we disregard the last two values. To find the proper vectors belonging to $\lambda_1 = 4$, we construct system (9), which becomes

$$\begin{aligned} \xi_1 - \xi_2 + 3\xi_3 &= 0 . \\ -3\xi_1 + 3\xi_2 + \xi_3 &= 0 , \\ -2\xi_1 + 2\xi_2 + 4\xi_3 &= 0 . \end{aligned}$$

Solving this system, we find

$$\xi_2 = \xi_1 , \quad \xi_3 = 0 ,$$

where ξ_1 is arbitrary. Thus the vector $\xi_1 a_1 + \xi_1 a_2$, for arbitrary ξ_1, is a proper vector of $\mathscr{A}$ belonging to the proper value $\lambda_1 = 4$.

• EXAMPLES AND PROBLEMS

1. Let the linear transformation $\mathscr{A}$ have the matrix

* A shorter proof may be given in the following way. The condition $a\mathscr{A} = \zeta a$ may be written in the form $a(\zeta\mathscr{E} - \mathscr{A}) = 0$. This shows that a proper vector a belongs to the kernel of the transformation $\zeta\mathscr{E} - \mathscr{A}$. But the kernel contains a nonzero vector if and only if the transformation is singular (See Section 41)—that is, if and only if $|\zeta E - A| = 0$.

$$A = \begin{bmatrix} 1 & 0 & 2 & -1 \\ 0 & 1 & 4 & -2 \\ 2 & -1 & 0 & 1 \\ 2 & -1 & -1 & 2 \end{bmatrix}$$

in a complex space $\mathfrak{L}$ with basis a_1, a_2, a_3, a_4. Find the proper values and proper vectors of $\mathscr{A}$. Also show that the subspace spanned by the vectors $2a_1 - a_2$, $-a_3 + a_4$ is invariant under $\mathscr{A}$.

2. Suppose that the space $\mathfrak{L}$ has a basis consisting of proper vectors of the transformation $\mathscr{A}$. What will the matrix of $\mathscr{A}$ be, relative to this basis?

3. If in the space $\mathfrak{L}$ with coordinate system $a_1, \cdots, a_n$ the matrix of a linear transformation $\mathscr{A}$ has the semidecomposable block form

$$A = \begin{bmatrix} A_1 & B_1 \\ 0 & A_2 \end{bmatrix},$$

where A_2 is a square matrix of order m, then the subspace spanned by the last m coordinate vectors, $a_{n-m+1}, \cdots, a_n$, is invariant under $\mathscr{A}$.

4. If the transformation $\mathscr{A}$ is nonsingular, then every subspace invariant under $\mathscr{A}$ is also invariant under $\mathscr{A}^{-1}$.

5. If the subspace $\mathfrak{A}$ is invariant under a transformation $\mathscr{A}$, then the image and pre-image of $\mathfrak{A}$ are also invariant under $\mathscr{A}$.

6. In a complex linear space every linear transformation has at least one nonzero proper vector.

7. In the coordinate system $a_1, \cdots, a_n$ let the matrix of a transformation $\mathscr{A}$ have diagonal form with distinct diagonal elements. Find all subspaces invariant under $\mathscr{A}$, and show that their number is 2^n.

8. Nonzero proper vectors belonging to distinct proper values are linearly independent.

9. If a linear transformation $\mathscr{A}$ of an n-dimensional space $\mathfrak{L}$ has n distinct proper values, then its matrix, in a suitable coordinate system, is diagonal.

6. *Transformations with Matrices in Normal Form*

In the present paragraph we will examine the properties of linear transformations whose matrices have the so-called Jordan normal form relative to some fixed coordinate system. Thus the possibility of reducing the matrices of the transformations under consideration to the required form is presupposed. In Section 59 it will be shown that over the field of complex numbers such a reduction is always possible.

47. Diagonal Form

The simplest characteristic of transformations whose matrices can be reduced to diagonal form is given by

THEOREM 1. *If a linear transformation of an n-dimensional space has n linearly independent proper vectors, then, taking these vectors as coordinates, the matrix of the transformation assumes diagonal form. Conversely, if the matrix of a transformation has diagonal form relative to some coordinate system, then the vectors of the coordinate system are proper vectors of the transformation.*

The proof is obvious. A more difficult problem is to recognize, given the matrix of a transformation computed in some coordinate system, whether or not the transformation has proper vectors that form a basis for the space. This problem will be solved in Section 59, but here we examine one special case.

THEOREM 2. *Proper vectors belonging to distinct proper values of a linear transformation are linearly independent.*

Let $\rho_1, \cdots, \rho_m$ be distinct proper values and $a_1, \cdots, a_m$ be corresponding nonzero proper vectors of the linear transformation $\mathscr{A}$. Assume that $a_1, \cdots, a_{m-1}$ are linearly independent (the case of one proper vector is trivial), and suppose that $a_1, \cdots, a_m$ satisfy the relation

$$\alpha_1 a_1 + \cdots + \alpha_{m-1} a_{m-1} + \alpha_m a_m = \theta .$$

Operating on both sides with $\mathscr{A}$, we obtain

$$\alpha_1 \rho_1 a_1 + \cdots + \alpha_{m-1} \rho_{m-1} a_{m-1} + \alpha_m \rho_m a_m = \theta .$$

Eliminating a_m, we have

$$\alpha_1(\rho_1 - \rho_m)a_1 + \cdots + \alpha_{m-1}(\rho_{m-1} - \rho_m)a_{m-1} = \theta .$$

By the linear independence of $a_1, \cdots, a_{m-1}$, this yields $\alpha_1 = \cdots = \alpha_{m-1} = 0$, and hence $\alpha_m = 0$, which completes the proof.

Comparing the two theorems, we obtain the

COROLLARY: *If the characteristic polynomial of a linear transformation of an n-dimensional linear space has n distinct zeros, then the matrix of the transformation reduces to diagonal form in an appropriate coordinate system.*

For example, the characteristic polynomial of the matrix

$$A = \begin{bmatrix} 1 & 3 & 1 & 2 \\ & -1 & 1 & 3 \\ & & 2 & 5 \\ & & & -2 \end{bmatrix}$$

has zeros ± 1, ± 2; the corresponding proper vectors have coordinate rows [6, 3, − 3, 1], [0, − 3, 1, 1], [0, 0, 4, 1], [0, 0, 0, 1]. Taking these proper vectors as a coordinate system, the matrix A reduces to diagonal form with 1, − 1, 2, − 2 on the main diagonal.

48. Jordan Blocks

A matrix of the form

$$A = \begin{bmatrix} \rho & 1 & 0 & \cdots & 0 \\ & \rho & 1 & \cdots & 0 \\ & & \rho & \cdots & 0 \\ \cdot & \cdot & \cdot & \cdot & \cdot \\ & & & \rho & 1 \\ & & & & \rho \end{bmatrix} \qquad (1)$$

is called a ***Jordan Block***. Its characteristic polynomial is $(\lambda - \rho)^n$, where n is the order of the matrix. Thus ρ is its only proper value, and has multiplicity n.

Let $\mathfrak{L}$ be a linear space with basis $e_1, \cdots, e_n$, and let $\mathscr{A}$ be a linear transformation having in this basis the matrix A of (1). Then

$$e_1\mathscr{A} = \rho e_1 + e_2, \cdots, e_{n-1}\mathscr{A} = \rho e_{n-1} + e_n, \quad e_n\mathscr{A} = \rho e_n, \qquad (2)$$

and consequently

$$e_1(\mathscr{A} - \rho\mathscr{E}) = e_2, \; e_1(\mathscr{A} - \rho\mathscr{E})^2 = e_3, \cdots, e_1(\mathscr{A} - \rho\mathscr{E})^{n-1} = e_n. \qquad (3)$$

Since $\mathscr{A}$ is a zero of its characteristic polynomial, $(\mathscr{A} - \rho\mathscr{E})^n = \mathscr{O}$. The minimal polynomial of $\mathscr{A}$ divides the characteristic polynomial, and hence must have the form $(\lambda - \rho)^s$, where $0 < s \leqq n$. The last equality of (3) shows that $(\mathscr{A} - \rho\mathscr{E})^{n-1} \neq \mathscr{O}$, and therefore $s = n$; that is, *the minimal polynomial of a Jordan block is identical with its characteristic polynomial* $(\lambda - \rho)^n$.

Denote by $\mathfrak{L}_i$ the subspace spanned by the basis vectors $e_i, e_{i+1}, \cdots, e_n$, for $i = 1, \cdots, n$. It is a consequence of equalities (2), or simply of the form of the matrix A, that all these subspaces are invariant. From relations (3) it is easy to verify that $\mathfrak{L}_i$ consists exactly of those vectors x for which

$$x(\mathscr{A} - \rho\mathscr{E})^{n-i+1} = \theta.$$

This shows that the chain of subspaces $\mathfrak{L} = \mathfrak{L}_1 \supset \mathfrak{L}_2 \supset \cdots \supset \mathfrak{L}_n \supset \theta$ is completely determined by the transformation $\mathscr{A}$, and does not depend on the choice of a coordinate system.

We now show that the transformation has no other invariant subspaces. Let $\mathfrak{M}$ be any invariant subspace for $\mathscr{A}$. Let i be such that $\mathfrak{M} \supset \mathfrak{L}_i$, $\mathfrak{M} \not\supset \mathfrak{L}_{i-1}$, setting $\mathfrak{L}_{n+1} = \theta$. We show that $\mathfrak{M} = \mathfrak{L}_i$. Consider an arbitrary vector in $\mathfrak{M}$:

$$a = \alpha_j e_j + \alpha_{j+1}e_{j+1} + \cdots + \alpha_n e_n, \qquad (4)$$

where $\alpha_j \neq 0$. If $j \geqq i$, then $a \in \mathfrak{L}_i$. Suppose that $j < i$. Operating on both sides of (4) with $(\mathscr{A} - \rho\mathscr{E})^{i-j-1}$, we obtain

$$a(\mathscr{A} - \rho\mathscr{E})^{i-j-1} = \alpha_j e_{i-1} + \alpha_{j+1}e_i + \cdots + \alpha_{n-i+j+1}e_n \in \mathfrak{M}.$$

Since, by assumption, $e_i, \cdots, e_n \in \mathfrak{M}$, then $e_{i-1} \in \mathfrak{M}$, and consequently, $\mathfrak{L}_{i-1} \subset \mathfrak{M}$, which is a contradiction. Therefore $j \geqq i$, $\mathfrak{M} \subset \mathfrak{L}_i$, and hence $\mathfrak{M} = \mathfrak{L}_i$.

We observe further that *the matrix of the transformation* $\mathscr{A}$ *is not decomposable in any coordinate system.*

Indeed, the decomposition of the matrix of $\mathscr{A}$ is equivalent to the decomposition of $\mathfrak{L}$ into the direct sum of invariant subspaces, and this is impossible, since one of any two invariant subspaces is contained in the other; that is, any two invariant subspaces have a nontrivial intersection.

49. Root Subspaces

In general, linear transformations whose matrices are reducible to diagonal form or to Jordan block form do not exhaust the entire set of matrices. However, over the field of complex numbers it is possible to reduce the matrix of an arbitrary linear transformation (hence, an arbitrary matrix) to a blockdiagonal form with Jordan blocks on the diagonal. This form is called the ***Jordan normal form***, and matrices of this form are called ***Jordan matrices***.

Suppose the matrix of the transformation $\mathscr{A}$ relative to some basis $e_1, \cdots, e_n$ has the Jordan normal form

$$A = A_1 \dotplus \cdots \dotplus A_s\,, \tag{5}$$

where A_i is a Jordan block of order n_i with proper value ρ_i, where $i = 1, \cdots, s$, and $n_1 + \cdots + n_s = n$. The block A_i corresponds to the invariant subspace $\mathfrak{L}^{(i)}$ spanned by the vectors $e_{p_i+1}, e_{p_i+2}, \cdots, e_{q_i}$, where $p_i = n_1 + \cdots + n_{i-1}$ and $q_i = p_i + n_i$. The transformation $\mathscr{A}$ induces in the subspace $\mathfrak{L}^{(i)}$ a transformation $\mathscr{A}_i$, whose matrix is the block A_i. By the preceding, each vector x in $\mathfrak{L}^{(i)}$ satisfies the relation

$$x(\mathscr{A}_i - \rho_i \mathscr{E})^{n_i} = \theta\,,$$

and hence also the relation

$$x(\mathscr{A} - \rho_i \mathscr{E})^{n_i} = \theta\,. \tag{6}$$

However, it is now impossible to say that relation (6) characterizes only the vectors in $\mathfrak{L}^{(i)}$, since there may be other diagonal blocks of A with the same proper value. To analyze the question in some detail, we introduce the following definition.

A vector a is called a ***root vector*** *of height h, belonging to the proper value ρ of the transformation, $\mathscr{A}$, if*

$$a(\rho\mathscr{E} - \mathscr{A})^h = \theta\,.$$

The notion of root vector is a generalization of the notion of proper vector, since proper vectors are root vectors of height 1.

The set of all root vectors belonging to some fixed proper value ρ of a transformation $\mathscr{A}$ is an invariant subspace $\mathfrak{L}_\rho$, called a **root subspace** *of the transformation $\mathscr{A}$.*

Indeed, if x, y belong to $\mathfrak{L}_\rho$, and have heights h_1, h_2 respectively, then for $h = \max(h_1, h_2)$ we have

$$(\alpha x + \beta y)(\rho\mathscr{E} - \mathscr{A})^h = x(\rho\mathscr{E} - \mathscr{A})^h \cdot \alpha + y(\rho\mathscr{E} - \mathscr{A})^h \cdot \beta = \theta\,,$$
$$x\mathscr{A}(\rho\mathscr{E} - \mathscr{A})^h = x(\rho\mathscr{E} - \mathscr{A})^h \mathscr{A} = \theta\,.$$

Root vectors belonging to distinct proper values are evidently linearly independent. More than this, the following stronger theorem also holds.

THEOREM 3. *If the sum* $x_1 + \cdots + x_m = x$ *of root vectors belonging to distinct proper values* $\rho_1, \cdots, \rho_m$ *of a transformation* $\mathscr{A}$ *is contained in an invariant subspace* $\mathfrak{M}$, *then each summand is contained in* $\mathfrak{M}$.

We show that, say, x_m is contained in $\mathfrak{M}$. Set

$$\varphi(\lambda) = (\lambda - \rho_1)^{h_1}(\lambda - \rho_2)^{h_2}\cdots(\lambda - \rho_{m-1})^{h_{m-1}} .$$

By assumption, $x\varphi(\mathscr{A}) \in \mathfrak{M}$, and at the same time

$$x_1\varphi(\mathscr{A}) = x_2\varphi(\mathscr{A}) = \cdots = x_{m-1}\varphi(\mathscr{A}) = \theta;$$

consequently, $x_m\varphi(\mathscr{A}) \in \mathfrak{M}$. Since the polynomials $\varphi(\lambda)$ and $(\lambda - \rho_m)^{h_m}$ are relatively prime, there exist polynomials $F(\lambda)$, $G(\lambda)$ such that

$$1 = \varphi(\lambda)F(\lambda) + (\lambda - \rho_m)^{h_m}G(\lambda) .$$

Hence

$$\mathscr{E} = \varphi(\mathscr{A})F(\mathscr{A}) + (\mathscr{A} - \rho_m\mathscr{E})^{h_m}G(\mathscr{A}) ,$$

and finally,

$$x_m = x_m\varphi(\mathscr{A})F(\mathscr{A}) + x_m(\mathscr{A} - \rho_m\mathscr{E})^{h_m}G(\mathscr{A}) = x_m\varphi(\mathscr{A})F(\mathscr{A}) \in \mathfrak{M} ,$$

which was to be proved.

The assertion of the linear independence of $x_1, \cdots, x_n$ is obtained from the theorem by setting $\mathfrak{M} = \theta$. As a consequence, we observe also that *distinct root subspaces have trivial intersection.*

We return now to the case when the matrix of the transformation $\mathscr{A}$ has the Jordan normal form (5) in some basis. Two series of subspaces were defined above: the root subspaces $\mathfrak{L}_{\rho_1}, \cdots, \mathfrak{L}_{\rho_m}$ and the subspaces $\mathfrak{L}^{(1)}, \cdots, \mathfrak{L}^{(s)}$, corresponding to the diagonal blocks of the matrix A. To clarify the connection between them, denote by $\mathfrak{M}^{(1)}$ the sum of those subspaces $\mathfrak{L}^{(i)}$ that correspond to blocks with proper value ρ_1, and define $\mathfrak{M}^{(2)}, \cdots, \mathfrak{M}^{(m)}$ similarly. Collecting in this way the terms of the decomposition

$$\mathfrak{L} = \mathfrak{L}^{(1)} \dotplus \cdots \dotplus \mathfrak{L}^{(s)} ,$$

we obtain the decomposition

$$\mathfrak{L} = \mathfrak{M}^{(1)} \dotplus \cdots \dotplus \mathfrak{M}^{(m)} . \tag{7}$$

It is clear that $\mathfrak{M}^{(i)} \subseteq \mathfrak{L}_{\rho_i}$, for $i = 1, \cdots, m$. Therefore, by (7),

$$\mathfrak{L} = \mathfrak{L}_{\rho_1} + \cdots + \mathfrak{L}_{\rho_m} . \tag{8}$$

But by Theorem 3 the sum (8) is direct, and comparing it with (7) we obtain $\mathfrak{M}^{(i)} = \mathfrak{L}_{\rho_i}$.

Thus, if the matrix of a transformation $\mathscr{A}$ can be reduced to Jordan normal form, the space $\mathfrak{L}$ is the direct sum of the root subspaces of $\mathscr{A}$, moreover, each root subspace in turn is the direct sum of subspaces corresponding to the Jordan blocks which have the given proper value.

The argument above also shows that the root subspaces are uniquely determined by the transformation $\mathscr{A}$, and do not depend on the choice of a coordinate system. As regards the subspaces $\mathfrak{L}^{(i)}$, in general they depend not only on $\mathscr{A}$ but also on the method of reducing the matrix to normal form.

● EXAMPLES AND PROBLEMS

1. Relative to the basis $e_1, \cdots, e_6$, let the transformation $\mathscr{A}$ have the matrix $A = A_1 \dotplus A_2 \dotplus A_3$, where $A_1 = A_2 = \begin{bmatrix} 6 & 1 \\ 0 & 6 \end{bmatrix}$, $A_3 = \begin{bmatrix} 7 & 1 \\ 0 & 7 \end{bmatrix}$. The root subspaces of $\mathscr{A}$ are $\mathfrak{L}_6 = Ke_1 + Ke_2 + Ke_3 + Ke_4$ and $\mathfrak{L}_7 = Ke_5 + Ke_6$, where K is the base field, and $\mathfrak{L}^{(1)} = Ke_1 + Ke_2$, $\mathfrak{L}^{(2)} = Ke_3 + Ke_4$. In the new basis,
$$e_1' = e_1 + e_3\,,\quad e_2' = e_2 + e_4\,,\quad e_3' = e_1 - e_3\,,\quad e_4' = e_2 - e_4\,,\quad e_5' = e_5\,,\quad e_6' = e_6\,,$$
the matrix of $\mathscr{A}$ will be the same; however, the subspaces $Ke_1' + Ke_2'$, $Ke_3' + Ke_4'$, corresponding to the Jordan blocks, will be different.
2. Find the minimal polynomials of the matrices
$$\begin{bmatrix} 2 & 1 & 1 \\ & 2 & 1 \\ & & 2 \end{bmatrix}, \quad \begin{bmatrix} 2 & 1 & 1 \\ & 3 & 1 \\ & & 4 \end{bmatrix}, \quad \begin{bmatrix} 2 & 1 & 1 \\ & 2 & 1 \\ & & 3 \end{bmatrix}, \quad \begin{bmatrix} 2 & 1 & 1 \\ & 2 & 0 \\ & & 2 \end{bmatrix}.$$
3. A matrix over the field of complex numbers is reducible to diagonal form if and only if its minimal polynomial does not have multiple zeros.
4. If the matrix of a transformation is reducible to Jordan normal form, then each invariant subspace is the direct sum of the intersections of this subspace will all of the root subspaces.

4 POLYNOMIAL MATRICES

Until now, almost all the matrices we have encounted have had their entries drawn from the base field K. Only in connection with the notion of a characteristic polynomial was it necessary to consider the characteristic matrix $\lambda E - \dot{A}$, whose elements were not scalars in K, but polynomials in λ with coefficients in K. In the present chapter we shall systematically study the properties of polynomial matrices; the results will then be applied to the problem of finding the Jordan form of the matrix of a linear trans formation.

1. *Invariant Factors*

50. Equivalence

Consider the nth order square matrix

$$\begin{bmatrix} f_{11}(\lambda) & \cdots & f_{1n}(\lambda) \\ \vdots & & \vdots \\ f_{n1}(\lambda) & \cdots & f_{nn}(\lambda) \end{bmatrix},$$

whose elements are polynomials in λ with coefficients in the base field K. This is a ***polynomial matrix*** or λ-***matrix****. It is often necessary to perform the following transformations on λ-matrices:

I. Multiplication of a row by a nonzero scalar in K.

II. Addition of one row, multiplied by an arbitrary polynomial $f(\lambda)$, to another row.

---

* We assume throughout that the matrices considered are square, although many results carry over immediately to rectangular λ-matrices.

III. Multiplication of a column by a nonzero scalar in K.

IV. Addition of one column, multiplied by an arbitrary polynomial $f(\lambda)$, to another column.

These transformations are called the ***elementary transformations*** of λ-matrices. The result of performing an elementary transformation on a λ-matrix is again a λ-matrix; this new matrix can again be operated on by an elementary transformation, and so on. We say that a λ-matrix F is ***equivalent*** to a λ-matrix G if F can be obtained from G by a series of elementary transformations. The following lemma turns out to be very useful.

LEMMA: *Any two rows of a λ-matrix can be interchanged by using the elementary transformations* I *and* II; *any two columns can be interchanged by using* III *and* IV.

Suppose we wish to interchange the ith and jth rows. It is easy to see that this is accomplished by applying the following series of elementary transformations: 1) add the jth row to the ith; 2) add -1 times the new ith row to the jth; 3) multiply the new jth row by -1; 4) add -1 times the jth row to the new ith row. The ith and jth columns are interchanged by applying similar operations to the columns. This proves the lemma.

It is a consequence of this lemma that *if F differs from G only in the ordering of rows or columns, then F is equivalent to G.*

The following properties are immediate consequences of the definition of equivalence,

1) *The relation of equivalence is transitive*: if F is equivalent to G, and G is equivalent to H, then F is equivalent to H.

By assumption, G can be obtained from H, and F from G, by a series of elementary transformations; consequently, F can be obtained from H by a series of elementary transformations.

2) *The relation of equivalence is symmetric*: if F is equivalent to G, then G is equivalent to F. In other words, if F can be obtained from G by a series of elementary transformations, then also can G be obtained from F by a series of elementary transformations.

We show first that if F can be obtained from G by a single elementary transformation, then also can G be obtained from F by a single transformation. To do this we consider each of the four types of elementary transformations. Let F be obtained from G by a transformation of type I, by the multiplication of the ith row of G by a nonzero scalar α. Then multiplying the ith row of F by α^{-1} will obviously yield G. Now let F be obtained from G by a transformation of type II, for example by adding $f(\lambda)$ times the jth row of G to the ith row. In this case, adding $-f(\lambda)$ times the jth row of F to the ith row yields G. The same statements can be made for operations of types III and IV. Consequently, for each elementary transformation there exists an elementary transformation inverse to it; thus, if F is obtained from G by a series of elementary transformations, applying the inverse transformations in the opposite order will yield G from F, which was to be proved.

3) *The relation of equivalence is reflexive: each λ-matrix is equivalent to itself.* For example, applying to F two transformations which are inverse to each other, we again obtain F.

51. Diagonal Forms

It has been shown that the relation of equivalence is transitive, symmetric, and reflexive; thus the λ-matrices may be divided into equivalence classes. The question arises as to whether there is a certain form of a λ-matrix such that each equivalence class contains one and only one matrix of this form. A form with this property is called ***canonical.*** We show that for λ-matrixes, a diagonal form with certain additional divisibility conditions is a canonical form in this sense.

Definition. A λ-matrix of the form

$$\begin{bmatrix} f_1(\lambda) & & & \\ & f_2(\lambda) & & \\ & & \ddots & \\ & & & f_n(\lambda) \end{bmatrix}$$

is called a canonical diagonal λ-matrix if each diagonal element $f_i(\lambda)$ is a divisor of the next element $f_{i+1}(\lambda)$, and if all non-zero diagonal elements have leading coefficient 1.

It is clear that if the diagonal contains zero polynomials, they must occur in the last places, since 0 is not a divisor of any nonzero polynomial. On the other hand, if the diagonal contains scalars different from 0, then they must equal 1 and occupy the first places, since the only polynomial with leading coefficient 1 which divides 1 is the polynomial 1. Consequently, the general canonical diagonal matrix has the form

$$\begin{bmatrix} 1 & & & & & & & & \\ & \ddots & & & & & & & \\ & & 1 & & & & & & \\ & & & f_1(\lambda) & & & & & \\ & & & & \ddots & & & & \\ & & & & & f_k(\lambda) & & & \\ & & & & & & 0 & & \\ & & & & & & & \ddots & \\ & & & & & & & & 0 \end{bmatrix}$$

where $f_1(\lambda), \cdots, f_k(\lambda)$ are nonconstant polynomials with leading coefficients 1 such that each of them divides the next.

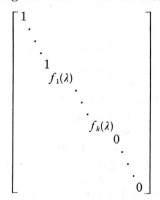

THEOREM 1. *Every λ-matrix can be reduced to canonical diagonal form by a finite number of elementary transformations.*

Let G be the given λ-matrix. If $G = 0$, there is nothing to prove, since 0 is already in normal form. Hence assume that $G \neq 0$. Among all λ-matrices equivalent to G, choose one in which the element in the upper left corner is nonzero and of least degree. Let this matrix be

$$F = \begin{bmatrix} f_{11}(\lambda) & \cdots & f_{1n}(\lambda) \\ \vdots & & \vdots \\ f_{n1}(\lambda) & \cdots & f_{nn}(\lambda) \end{bmatrix}.$$

We show that all the elements of the first row and first column of F are divisible without remainder by $f_{11}(\lambda)$. Let

$$f_{1i}(\lambda) = f_{11}(\lambda)\, q_i(\lambda) + r_i(\lambda) \qquad (i = 1, \cdots, n), \tag{1}$$

where $q_i(\lambda)$, $r_i(\lambda)$ are the quotient and remainder on dividing $f_{1i}(\lambda)$ by $f_{11}(\lambda)$. Operate on F with the following elementary transformation: subtract $q_i(\lambda)$ times the first column from the ith column. Equality (1) shows that the element in the 1st row and ith column of the new matrix is $r_i(\lambda)$. If $r_i(\lambda) \neq 0$, then the degree of $r_i(\lambda)$ is less than the degree of the divisor $f_{11}(\lambda)$. Interchanging the 1st and ith columns, we obtain a matrix equivalent to F and having in the upper left corner an element $r_i(\lambda)$ of degree less than that of $f_{11}(\lambda)$, which contradicts the definition of F. Thus $r_i(\lambda) = 0$. A similar argument shows that $f_{11}(\lambda)$ divides all the elements of the first column.

With $q_i(\lambda)$ as before, perform these elementary transformations on F: subtract $q_2(\lambda)$ times the first column from the second, then subtract $q_3(\lambda)$ times the first column from the third, and so on. Then perform analogous transformations on the rows. As a result, F is transformed into the equivalent matrix

$$H = \begin{bmatrix} f_{11}(\lambda) & 0 & \cdots & 0 \\ 0 & h_{22}(\lambda) & \cdots & h_{2n}(\lambda) \\ \vdots & \vdots & & \vdots \\ 0 & h_{n2}(\lambda) & \cdots & h_{nn}(\lambda) \end{bmatrix}, \tag{2}$$

where the $h_{ij}(\lambda)$ are certain polynomials.

All the $h_{ij}(\lambda)$ are divisible by $f_{11}(\lambda)$. If, say, $h_{ij}(\lambda)$ were not divisible by $f_{11}(\lambda)$, then, adding the ith row of H to the first, we would obtain a matrix $\bar{H}$ with these properties: (1) $\bar{H}$ is equivalent to G; (2) the upper left element of $\bar{H}$ is nonzero and of least degree; (3) in the first row of $\bar{H}$ is an element $h_{ij}(\lambda)$, which is not divisible by the first element of this row.

However, by the preceding argument, the third property contradicts the first two, and our assertion is proved. Thus we have shown that for each λ-matrix G there exists an equivalent matrix H of the form (2), where all the $h_{ij}(\lambda)$ are divisible by $f_{11}(\lambda)$. We now perform elementary transformations on the matrix

$$H_1 = \begin{bmatrix} h_{22}(\lambda) & \cdots & h_{2n}(\lambda) \\ \vdots & & \vdots \\ h_{n2}(\lambda) & \cdots & h_{nn}(\lambda) \end{bmatrix}.$$

Each elementary transformation of H_1 may also be considered an elementary transformation of H. It is easy to see that the first row and column of H are left fixed. Moreover, since all the elements of H_1 are divisible by $f_{11}(\lambda)$, then all the elements of the new matrices, arising from H_1 as the result of elementary transformations, will also be divisible by $f_{11}(\lambda)$.

Applying the result proved above to the matrix H_1, we see that by elementary transformations we may obtain from H_1 a matrix of the form

$$K_1 = \begin{bmatrix} k_{22}(\lambda) & 0 & \cdots & 0 \\ 0 & p_{33}(\lambda) & \cdots & p_{3n}(\lambda) \\ \vdots & \vdots & & \vdots \\ 0 & p_{n3}(\lambda) & \cdots & p_{nn}(\lambda) \end{bmatrix},$$

and from H, consequently, a matrix of the form

$$L = \begin{bmatrix} f_{11}(\lambda) & & & & \\ & k_{22}(\lambda) & & & \\ & & p_{33}(\lambda) & \cdots & p_{3n}(\lambda) \\ & & \vdots & & \vdots \\ & & p_{n3}(\lambda) & \cdots & p_{nn}(\lambda) \end{bmatrix},$$

where all the $p_{ij}(\lambda)$ are divisible by $k_{22}(\lambda)$, and $k_{22}(\lambda)$ is divisible by $f_{11}(\lambda)$. Continuing this process, after a finite number of steps we obtain the required canonical diagonal form.

It is not hard to extract from our proof a practical method for reducing a λ-matrix to a canonical diagonal form. The idea is to use elementary transformations, first to get an upper left element of lowest degree, then to obtain zeros in the remaining places in the first row and column, and, after this is achieved, to apply the same method to the matrix H_1, and so on.

Theorem 1 asserts that *each equivalence class of matrices contains at least one matrix in canonical diagonal form*. In the following section we show that this matrix is unique.

52. Greatest Common Divisor of Minors

Let F be a λ-matrix of order n. Construct from F all possible minors of order k. These minors are polynomials in λ. Denote their greatest common divisor by $D_k(\lambda)$.* If it turns out that all minors of order k are zero, then we define $D_k(\lambda) = 0$. In particular, $D_1(\lambda)$ is the greatest common divisor of the elements of the matrix F; $D_n(\lambda)$ equals the determinant of F divided by its leading coefficient (unless $D_n(\lambda) = 0$).

* The greatest common divisor here is the common divisor of highest degree with *leading coefficient* 1. Therefore all the nonzero polynomials $D_k(\lambda)$ have leading coefficient 1.

THEOREM 2. *Equivalent λ-matrices have identical greatest common divisors of kth order minors, $k = 1, \cdots, n$.*

Let F_1, F_2 be two equivalent λ-matrices. Denote the greatest common divisors of their kth order minors respectively by $D_{k1}(\lambda)$ and $D_{k2}(\lambda)$. It is required to show that $D_{k1}(\lambda) = D_{k2}(\lambda)$. We know that F_2 can be obtained from F_1 by a series of elementary transformations. Suppose first that this series consists of one elementary transformation. For example, let F_2 be obtained from F_1 by multiplying the ith row of F_1 by a scalar $\alpha \neq 0$. The corresponding minors of F_1 and F_2 are then either identical or differ only by a constant factor α. However, a constant factor does not influence the calculation of the greatest common divisor, and therefore $D_{k1} = D_{k2}$. The situation is the same when F_2 is obtained from F_1 by multiplying a column of F_1 by α. Suppose now that F_2 is obtained from F_1 by a transformation of type II or IV; for example, let F_2 be the result of adding $f(\lambda)$ times the jth row of F_1 to the ith row. We show that D_{k1} divides D_{k2}.

The kth order minors of F_1, F_2 may be divided into three classes. In the first we put those which do not contain elements of the ith row. In this case, corresponding minors of F_1, F_2 are evidently equal. In the second class we put those minors which contain elements of both the ith and the jth rows. Corresponding minors of F_1, F_2 in this class are again equal, since a determinant is not changed by adding a multiple of one row to another row. Finally, in the third class we put those minors that contain elements of the ith row but not elements of the jth row. Corresponding minors in this class have the forms

$$M_1 = \begin{vmatrix} \cdots\cdots \\ f_{i\nu_1} \cdots f_{i\nu_k} \\ \cdots\cdots \end{vmatrix}, \quad M_2 = \begin{vmatrix} \cdots\cdots\cdots\cdots \\ f_{i\nu_1} + f_{j\nu_1} \cdot f(\lambda) \cdots f_{i\nu_k} + f_{j\nu_k} \cdot f(\lambda) \\ \cdots\cdots\cdots\cdots \end{vmatrix},$$

where the corresponding rows which are not written out are identical. By a fundamental theorem on addition of determinants,

$$M_2 = \begin{vmatrix} \cdots\cdots \\ f_{i\nu} \cdots f_{i\nu_k} \\ \cdots\cdots \end{vmatrix} + f(\lambda) \begin{vmatrix} \cdots\cdots \\ f_{j\nu_1} \cdots f_{j\nu_k} \\ \cdots\cdots \end{vmatrix} = M_1 \pm f(\lambda) N_1,$$

where N_1 is some minor of the matrix F_1. All kth order minors of F_1 are divisible by D_{k1}. It is now evident that all kth order minors of F_2 are divisible by D_{k1}. This means that D_{k1} divides the greatest common divisor of the kth order minors of F_2 that is, that D_{k1} divides D_{k2}. Applying the inverse elementary transformation (which is also of type II) to F_2, we obtain F_1. Therefore D_{k2} divides D_{k1}, and hence $D_{k1} = D_{k2}$. This takes care of the case when F_2 is obtained from F_1 by a single elementary transformation. However, if $D_k(\lambda)$ is not affected by each separate elementary transformation in a series, it is obviously not affected by the series of elementary transformations. This completes the proof of Theorem 2.

We compute the polynomials $D_1(\lambda), \cdots, D_n(\lambda)$ for a matrix having the canonical form

$$D = \begin{bmatrix} d_1(\lambda) & & & & \\ & d_2(\lambda) & & & \\ & & \cdot & & \\ & & & \cdot & \\ & & & & \cdot \\ & & & & & d_n(\lambda) \end{bmatrix}.$$

To obtain a kth order minor, we must strike out $n-k$ rows and $n-k$ columns. If the ith row is crossed out, then the remaining ith column contains only zeros. Therefore, to obtain a minor different from zero, we must strike out corresponding rows and columns. Thus the nonzero kth order minors must have the form

$$\begin{vmatrix} d_{\nu_1}(\lambda) & & & & \\ & d_{\nu_2}(\lambda) & & & \\ & & \cdot & & \\ & & & \cdot & \\ & & & & \cdot \\ & & & & & d_{\nu_k}(\lambda) \end{vmatrix} = d_{\nu_1}(\lambda) d_{\nu_2}(\lambda) \cdots d_{\nu_k}(\lambda), \tag{3}$$

and $D_k(\lambda)$ is the greatest common divisor of these minors. From the inequalities $1 \leqq \nu_1 < \cdots < \nu_k \leqq n$ it follows that $1 \leqq \nu_1$, $2 \leqq \nu_2$, $\cdots$, $k \leqq \nu_k$. Therefore $d_{\nu_i}(\lambda)$ is divisible by $d_i(\lambda)$, and this means that $d_{\nu_1}(\lambda) \cdots d_{\nu_k}(\lambda)$ is divisible by $d_1(\lambda) \cdots d_k(\lambda)$. Consequently, every kth order minor of the matrix D is divisible by the kth order minor

$$\begin{vmatrix} d_1(\lambda) & & & \\ & \cdot & & \\ & & \cdot & \\ & & & \cdot \\ & & & & d_k(\lambda) \end{vmatrix} = d_1(\lambda) \cdots d_k(\lambda). \tag{4}$$

If this minor equals zero, then all the kth order minors of D are zero, and by definition $D_k(\lambda) = 0$. If the minor (4) is not zero, then the polynomials $d_1(\lambda), \cdots, d_k(\lambda)$ are nonzero and have leading coefficient 1. Since every minor (3) is divisible by (4), $D_k(\lambda)$ coincides with (4). Consequently we have

$$D_k(\lambda) = d_1(\lambda) \cdots d_k(\lambda) \tag{5}$$

Consider now an arbitrary λ-matrix F. Denote the greatest common divisor of the kth order minors of this matrix by $D_k(\lambda)$. By Theorem 1, F can be reduced by elementary transformations to the canonical diagonal form

$$D = \begin{bmatrix} d_1(\lambda) & & & \\ & \cdot & & \\ & & \cdot & \\ & & & \cdot \\ & & & & d_n(\lambda) \end{bmatrix}.$$

By Theorem 2, the polynomials $D_k(\lambda)$, computed for the matrix D, are identical with the corresponding polynomials $D_k(\lambda)$ computed for the matrix F. Thus, *the polynomials* $D_k(\lambda)$ *of the matrix* F *and the diagonal elements of the canonical diagonal matrix D to which F can be reduced, are connected by relation* (5).

Let $D_1(\lambda), \cdots, D_r(\lambda)$ be different from zero, and the remaining polynomials $D_{r+1}(\lambda), \cdots, D_n(\lambda)$, if there are any, be zero. Then from (5) we have

$$\begin{aligned} D_1(\lambda) &= d_1(\lambda), & d_1(\lambda) &= D_1(\lambda), \\ D_2(\lambda) &= d_1(\lambda)\, d_2(\lambda), & d_2(\lambda) &= D_2(\lambda)/D_1(\lambda), \\ &\vdots & &\vdots \\ D_r(\lambda) &= d_1(\lambda)\, d_2(\lambda) \cdots d_r(\lambda), & d_r(\lambda) &= D_r(\lambda)/D_{r-1}(\lambda), \\ D_{r+1}(\lambda) &= d_1(\lambda)\, d_2(\lambda) \cdots d_r(\lambda)\, d_{r+1}(\lambda), & d_{r+1}(\lambda) &= D_{r+1}(\lambda)/D_r(\lambda), \end{aligned}$$

Since $d_{r+1}(\lambda) = 0$, then $d_{r+2}(\lambda), \cdots, d_n(\lambda)$ are also zero, and we have finally

$$\begin{gathered} d_1(\lambda) = D_1(\lambda),\ d_2(\lambda) = D_2(\lambda)/D_1(\lambda), \cdots, d_r(\lambda) = D_r(\lambda)/D_{r-1}(\lambda), \\ d_{r+1}(\lambda) = \cdots = d_n(\lambda) = 0, \end{gathered} \tag{6}$$

We have obtained the following theorem.

THEOREM 3. *If the greatest common divisors $D_k(\lambda)$ of the kth order minors of the λ-matrix F are different from zero for $k = 1, \cdots, r$, and $D_{r+1}(\lambda) = 0$, then the diagonal elements $d_k(\lambda)$ of the canonical diagonal matrix to which F can be reduced by elementary transformations are expressed in terms of the $D_k(\lambda)$ by* (6), *and thus are uniquely determined by the matrix F.*

The polynomials $d_1(\lambda), \cdots, d_n(\lambda)$ are called the ***invariant factors*** of the matrix F.

The number r appearing in (6) has a very simple meaning: it is the rank of the matrix F. Indeed, the rank of F is the highest of the orders of the non-zero minors of F. If this order is r, then $D_r(\lambda) \neq 0$, $D_{r+1}(\lambda) = 0$. Conversely, if $D_r(\lambda) \neq 0$ and $D_{r+1}(\lambda) = 0$, then some rth order minor of F is nonzero, every $(r+1)$st order minor equals zero, and F has rank r.

53. Conditions for Equivalence

Using the results of the preceding section, it is easy to find conditions under which two given λ-matrices are equivalent. We present these conditions in two forms.

First condition for equivalence. *Two polynomial matrices of order n are equivalent if and only if the greatest common divisors of their kth order minors are identical for $k = 1, \cdots, n$.*

Since equality of the greatest common divisors of the minors is equivalent to equality of the invariant factors, this first condition may also be stated in the following form: *two λ-matrices are equivalent if and only if their corresponding invariant factors are equal.*

The proof is evident since if two λ-matrices F and G are equivalent, their greatest common divisors $D_k(\lambda)$ are identical (Theorem 2). Conversely, if the polynomials $D_k(\lambda)$ of F and of G are equal, then F and G can be reduced by elementary transformations to the same canonical diagonal matrix (Theorem 3) and two matrices equivalent to a third are equivalent to each other.

Second condition for equivalence. *The polynomial matrices F and G are equivalent if and only if they satisfy a relation*

$$G = PFQ$$

*where P and Q are polynomial matrices with constant nonzero determinants.**

Before proving this assertion, we make several observations. Let

$$A = \begin{bmatrix} 1 & & & & & & \\ & \cdot & & & & & \\ & & 1 & & & & \\ & & & \alpha & & & \\ & & & & 1 & & \\ & & & & & \cdot & \\ & & & & & & 1 \end{bmatrix} \quad i\text{th row},$$

where α is a nonzero scalar. Multiplying an arbitrary matrix F on the left by A, we see that all elements of F are left unchanged except those in the ith row, which are multiplied by α. Thus, *performing an elementary transformation of type I on F is equivalent to multiplying F on the left by a suitable matrix A.* Similarly, if we multiply the matrix F on the left by the matrix

$$B = \begin{bmatrix} 1 & \cdots & 0 & \cdots & 0 & \cdots & 0 \\ \vdots & & \vdots & & \vdots & & \vdots \\ 0 & \cdots & 1 & \cdots & f(\lambda) & \cdots & 0 \\ \vdots & & \vdots & & \vdots & & \vdots \\ 0 & \cdots & 0 & \cdots & 1 & \cdots & 0 \\ \vdots & & \vdots & & \vdots & & \vdots \\ 0 & \cdots & 0 & \cdots & 0 & \cdots & 1 \end{bmatrix}, \quad \begin{matrix} i\text{th row} \\ \\ j\text{th row} \end{matrix}$$

where the diagonal elements are 1, the element in the ith row and jth column is $f(\lambda)$, and the remaining elements are zero, then the result is the addition of $f(\lambda)$ times the jth row to the ith row. Consequently, performing an elementary transformation of type II on F is equivalent to multiplying the matrix F on the left by a suitable matrix B.

Finally, it is easy to see that performing an elementary transformation of type III or IV on F is equivalent to multiplying the matrix F on the right by a suitable matrix A or B.

We proceed now to the proof of the second condition for equivalence.

* Equivalence of λ-matrices was defined above by using elementary transformations. It is often defined in another way: two λ-matrices G, F are equivalent if there exist nonsingular matrices P, Q with constant determinants such that $G = PFQ$. Thus the second condition above may be interpreted as a theorem on the equivalence of these definitions.

Necessity. Let the matrix G be equivalent to the matrix F. This means that G can be obtained from F by a series of elementary transformations. Each elementary transformation can be applied by multiplying F on the right or left by a suitable matrix of the form A or B. Thus we obtain

$$G = P_1 \cdots P_p F Q_1 \cdots Q_q, \tag{7}$$

where each P_i, Q_j has the form A or B, for $i, j = 1, 2, \cdots$. Set

$$P = P_1 \cdots P_p, \quad Q = Q_1 \cdots Q_q.$$

Since the determinant of a matrix of type B is 1, and the determinant of a matrix of type A is a nonzero constant, the determinants of P and Q are also nonzero constants. Relation (7) gives

$$G = PFQ,$$

and this proves the necessity of the condition.

Sufficiency. Suppose, conversely, that

$$G = PFQ, \tag{8}$$

where P and Q are polynomial matrices with nonzero constant determinants. The greatest common divisor $D_n(\lambda)$ of all nth order minors of the matrix P equals the determinant of P divided by its leading coefficient. Since this determinant is a constant, then $D_n(\lambda) = 1$. From (5) for $k = n$, we have

$$D_n(\lambda) = d_1(\lambda) \cdots d_n(\lambda) = 1,$$

and hence

$$d_1(\lambda) = \cdots = d_n(\lambda) = 1,$$

where $d_1(\lambda), \cdots, d_n(\lambda)$ are the invariant factors of P. But the invariant factors of the identity matrix E are all equal to 1, since E has canonical diagonal form. By the first condition for equivalence, P is equivalent to E, and this means that P can be obtained from E by a series of elementary transformations. Each elementary transformation can be applied by multiplying by a matrix of type A or B. Hence P can be represented in the following way:

$$P = P_1 \cdots P_k E Q_1 \cdots Q_l = P_1 \cdots P_k Q_1 \cdots Q_l,$$

where the P_i, Q_j are matrices of type A or B.

Applying the same argument to the matrix Q, we obtain the expression

$$Q = M_1 \cdots M_s N_1 \cdots N_t,$$

Substituting these expressions in (8), we have

$$G = P_1 \cdots P_k Q_1 \cdots Q_l F M_1 \cdots \mathrm{M}_s N_1 \cdots N_t. \tag{9}$$

Thus G is obtained from F by multiplying F successively by matrices P_i, Q_i, M_i, N_i of types A and B. But each of these multiplications is equivalent to some elementary transformation. Consequently, G is equivalent to F, and the proof is complete.

● EXAMPLES AND PROBLEMS

1. Using elementary transformations, reduce the following matrices to canonical diagonal form:

$$\begin{bmatrix} \lambda-2 & -1 & 0 \\ 0 & \lambda-2 & -1 \\ 0 & 0 & \lambda-2 \end{bmatrix}, \quad \begin{bmatrix} \lambda(\lambda+1) & 0 & 0 \\ 0 & \lambda & 0 \\ 0 & 0 & (\lambda+1)^2 \end{bmatrix}, \quad \begin{bmatrix} 1-\lambda & \lambda^2 & \lambda \\ \lambda & \lambda & -\lambda \\ 1+\lambda^2 & \lambda^2 & -\lambda^2 \end{bmatrix}.$$

2. Using the greatest common divisor of minors, find the canonical diagonal form of the λ-matrices

$$\begin{bmatrix} \lambda & 1 & 0 & 0 \\ 0 & \lambda & 1 & 1 \\ 0 & 0 & \lambda & 1 \\ 5 & 4 & 3 & \lambda+2 \end{bmatrix}, \quad \begin{bmatrix} \alpha+\lambda & \beta & 1 & 0 \\ -\beta & \alpha+\lambda & 0 & 1 \\ 0 & 0 & \alpha+\lambda & \beta \\ 0 & 0 & -\beta & \alpha+\lambda \end{bmatrix}$$

3. Show that every rectangular λ-matrix with m rows and n columns can be reduced by elementary transformations to the form

$$\begin{bmatrix} d_1(\lambda) & 0 & \cdots & 0 & \cdots & 0 \\ 0 & d_2(\lambda) & \cdots & 0 & \cdots & 0 \\ \cdots & \cdots & \cdots & \cdots & \cdots & \cdots \\ 0 & 0 & \cdots & d_m(\lambda) & \cdots & 0 \end{bmatrix} \quad \text{or} \quad \begin{bmatrix} d_1(\lambda) & 0 & \cdots & 0 \\ 0 & d_2(\lambda) & \cdots & 0 \\ \cdots & \cdots & \cdots & \cdots \\ 0 & 0 & \cdots & d_n(\lambda) \\ \cdots & \cdots & \cdots & \cdots \\ 0 & 0 & \cdots & 0 \end{bmatrix}.$$

How must the second condition for equivalence be formulated for these matrices?

4. Show that every square λ-matrix can be reduced by elementary transformations of types I and II to the form

$$\begin{bmatrix} f_{11}(\lambda) & f_{12}(\lambda) & \cdots & f_{1n}(\lambda) \\ 0 & f_{22}(\lambda) & \cdots & f_{2n}(\lambda) \\ \cdots & \cdots & \cdots & \cdots \\ 0 & 0 & \cdots & f_{nn}(\lambda) \end{bmatrix}$$

5. Instead of λ-matrices, consider integer matrices; that is matrices whose terms are whole numbers. The elementary transformations of integer matrices are defined in the following way: I, multiplication of a row by ± 1; II, addition of an integer times one row to another row; III, IV are analogous transformations of the columns. A diagonal integer matrix is called canonical if its diagonal elements are nonnegative and each divides the one following. Prove the following: a) each integer matrix can be reduced by a finite number of elementary transformations to canonical diagonal form; b) this canonical diagonal form is unique; c) two integer matrices F, G are equivalent if and only if they satisfy a relation $G = PFQ$, where P, Q are integer matrices with determinant ± 1.

2. *Elementary Divisors*

The invariant factors characterize a polynomial matrix F up to equivalence.

However, if F is decomposable into diagonal block form, then the dependence of the invariant factors of F on the invariant factors of the blocks turns out to be complicated. In some questions it is more convenient to consider not invariant factors, but the so-called elementary divisors of the matrix F, whose behavior is simpler when F decomposes.

54. The Connection with Invariant Factors

Consider an arbitrary λ-matrix F, whose elements are polynomials in λ with coefficients in the base field K. Here K is not restricted in any way. Denote the invariant factors of F by $d_1(\lambda), \cdots, d_n(\lambda)$. Some of these may be zero, so we suppose for definiteness that $d_1(\lambda), \cdots, d_r(\lambda)$ are nonzero and $d_{r+1}(\lambda) = \cdots = d_n(\lambda) = 0$. The number r, as we have seen above, is the rank of the matrix F. We factor each of the polynomials $d_1(\lambda), \cdots, d_r(\lambda)$ into factors irreducible over K. Let, for example,

$$d_i(\lambda) = [\varepsilon_1(\lambda)]^{n_1} \cdots [\varepsilon_k(\lambda)]^{n_k} ,$$

where $\varepsilon_1(\lambda), \cdots, \varepsilon_k(\lambda)$ are distinct irreducible factors with leading coefficients 1. The expressions $[\varepsilon_1(\lambda)]^{n_1}, \cdots, [\varepsilon_k(\lambda)]^{n_k}$ are called the ***elementary divisors*** of the invariant factor $d_i(\lambda)$.* The elementary divisors of all the nonconstant invariant factors of a matrix F are called the elementary divisors of F. For example, if the invariant factors of F are respectively $1, \lambda, \lambda^2(\lambda+1), \lambda^2(\lambda+1)^2$, then the elementary divisors of F are $\lambda, \lambda^2, \lambda^2, (\lambda+1)$, $(\lambda+1)^2$. Elementary divisors of the form $[\varepsilon(\lambda)]^k$, where $\varepsilon(\lambda)$ is an irreducible polynomial, are said to *belong to* the polynomial $\varepsilon(\lambda)$. In the example just given, the elementary divisors $\lambda, \lambda^2, \lambda^2$ belong to the polynomial λ, and $\lambda+1$ and $(\lambda+1)^2$ belong to $\lambda+1$.

We now take some λ-matrix F and write out all its elementary divisors. If some elementary divisor of F is contained in several invariant factors of F, then we write it a corresponding number of times. We show that the system of elementary divisors obtained in this way fully determines all the nonconstant invariant factors of the matrix F; this system, together with the order and rank of F, determines all the invariant factors of F.

THEOREM 1. *The system of elementary divisors of a λ-matrix F, along with its rank and order, fully determines the invariant factors of F, and, consequently, determine F to within equivalence.*

The proof is easily understood through the following example. Let F have order 6, rank 4, and elementary divisors $\lambda, \lambda^2, \lambda^2, \lambda+1, (\lambda+1)^3, \lambda-1$, $\lambda-1$. Since F has order 6, it has six invariant factors $d_1(\lambda), \cdots, d_6(\lambda)$; of these, $d_5(\lambda) = d_6(\lambda) = 0$, since F has rank 4. If $d_1(\lambda), \cdots, d_4(\lambda)$ are factored, the seven indicated elementary divisors must be obtained. However, since $d_4(\lambda)$ is divisible by $d_3(\lambda)$, $d_2(\lambda)$, and $d_1(\lambda)$, then $d_4(\lambda)$ contains all the elementary divisors belonging to all the irreducible polynomials and to the

* The elementary divisors of an arbitrary polynomial, used later on by the author, are defined in exactly the same way. (Ed.)

highest powers. Therefore $d_4(\lambda) = \lambda^2(\lambda+1)^3(\lambda-1)$. Among the remaining elementary divisors $\lambda, \lambda^2, (\lambda+1), \lambda-1$, the highest powers must be contained in $d_3(\lambda)$; consequently, $d_3(\lambda) = \lambda^2(\lambda+1)(\lambda-1)$. In turn, the highest powers of the remaining must be contained in $d_2(\lambda)$, or $d_2(\lambda) = \lambda$. Since all the elementary divisors have been distributed, $d_1(\lambda) = 1$. It is clear that this method applies to the general case and the proof is completed.

Elementary divisors depend on the base field K. For example, let the invariant factors of a λ-matrix F be λ^2+1 and $(\lambda^2+1)^2$. If the base field is the field of real numbers, then the polynomial λ^2+1 is irreducible, and the elementary divisors of F are λ^2+1 and $(\lambda^2+1)^2$. However, if the base field is the field of complex numbers, then $\lambda^2+1 = (\lambda+i)(\lambda-i)$, and the elementary divisors of F are $(\lambda+i)$, $(\lambda+i)^2$, $(\lambda-i)$, $(\lambda-i)^2$.

55. Elementary Divisors of Decomposable Matrices

To obtain the elementary divisors of a λ-matrix in canonical diagonal form, it is sufficient, by the definition, to take all the elementary divisors of the diagonal elements. We show that this is also true for arbitrary diagonal λ-matrices.

LEMMA 1. *The system of elementary divisors of an arbitrary diagonal λ-matrix F is the union of the elementary divisors of the diagonal elements.*

Let F have diagonal elements $f_1(\lambda), \cdots, f_n(\lambda)$. Without loss of generality we may assume that all these polynomials are different from zero and that each has leading coefficient 1. Let $D_k(\lambda)$ be the greatest common divisor of the kth order minors of F. Since the leading coefficients of all the polynomials $f_1(\lambda), \cdots, f_n(\lambda)$ are 1, $D_n(\lambda)$ is the determinant of F, or

$$D_n(\lambda) = f_1(\lambda) \cdots f_n(\lambda).$$

But

$$D_n(\lambda) = d_1(\lambda) \cdots d_n(\lambda),$$

where $d_1(\lambda), \cdots, d_n(\lambda)$ are the invariant factors of F. Therefore, denoting the distinct irreducible factors of the polynomials $f_1(\lambda), \cdots, f_n(\lambda)$ by $\varepsilon_1(\lambda), \cdots, \varepsilon_s(\lambda)$, we see that each elementary divisor of F is a power of one of the polynomials $\varepsilon_1(\lambda), \cdots, \varepsilon_s(\lambda)$. We now factor out the highest power of $\varepsilon_1(\lambda)$ contained in $f_1(\lambda), \cdots, f_n(\lambda)$. Let

$$f_i(\lambda) = [\varepsilon_1(\lambda)]^{s_i} g_i(\lambda),$$

where $g_i(\lambda)$ is not divisible by $\varepsilon_1(\lambda)$. We wish to show that $[\varepsilon_1(\lambda)]^{s_1}, \cdots, [\varepsilon_1(\lambda)]^{s_n}$ are the elementary divisors of F which belong to the polynomial $\varepsilon_1(\lambda)$. Since the elementary divisors of F do not depend on the order of the rows and columns, we assume that the rows and columns are ordered in such a way that

$$s_1 \leqq s_2 \leqq \cdots \leqq s_n. \qquad (1)$$

We now find the power of $\varepsilon_1(\lambda)$ contained in $D_k(\lambda)$. By definition, $D_k(\lambda)$

is the greatest common divisor of the kth order minors of F; those kth order minors different from zero, as we have seen above (Section 54), have the form

$$f_{\nu_1}(\lambda) \cdots f_{\nu_k}(\lambda) = [\varepsilon_1(\lambda)]^{s_{\nu_1}+\cdots+s_{\nu_k}} g_{\nu_1}(\lambda) \cdots g_{\nu_k}(\lambda).$$

From inequality (1), the smallest power of $\varepsilon_1(\lambda)$ is contained in the minor

$$f_1(\lambda) \cdots f_k(\lambda) = [\varepsilon_1(\lambda)]^{s_1+\cdots+s_k} g_1(\lambda) \cdots g_k(\lambda).$$

Consequently, $D_k(\lambda)$ contains $\varepsilon_1(\lambda)$ to the power $s_1 + \cdots + s_k$. But the invariant factor $d_k(\lambda)$ equals $D_k(\lambda)$ divided by $D_{k-1}(\lambda)$. Therefore, $d_k(\lambda)$ contains $\varepsilon_1(\lambda)$ exactly to the power s_k. Thus, the elementary divisors of the matrix F belonging to the irreducible polynomial $\varepsilon_1(\lambda)$ coincide with the elementary divisors of the diagonal elements of F belonging to $\varepsilon_1(\lambda)$. Since our argument is valid also for the remaining polynomials $\varepsilon_2(\lambda), \cdots, \varepsilon_s(\lambda)$, the lemma is proved.

THEOREM 2. *The system of elementary divisors of a decomposable matrix is the union of the systems of elementary divisors of the blocks.*

Let the λ-matrix F have the blockdiagonal form

$$F = \begin{bmatrix} F_1 & & & & \\ & F_2 & & & \\ & & \cdot & & \\ & & & \cdot & \\ & & & & F_m \end{bmatrix}$$

Elementary transformations of the separate blocks $F_1, \cdots, F_m$ may be considered as transformations of the whole matrix F. These transformations do not affect the block diagonal form of the matrix F, and a transformation applied to one block does not change the form of the remaining blocks. Therefore all the blocks may be reduced to diagonal form by elementary transformations of the matrix F. By Lemma 1, the elementary divisors of the diagonal matrices resulting from the matrices $F, F_1, \cdots, F_m$ are the unions of the elementary divisors of the diagonal elements. In particular, the elementary divisors of F are obtained as the union of the elementary divisors of the blocks $F_1, \cdots F_m$, which was to be proved.

● EXAMPLES AND PROBLEMS

1. Find the elementary divisors of the following matrices:

$$\begin{bmatrix} \lambda & 1 & & \\ & \lambda & 1 & \\ & & \lambda & 1 \\ & & & \lambda \end{bmatrix}, \quad \begin{bmatrix} 0 & 0 & 1 & \lambda+2 \\ 0 & 1 & \lambda+2 & \\ 1 & \lambda+2 & & \\ \lambda+2 & & & \end{bmatrix}, \quad \begin{bmatrix} 0 & 0 & 0 & \lambda^2 \\ 0 & 0 & \lambda(\lambda-1) & \\ 0 & (\lambda-1)^2 & & \\ \lambda(\lambda-1) & & & \end{bmatrix},$$

2. Find the invariant factors of the matrices

$$\begin{bmatrix} \lambda(\lambda+1) & & & \\ & \lambda^2 & & \\ & & (\lambda+1)^2 & \\ & & & \lambda(\lambda-1) \end{bmatrix}, \quad \begin{bmatrix} \lambda & 1 & 2 & 3 \\ & \lambda & 1 & 2 \\ & & \lambda & 1 \\ & & & \lambda \end{bmatrix}, \quad \begin{bmatrix} \lambda & 1 & 0 & 0 \\ 0 & \lambda & 1 & 0 \\ 0 & 1 & \lambda & 0 \\ 0 & 0 & 1 & \lambda \end{bmatrix}.$$

3. Find the elementary divisors of the matrix

$$\begin{bmatrix} \lambda^2+2 & \lambda^2+1 & \lambda^2+1 \\ 3 & \lambda^2+1 & 3 \\ \lambda^2+1 & \lambda^2+1 & \lambda^2+1 \end{bmatrix}$$

over the field of rational numbers, the field of real numbers, and the field of complex numbers.

3. Normal Forms for the Matrix of a Linear Transformation

56. Division with λ-Matrices

An expression of the form

$$F(\lambda) = A_0\lambda^m + A_1\lambda^{m-1} + \cdots + A_m , \tag{1}$$

where $A_0, \cdots, A_m$ are square matrices all of the same order with elements from a base field K, is called a matrix polynomial in λ, or a matrix λ-polynomial. Two λ-polynomials are regarded as equal if the matrices standing before like powers of λ are equal, and λ-polynomials are added and multiplied in the usual way. It is clear that each λ-polynomial may be written in the form of a single matrix whose elements are ordinary polynomials in λ, and conversely. For example,

$$\begin{bmatrix} 1 & 0 \\ 0 & 1 \end{bmatrix}\lambda^2 + \begin{bmatrix} 5 & 6 \\ 2 & -2 \end{bmatrix}\lambda + \begin{bmatrix} 1 & 2 \\ 0 & 3 \end{bmatrix} = \begin{bmatrix} \lambda^2+5\lambda+1 & 6\lambda+2 \\ 2\lambda & \lambda^2-2\lambda+3 \end{bmatrix}.$$

Therefore, the matrix λ-polynomials are only particular ways of writing λ-matrices.

If the matrix A_0 in (1) is different from zero, then the degree of the matrix polynomial is m. The polynomial $F(\lambda)$ is called ***regular*** if A_0 is invertible.

It is evident that the degree of the sum of matrix λ-polynomials does not exceed the maximum of the degrees of the summands. It is easy to convince oneself by examples that the degree of the product of matrix λ polynomials may be less than the sum of the degrees of the factors. However, *if one of the two factors in a product is regular, then the degree of the product is equal to the sum of the degrees of the factors.* If

$$A(\lambda) = A_0\lambda^m + A_1\lambda^{m-1} + \cdots + A_m,$$
$$B(\lambda) = B_0\lambda^p + B_1\lambda^{p-1} + \cdots + B_p, \tag{2}$$

then the leading term of the product $A(\lambda)B(\lambda)$ is $A_0B_0\lambda^{m+p}$; if the matrix

B_0 is invertible, then $A_0B_0 = 0$ would imply that $0 = A_0B_0B_0^{-1} = A_0$, contrary to assumption.

THEOREM 1. *For an arbitrary matrix λ-polynomial $A(\lambda)$ and regular matrix λ-polynomial $B(\lambda)$ there exist λ-polynomials $P(\lambda)$, $S(\lambda)$, $Q(\lambda)$, $R(\lambda)$, which satisfy the conditions*:

a) $A(\lambda) = P(\lambda)B(\lambda) + S(\lambda)$, $A(\lambda) = B(\lambda)Q(\lambda) + R(\lambda)$;

b) *either $S(\lambda) = 0$ or the degree of $S(\lambda)$ is less than the degree of $B(\lambda)$; either $R(\lambda) = 0$ or the degree of $R(\lambda)$ is less than the degree of $B(\lambda)$.*

Conditions a) *and* b) *determine the indicated polynomials uniquely*; *$P(\lambda)$, $S(\lambda)$ are called the right quotient and right remainder, $Q(\lambda)$, $R(\lambda)$ the left quotient and left remainder, upon division of $A(\lambda)$* by *$B(\lambda)$.*

To prove this, we indicate the process of finding the quotient and remainder, which is similar to the division algorithm for ordinary polynomials. Suppose, for example, that $A(\lambda)$, $B(\lambda)$ have the form (*2*). If $m < p$, then we may take $P(\lambda) = 0$, $S(\lambda) = A(\lambda)$. Therefore, let $m \geqq p$. We construct the sequence of differences

$$S_1(\lambda) = A(\lambda) - A_0B_0^{-1}\lambda^{m-p}B(\lambda) = C_0^{(1)}\lambda^{m_1} + \cdots ,$$
$$S_2(\lambda) = S_1(\lambda) - C_0^{(1)}B_0^{-1}\lambda^{m_1-p}B(\lambda) = C_0^{(2)}\lambda^{m_2} + \cdots ,$$
$$\vdots$$
$$S_{t+1}(\lambda) = S_t(\lambda) - C_0^{(t)}B_0^{-1}\lambda^{m_t-p}B(\lambda) = C_0^{(t+1)}\lambda^{m_{t+1}} + \cdots ,$$

where $t+1$ is the first integer for which $m_{t+1} < p$. Adding these equalities and setting

$$S(\lambda) = S_{t+1}(\lambda) ,$$
$$P(\lambda) = A_0B_0^{-1}\lambda^{m-p} + C_0^{(1)}B_0^{-1}\lambda^{m_1-p} + \cdots + C_0^{(t)}B_0^{-1}\lambda^{m_t-p} ,$$

we obtain the first relation of a); $Q(\lambda)$, $R(\lambda)$ are found analogously.

Uniqueness remains to be shown. If

$$A(\lambda) = P(\lambda)B(\lambda) + S(\lambda) = P_*(\lambda)B(\lambda) + S_*(\lambda) ,$$

then

$$[P(\lambda) - P_*(\lambda)]B(\lambda) = S_*(\lambda) - S(\lambda) .$$

Since the polynomial $B(\lambda)$ is regular, then if the difference $P(\lambda) - P_*(\lambda)$ were not zero, the left side would be not less than the degree of $B(\lambda)$, while the degree of the right side is less than the degree of $B(\lambda)$. Therefore $P(\lambda) = P_*(\lambda)$ and $S(\lambda) = S_*(\lambda)$.

57. Scalar Equivalence

According to Section 53, two λ-matrices $A(\lambda)$, $B(\lambda)$ are equivalent if and only if these exist λ-matrices $U(\lambda)$, $V(\lambda)$ with nonzero constant determinants, such that

$$A(\lambda) = U(\lambda)B(\lambda)V(\lambda) . \tag{3}$$

We say that matrices $A(\lambda)$, $B(\lambda)$ are ***scalar-equivalent*** if there exist non-singular matrices U, V, *whose elements are constants,* such that

$$A(\lambda) = UB(\lambda)V,$$

The matrices U, V are called ***scalar matrices.***

THEOREM 2. *If two first-degree λ-polynomials $A\lambda + B$, $C\lambda + D$ are regular and equivalent, then they are scalar-equivalent.*

By assumption,

$$A\lambda + B = U(\lambda)(C\lambda + D)V(\lambda), \tag{4}$$

where $U(\lambda)$, $V(\lambda)$ are matrices with nonzero constant determinants. Denote by P, S the left quotient and left remainder upon dividing $U(\lambda)$ by $A\lambda + B$, and denote by Q, R the right quotient and right remainder upon dividing $V(\lambda)$ by $A\lambda + B$. Then

$$U = (A\lambda + B)P + S, \qquad V = Q(A\lambda + B) + R. \tag{5}$$

S and R are scalar matrices, since their degree is less than 1. We show that

$$A\lambda + B = S(C\lambda + D)R. \tag{6}$$

If we multiply both sides of (4) on the left by U^{-1} and substitute for V its expression from (5), we obtain, transposing a term,

$$[U^{-1} - (C\lambda + D)Q](A\lambda + B) = (C\lambda + D)R.$$

Comparing the degrees of the left and right sides, we see that the expression in square brackets must be a scalar matrix T, and we have

$$T = U^{-1} - (C\lambda + D)Q, \qquad T(A\lambda + B) = (C\lambda + D)R. \tag{7}$$

Hence, making use of (4),

$$\begin{aligned} E = U(C\lambda + D)Q + UT &= (A\lambda + B)V^{-1}Q + UT \\ &= (A\lambda + B)V^{-1}Q + [(A\lambda + B)P + S]T, \end{aligned}$$

or

$$E = (A\lambda + B)[V^{-1}Q + PT] + ST.$$

But the right side can have degree zero only if the expression in square brackets is zero; hence

$$E = ST, \qquad T = S^{-1}.$$

Comparing with (7), we obtain (6), where S, and similarly, R, are invertible scalar matrices.

58. Similar Matrices

According to Section 9, square matrices A, B over a field K are ***similar*** if there exists an invertible matrix with elements from K such that

$$A = T^{-1}BT . \tag{8}$$

The importance of finding conditions under which given matrices will be similar was explained in Chapter III. With the results now obtained, it is easy to give necessary and sufficient conditions for similarity, and thus to solve one of the fundamental problems in the theory of matrices.

THEOREM 3. *Two matrices A, B over a field K are similar if and only if their characteristic matrices $\lambda E - A$ and $\lambda E - B$ are equivalent.*

The necessity of the condition is evident, since from (8) it follows that

$$\lambda E - A = T^{-1}(\lambda E - B)T,$$

so that $\lambda E - A$ and $\lambda E - B$ are equivalent, and even scalar-equivalent. Conversely, let the matrices $\lambda E - A$ and $\lambda E - B$ be equivalent. Since these are regular, first-degree, equivalent matrix λ-polynomials, by Theorem 2 they are scalar-equivalent—that is, there are nonsingular scalar matrices S, R such that

$$\lambda E - A = S(\lambda E - B)R .$$

Comparing the coefficients of λ and the constant terms, we obtain

$$E = SR , \quad A = SBR ,$$

and therefore

$$A = R^{-1}BR , \tag{9}$$

which was to be proved.

From the proof of the theorem it is possible to extract the following algorithm for deciding the similarity of matrices A, B: construct the characteristic matrices $\lambda E - A$, $\lambda E - B$ and reduce them to canonical diagonal form (see Sections 51, 52). If these forms are identical, then A and B are similar; if the forms differ, A and B are not similar.

It is sometimes required to find the matrix T for which $B = T^{-1}AT$. If the order of the matrices A, B is not too large, then, setting $T = \| t_{ij} \|$, one can write the matrix equality $B = T^{-1}AT$ in the form of n^2 equalities between the elements of TB and AT, and consider these equalities as linear homogeneous equations in the unknowns t_{ij}. Solving this system yields T.

For large n this method is too cumbersome, and the method suggested in the proof of Theorem 3 is preferable. First of all, knowing the elementary transformations which reduce the matrices $\lambda E - A$, $\lambda E - B$ to canonical diagonal form, and, consequently, the elementary transformations which carry $\lambda E - A$ into $\lambda E - B$, one can find, by Section 53, λ-matrices $U(\lambda)$, $V(\lambda)$ for which

$$\lambda E - A = U(\lambda)(\lambda E - B)V(\lambda) .$$

Computing the right remainder R upon dividing $V(\lambda)$ by $\lambda E - A$, we have, by (9), $A = R^{-1}BR$; that is, R will serve as the desired matrix.

We remark that to find R it is not actually necessary to divide $V(\lambda)$ by

$\lambda E - A$. If we write $V(\lambda)$ in the form.

$$V(\lambda) = V_0\lambda^k + V_1\lambda^{k-1} + \cdots + V_k$$

and apply the scheme of division of Section 56, we obtain

$$R = V_0 A^k + V_1 A^{k-1} + \cdots + V_k \,. \tag{10}$$

Similarly, if we write the polynomial $U(\lambda)$ in the "left" form

$$U(\lambda) = \lambda^l U_0 + \lambda^{l-1} U_1 + \cdots + U_l$$

and carry out left division by $\lambda E - A$, we obtain for the left remainder S the expression

$$S = A^l U_0 + A^{l-1} U_1 + \cdots + U_l \,. \tag{11}$$

These formulas for the remainder on division of a matrix λ-polynomial by a binomial $\lambda E - A$ are very similar to Bezout's formula $r = f(a)$ for the remainder on division of an ordinary polynomial $f(\lambda)$ by a binomial $\lambda - a$. For this reason (10), (11) are sometimes called the matrix form of Bezout's remainder formula.

59. Jordan Normal Form

Matrices of a certain form, called Jordan matrices, were introduced in Section 48, with a discussion of several properties of linear transformations whose matrices, in a suitable coordinate system, were Jordan matrices. However, the fundamental question of the conditions under which the matrix of a transformation could be reduced to Jordan form was left open. We now have all the necessary means to answer this question.

THEOREM 4. *Each square matrix over the field of complex numbers, or over any other algebraically closed field, is similar to a Jordan matrix. Two Jordan matrices are similar if and only if they are constructed from the same Jordan blocks and differ at most in the distribution of these blocks on their main diagonals.*

To prove this we need two lemmas, which are, however, interesting in themselves.

LEMMA 1. *The characteristic matrix of a Jordan block has only one elementary divisor, $(\lambda - \rho)^n$, where n, ρ are respectively the order and the proper value of the block.*

The characteristic matrix of the given Jordan block (see Section 48) has the form

$$\lambda E - A = \begin{bmatrix} \lambda-\rho & -1 & 0 \cdots & 0 & 0 \\ 0 & \lambda-\rho & -1 \cdots & 0 & 0 \\ \cdots & \cdots & \cdots & \cdots & \cdots \\ 0 & 0 & 0 \cdots & \lambda-\rho & -1 \\ 0 & 0 & 0 \cdots & 0 & \lambda-\rho \end{bmatrix}.$$

We compute the greatest common divisor $D_k(\lambda)$ of the kth order minors of the matrix $\lambda E - A$. First of all, we have

$$D_n(\lambda) = |\lambda E - A| = (\lambda - \rho)^n.$$

$D_{n-1}(\lambda)$ is the greatest common divisor of all minors of degree $n-1$ and among these is the minor

$$\begin{bmatrix} -1 & 0 & \cdots & 0 & 0 \\ \lambda-\rho & -1 & \cdots & 0 & 0 \\ 0 & \lambda-\rho & \cdots & 0 & 0 \\ \cdots & \cdots & \cdots & -1 & 0 \\ 0 & 0 & \cdots & \lambda-\rho & -1 \end{bmatrix} = (-1)^{n-1},$$

obtained by striking out the first column and last row of $\lambda E - A$. Since this minor is ± 1, $D_{n-1}(\lambda) = 1$. Let $d_1(\lambda), \cdots, d_n(\lambda)$ be the invariant factors of $\lambda E - A$. As a consequence of the relations

$$D_{n-1}(\lambda) = d_1(\lambda) \cdots d_{n-1}(\lambda) = 1,$$
$$D_n(\lambda) = d_1(\lambda) \cdots d_{n-1}(\lambda) d_n(\lambda) = (\lambda - \rho)^n,$$

we have $d_1(\lambda) = \cdots = d_{n-1}(\lambda) = 1$, $d_n(\lambda) = (\lambda - \rho)^n$. Consequently, $\lambda E - A$ has only one elementary divisor, namely $(\lambda - \rho)^n$.

LEMMA 2. *The system of elementary divisors of the characteristic matrix of a Jordan matrix A consists of the elementary divisors of the characteristic matrices of the Jordan blocks of A. These elementary divisors determine A uniquely up to the ordering of its Jordan blocks on the main diagonal.*

By definition, A is a block diagonal matrix constructed from Jordan blocks. Therefore, the characteristic matrix $\lambda E - A$ decomposes into the characteristic matrices of the separate Jordan blocks of A. By Section 55, the system of elementary divisors of $\lambda E - A$ consists of the elementary divisors of the separate Jordan blocks; there is one for each block. At the same time, these elementary divisors of the characteristic matrices of the Jordan blocks determine the form of the matrix A uniquely up to the ordering of the Jordan blocks on the main diagonal.

The characteristic matrices of similar matrices are equivalent, and therefore have identical systems of elementary divisors. Hence similar Jordan matrices must be constructed from identical Jordan blocks, and to complete the proof of Theorem 4 there remains only to construct, for an arbitrary matrix A, a Jordan matrix similar to it. Let $(\lambda - \rho_1)^{n_1}, \cdots, (\lambda - \rho_s)^{n_s}$ be a complete enumeration of the elementary divisors of the matrix $\lambda E - A$. Let B be a Jordan matrix such that the characteristic matrices of its Jordan blocks have the indicated elementary divisors. Then the matrices $\lambda E - A$, $\lambda E - B$ have the same elementary divisors, and hence by Section 54 they are equivalent. Finally, by Section 58, A is similar to the Jordan matrix B; this completes the proof.

Our argument also gives an answer to the question of how to find the

Jordan matrix similar to a given matrix A. One has only to construct the characteristic matrix $\lambda E - A$, reduce it by elementary transformations to canonical diagonal form, factor the diagonal polynomials, find the elementary divisors, and construct a Jordan matrix from them. For example, let

$$A = \begin{bmatrix} 3 & 1 & -3 \\ -7 & -2 & 9 \\ -2 & -1 & 4 \end{bmatrix},$$

We construct the characteristic matrix

$$\lambda E - A = \begin{bmatrix} \lambda-3 & -1 & 3 \\ 7 & \lambda+2 & -9 \\ 2 & 1 & \lambda-4 \end{bmatrix},$$

and seek its invariant factors. It is easy to see that these factors are $1, 1, (\lambda - 1)(\lambda - 2)^2$. Consequently, the elementary divisors are $(\lambda - 1)$, $(\lambda - 2)^2$, and the Jordan matrix has the form

$$\begin{bmatrix} 1 & 0 & 0 \\ 0 & 2 & 1 \\ 0 & 0 & 2 \end{bmatrix}.$$

We make one further observation. If the elementary divisors of the matrix $\lambda E - A$ turn out to be of first degree, then the Jordan block of the corresponding Jordan matrix will be of order 1, i. e. the matrix B will be diagonal. Conversely, if the corresponding Jordan matrix is diagonal, then the elementary divisors will be of first degree. Thus, *a given matrix is similar to a diagonal matrix if and only if all the elementary divisors of its characteristic matrix are of first degree.*

* * *

60. Natural Normal Form

Over the field of complex numbers, every matrix is similar to some Jordan matrix*. If an arbitrary number field is taken for the base field K, the reduction to Jordan form may sometimes be impossible. In general, in order that the reduction be possible, it is necessary and sufficient that the characteristic polynomial of the matrix factor into linear factors over K. Therefore, there arises the problem of indicating a normal form such that, over the given base field, every matrix may be reduced to it. An infinite number of these normal forms exist. The simplest one to construct is called the natural normal form.

Let

$$f(\lambda) = \alpha_0 + \alpha_1\lambda + \cdots + \alpha_{n-1}\lambda^{n-1} + \lambda^n$$

be an arbitrary nonconstant polynomial with leading coefficient 1. Let the coefficients of this polynomial lie in a field K. The matrix

* The same is true over any algebraically closed field (Theorem 4).

$$A = \begin{bmatrix} 0 & 1 & 0 & \cdots & 0 & 0 \\ 0 & 0 & 1 & \cdots & 0 & 0 \\ \cdots & \cdots & \cdots & \cdots & \cdots & \cdots \\ 0 & 0 & 0 & \cdots & 0 & 1 \\ -\alpha_0 & -\alpha_1 & -\alpha_2 & \cdots & -\alpha_{n-2} & -\alpha_{n-1} \end{bmatrix}$$

is called the ***companion matrix*** of the polynomial $f(\lambda)$.

LEMMA 3. *If $f(\lambda)$ is a nonconstant polynomial with leading coefficient 1, and A is its companion matrix, then the invariant factors of the characteristic matrix $\lambda E - A$ are* 1, 1, $\cdots$ 1, $f(\lambda)$.

Let $f(\lambda) = \alpha_0 + \alpha_1\lambda + \cdots + \alpha_{n-1}\lambda^{n-1} + \lambda^n$; then

$$\lambda E - A = \begin{bmatrix} \lambda & -1 & 0 & \cdots & 0 & 0 \\ 0 & \lambda & -1 & \cdots & 0 & 0 \\ \cdots & \cdots & \cdots & \cdots & \cdots & \cdots \\ 0 & 0 & 0 & \cdots & \lambda & -1 \\ \alpha_0 & \alpha_1 & \alpha_2 & \cdots & \alpha_{n-2} & \lambda + \alpha_{n-1} \end{bmatrix}.$$

Striking out the first column and last row, we obtain a minor equal to $(-1)^{n-1}$. Consequently, the greatest common divisor $D_{n-1}(\lambda)$ of the $(n-1)$st order minors is 1. So far as $D_n(\lambda)$ is concerned, this polynomial is the determinant of the matrix $\lambda E - A$ Expanding this determinant by the elements of the last row, we find that

$$D_n(\lambda) = \alpha_0 + \alpha_1\lambda + \cdots + \alpha_{n-1}\lambda^{n-1} + \lambda^n .$$

It follows from $D_{n-1}(\lambda) = 1$ that $d_1(\lambda) = \cdots = d_{n-1}(\lambda) = 1$, and from $D_n(\lambda) = f(\lambda)$ that $d_n(\lambda) = f(\lambda)$, which was to be proved.

We say that the matrix A has ***natural normal form*** if A decomposes into blocks $A_1, \cdots, A_s$, which are the companion matrices of polynomials $f_1(\lambda), \cdots, f_s(\lambda)$, each of which is divisible by the preceding. We show that the invariant factors of the characteristic matrix $\lambda E - A$ are 1, 1, $\cdots$ 1, $f_1(\lambda), f_2(\lambda), \cdots, f_s(\lambda)$, where the number of 1's is the sum of the degrees of the polynomials $f_1(\lambda), \cdots, f_s(\lambda)$ minus s. The characteristic matrix is

$$\lambda E - A = \begin{bmatrix} \lambda E_1 - A_1 & & & & \\ & \lambda E_2 - A_2 & & & \\ & & \cdot & & \\ & & & \cdot & \\ & & & & \lambda E_s - A_s \end{bmatrix},$$

By Lemma 3, each block $\lambda E_i - A_i$ can be reduced to diagonal form, with diagonal elements 1, $\cdots$, 1, $f_i(\lambda)$. If we then change the order of the rows and columns of $\lambda E - A$, we reduce it to a diagonal form with diagonal elements 1, $\cdots$, 1, $f_1(\lambda), \cdots, f_s(\lambda)$. Since each element here is divisible by the preceding, this is the canonical diagonal form, and the elements 1, $\cdots$, 1, $f_1(\lambda), \cdots, f_s(\lambda)$ are the invariant factors of the matrix $\lambda E - A$. Since the order of the matrix A is the sum of the degrees of the polynomials $f_1(\lambda)$, $\cdots, f_s(\lambda)$, and the number of invariant factors equals the order of the matrix, the number of 1's among the invariant factors is as indicated above.

From our argument it follows in particular that the natural normal form of a matrix is uniquely determined by the invariant factors of the characteristic matrix $\lambda E - A$.

We can now prove in a few lines the following theorem.

THEOREM 5. *Every matrix with elements from a field K reduces over this field to a unique natural normal form.*

Let $1, \cdots, 1, f_1(\lambda), \cdots, f_s(\lambda)$ be the invariant factors of the matrix $\lambda E - A$. Since the sum of the degrees of all the invariant factors must equal the order of the matrix A, the number of 1's equals the sum of the degrees of the polynomials $f_1(\lambda), \cdots, f_s(\lambda)$ minus s. We construct for each polynomial $f_i(s)$ the companion matrix B_i, and consider the block-diagonal matrix B with diagonal blocks $B_1, \cdots, B_s$. Since each of the polynomials $f_1(\lambda), \cdots, f_s(\lambda)$ is divisible by the preceding, B is a natural normal matrix. As was proved above, the invariant factors of the matrix $\lambda E - B$ equal, $1, \cdots, 1, f_1(\lambda), \cdots, f_s(\lambda)$, and thus coincide with the invariant factors of the matrix $\lambda E - A$. By Theorem 3, A is similar to B. This proves the possibility of reducing the matrix A to natural normal form. The uniqueness comes from the fact that the natural matrix B is uniquely determined by its invariant factors, which, in turn, are uniquely determined by the matrix A.

61. Other Normal Forms

The advantage of the natural normal form is its absolute uniqueness: not only the diagonal blocks themselves, but also their order on the main diagonal, are uniquely determined. It is necessary to mention the following shortcomings: this form does not give a reduction to blocks of smallest possible order, and the Jordan form is not a special case of the natural form.

The first of these shortcomings may be eliminated in the following way. We call a matrix B **quasi-natural** if B decomposes into blocks $B_1, \cdots, B_s$, which are the companion matrices of polynomials of the form $[\varepsilon_1(\lambda)]^{m_1}, \cdots, [\varepsilon_s(\lambda)]^{m_s}$, where $\varepsilon_1(\lambda), \cdots, \varepsilon_s(\lambda)$ are irreducible over the base field K and have leading coefficient 1. Since B_i is the companion matrix of the polynomial $[\varepsilon_i(\lambda)]^{m_i}$, the invariant factors of the characteristic matrix $\lambda E_i - B_i$ are $1, \cdots, 1, [\varepsilon_i(\lambda)]^{m_i}$. Consequently, $\lambda E_i - B_i$ has a single elementary divisor $[\varepsilon_i(\lambda)]^{m_i}$, and the elementary divisors of the matrix $\lambda E - B$ are $[\varepsilon_1(\lambda)]^{m_1}, \cdots, [\varepsilon_s(\lambda)]^{m_s}$. Since the rank of $\lambda E - B$ equals its order, and also equals the sum of the degrees of the polynomials $[\varepsilon_i(\lambda)]^{m_i}$, the quasi-natural matrix is uniquely determined by its elementary divisors, up to the ordering of the diagonal blocks.

As in the preceding section, it follows immediately that each matrix A with elements from a field K is reducible over K to a quasi-natural normal form. This form, up to the ordering of the diagonal blocks, is uniquely determined by the matrix A.

A block of a quasi-natural form cannot be split over K into blocks of smaller order; for if such a splitting were possible, then the characteristic matrix of the block would have not one, but at least two, elementary divisors.

We consider one more normal form, which may be regarded as a generalization of the Jordan form over an arbitrary number field K.* Let $\varepsilon(\lambda)$ be an irreducible polynomial with coefficients from K. We assume that $\varepsilon(\lambda)$ is nonconstant and has leading coefficient 1.

LEMMA 4. *If the characteristic polynomial of a matrix A, with coefficients from the number field K, is irreducible over K and equals $\varepsilon(\lambda)$, then the block matrix*

$$B = \begin{bmatrix} A & E & 0 & \cdots & 0 & 0 \\ 0 & A & E & \cdots & 0 & 0 \\ \cdots & \cdots & \cdots & \cdots & \cdots & \cdots \\ 0 & 0 & 0 & \cdots & A & E \\ 0 & 0 & 0 & \cdots & 0 & A \end{bmatrix},$$

where E is the identity matrix, has a characteristic matrix with a single elementary divisor $[\varepsilon(\lambda)]^m$, where m is the number of diagonal blocks of the matrix B.

Let $\lambda E - B = P$; then

$$\lambda E - B = \begin{bmatrix} P & -E & 0 & \cdots & 0 & 0 \\ 0 & P & -E & \cdots & 0 & 0 \\ \cdots & \cdots & \cdots & \cdots & \cdots & \cdots \\ 0 & 0 & 0 & \cdots & P & -E \\ 0 & 0 & 0 & \cdots & 0 & P \end{bmatrix}. \tag{12}$$

If in (12) we add to one column the product of another column with a λ-matrix, the result is evidently the same as the result of performing a series of elementary transformations of types II and IV on the matrix $\lambda E - B$, so that the new matrix obtained is equivalent to $\lambda E - B$. We make use of this observation, and perform successively the following transformations, starting with the matrix $\lambda E - B$: add P times the second column to the first; add P^2 times the third column of the new matrix to the first, and P times the third column to the second; and so on. The result of these transformations is the matrix

$$\begin{Vmatrix} 0 & -E & 0 & \cdots & 0 \\ 0 & 0 & -E & \cdots & 0 \\ 0 & 0 & 0 & \cdots & -E \\ P^m & P^{m-1} & P^{m-2} & \cdots & P \end{Vmatrix}$$

Now adding P^{m-1}, P^{m-2}, $\cdots$, respectively, times the second, third, $\cdots$ rows to the last row, and changing the order of the columns, we obtain the matrix

* Or, in general, over an arbitrary separable field.

$$\begin{bmatrix} -E & & & \\ & \ddots & & \\ & & -E & \\ & & & P^m \end{bmatrix}. \tag{13}$$

Since (13) has block diagonal form, and the beginning blocks have determinant ± 1, the elementary divisors of the matrix (13) are just the elementary divisors of the matrix $P^m = (\lambda E - A)^m$, which we now examine.

By assumption, the characteristic polynomial of the matrix A is $\varepsilon(\lambda)$, which is irreducible over the field K. It follows from this that all of its zeros in the field of complex numbers are distinct, and consequently there exists a complex matrix T such that TAT^{-1} has diagonal form, and

$$\lambda E = TAT^{-1} = \begin{bmatrix} \lambda-\alpha_1 & & & & \\ & \lambda-\alpha_2 & & & \\ & & \ddots & & \\ & & & & \lambda-\alpha_n \end{bmatrix}.$$

The matrix P^m is equivalent to the matrix $TP^mT^{-1} = (TPT^{-1})^m$, and the latter has the form

$$[T(\lambda E - A)T^{-1}]^m = (\lambda E - TAT^{-1})^m = \begin{bmatrix} (\lambda-\alpha_1)^m & & & \\ & (\lambda-\alpha_2)^m & & \\ & & \ddots & \\ & & & (\lambda-\alpha_n)^m \end{bmatrix}.$$

Therefore, the elementary divisors of the matrix P^m over the complex field are $(\lambda - \alpha_1)^m, \cdots, (\lambda - \alpha_n)^m$. All of them belong to distinct irreducible polynomials. The invariant factors of the matrix P^m are $1, \cdots, 1, (\lambda - \alpha_1)^m \cdots (\lambda - \alpha_n)^m = [\varepsilon(\lambda)]^m$. But the polynomial $\varepsilon(\lambda)$ is irreducible over K; consequently, over this field the matrix P^m has only one elementary divisor, namely $[\varepsilon(\lambda)]^m$. Thus, matrix (13)—and hence matrix (12)—has a single elementary divisor $[\varepsilon(\lambda)]^m$. This proves the lemma.

If A is the companion matrix of $\varepsilon(\lambda)$, then the matrix B is called a ***generalized Jordan block***, corresponding to the elementary divisor $[\varepsilon(\lambda)]^m$. We also say that a matrix has a ***generalized Jordan form*** if it decomposes into generalized Jordan blocks. It is clear that a generalized Jordan matrix is fully determined by its elementary divisors.

THEOREM 6. *Every matrix A with elements from a separable field K is reducible over this field to a generalized Jordan matrix. This matrix is uniquely determined by A up to the ordering of the blocks on the main diagonal.*

Let the elementary divisors of the matrix $\lambda E - A$ over the field K be the polynomials $[\varepsilon_1(\lambda)]^{m_1}, \cdots, [\varepsilon_s(\lambda)]^{m_s}$. Construct the corresponding generalized Jordan block B_i for each polynomial $[\varepsilon_i(\lambda)]^{m_i}$, and consider the block-diagonal matrix B with the blocks B_i on the main diagonal.

By Lemma 4, the elementary divisors of the matrix $\lambda E - B$ are equal to the corresponding elementary divisors of the matrix $\lambda E - A$. Since $\lambda E - B$ and $\lambda E - A$ also have the same rank and order, A is similar to B. Uniqueness follows from the fact that the matrix B is determined by the elementary divisors of A.

If the base field K is the field of complex numbers, then all the irreducible polynomials are of first degree. Consequently, the blocks in the generalized Jordan blocks are of order 1, and the generalized Jordan blocks turn into ordinary Jordan blocks.

We consider also the case where the base field K is the field of real numbers. The irreducible polynomials over K are of two forms: 1) polynomials $\lambda - \rho$ of first degree; the corresponding generalized Jordan blocks are ordinary Jordan blocks; 2) $\varepsilon(\lambda) = \lambda^2 + p\lambda + q$, where $p^2 - 4q < 0$; the companion block A has the form

$$\begin{bmatrix} 0 & 1 \\ -q & -p \end{bmatrix}, \tag{14}$$

and the generalized Jordan block corresponding to $(\lambda^2 + p\lambda + q)^m$ has the form of the matrix B of Lemma 4, where A may be replaced by a matrix of the form

$$A = \begin{bmatrix} \alpha & \beta \\ -\beta & \alpha \end{bmatrix};$$

α and β are the coefficients of the real and imaginary parts of a complex zero of the polynomial $\lambda^2 + p\lambda + q$. Such a replacement is possible, since the characteristic polynomial of this matrix is $\lambda^2 + p\lambda + q$:

$$\begin{bmatrix} \lambda - \alpha & -\beta \\ \beta & \lambda - \alpha \end{bmatrix} = \lambda^2 + p\lambda + q,$$

* * *

• EXAMPLES AND PROBLEMS

1. Indicate which of the following matrices are similar:

$$\begin{bmatrix} 3 & 1 & -3 \\ -4 & -2 & 6 \\ -1 & -1 & 5 \end{bmatrix}, \quad \begin{bmatrix} 42 & 130 & 25 \\ -8 & -24 & -5 \\ -23 & -73 & -13 \end{bmatrix}, \quad \begin{bmatrix} 2 & 1 & -1 \\ 7 & 4 & -22 \\ 2 & 1 & -5 \end{bmatrix},$$

$$\begin{bmatrix} 8 & -13 & 16 \\ -8 & 18 & -22 \\ -11 & 22 & -27 \end{bmatrix}, \quad \begin{bmatrix} 20 & -89 & -32 \\ 11 & -51 & 20 \\ 20 & -95 & -36 \end{bmatrix}, \quad \begin{bmatrix} 2 & 0 & 0 \\ 1 & 1 & 1 \\ 0 & -1 & 3 \end{bmatrix},$$

Find the Jordan matrices similar to them.

2. Show that the characteristic polynomial of a matrix A equals the product of all the invariant factors of the characteristic matrix $\lambda E - A$ and the minimal polynomial equals the last of the invariant factors.

3. Find the minimal polynomials of the matrices of problem 1.
4. Show that over the field of complex numbers a square matrix is similar to a diagonal matrix if and only if its minimal polynomial does not have multiple zeros.
5. Show that a matrix A is always similar to its transpose A'.
6. If A is nonsingular and B is arbitrary, then AB is similar to BA. Is AB similar to BA for arbitrary A and B?
7. Find the normal forms of the matrices

$$\begin{bmatrix} -3 & -1 & 3 \\ 22 & 9 & -27 \\ 5 & 2 & -6 \end{bmatrix}, \quad \begin{bmatrix} 1 & -1 & 1 & 3 \\ -1 & 1 & 3 & -1 \\ -1 & -3 & -1 & -1 \\ 3 & 1 & -1 & -1 \end{bmatrix}$$

over the field of rational numbers, the field of real numbers, and the field of complex numbers.

8. Show that for the construction of the normal form over the field of complex numbers it is possible to replace the Jordan blocks by blocks of the form

$$\begin{bmatrix} \rho & \alpha & 0 & \cdots & 0 & 0 \\ & \rho & \alpha & \cdots & 0 & 0 \\ & & & \cdots\cdots & & \\ & & & & \rho & \alpha \\ & & & & & \rho \end{bmatrix},$$

where α is an arbitrary, fixed, nonzero number.

9. Segre characteristic. Let $\mathscr{A}$ be a linear transformation of a complex vector space, with distinct proper values $\rho_1, \cdots, \rho_s$. Denote by $\sigma_{1k}, \sigma_{2k}, \cdots, \sigma_{jk}$ the orders of the Jordan blocks of the Jordan normal form of $\mathscr{A}$, belonging to the proper value ρ_k. The symbol

$$[(\sigma_{11}, \sigma_{21}, \cdots)(\sigma_{12}, \sigma_{22}, \cdots) \cdots (\sigma_{1s}, \sigma_{2s}, \cdots)]$$

is called the **Segre characteristic of the transformation** $\mathscr{A}$. For example, the matrices

$$\begin{bmatrix} 1 & 1 & & \\ 0 & 1 & & \\ & & 1 & \\ & & & 2 \end{bmatrix}, \quad \begin{bmatrix} 2 & 1 & & \\ 0 & 2 & & \\ & & 2 & 1 \\ & & 0 & 2 \end{bmatrix}, \quad \begin{bmatrix} 2 & 1 & 0 & \\ & 2 & 1 & \\ & & 2 & \\ & & & 3 \end{bmatrix}, \quad \begin{bmatrix} 2 & 1 & 0 & 0 \\ & 2 & 1 & 0 \\ & & 2 & 1 \\ & & & 2 \end{bmatrix}$$

have the Segre characteristics [(2, 1) (1)], [(2, 2)], [(3) (1)], [(4)]. Compute the Segre characteristics of the matrices of problem 1.

10. Weyr characteristic. Let $\mathscr{A}$ be as in the preceding problem. Denote the nullities of the transformations $(\mathscr{A} - \rho_i \mathscr{E})$, $(\mathscr{A} - \rho_i \mathscr{E})^2 \cdots$, $(\mathscr{A} - \rho_i \mathscr{E})^p$, where p is the multiplicity of the proper value ρ_i, by

$$\alpha_{i1}, \alpha_{i1} + \alpha_{i2}, \cdots, \alpha_{i1} + \alpha_{i2} + \cdots + \alpha_{ip}.$$

The row $\{\alpha_{i1}, \alpha_{i2}, \cdots, \alpha_{ip}\}$ is called the ***Weyr characteristic of the transformation*** $\mathscr{A}$, corresponding to the proper value ρ_i. Show that the

Weyr characteristics of the transformations in Problem 9 are respectively

$$[\{2, 1\}, \{1\}], [\{2, 2\}], [\{1, 1, 1\}, \{1\}], [\{1, 1, 1, 1\}].$$

11. Show that Segre characteristic and Weyr characteristic corresponding to the same proper value are related in the following way. Let the Segre characteristic be (6, 4, 3, 3). Construct the diagram

```
. . . . . .
. . . .
. . .
. . .
```

The number of dots in the successive columns is the Weyr characteristic; in this case {4, 4, 4, 2, 1, 1}.

12. A matrix with irreducible elementary divisors is called ***semisimple.*** Show that an arbitrary matrix A can be decomposed into the sum of a semisimple and a nilpotent matrix which permute with each other, and that this decomposition is unique.

4. *Matrix Functions*

We will now consider certain problems of the matrix calculus whose solutions depend on the possibility of reducing a matrix to Jordan form. Thus for the base field we take the field of complex numbers.

62. Polynomials in a Jordan Matrix

The simplest matrix functions are polynomials. Later we will give a more general definition of a matrix function, but for now we indicate an explicit expression for a polynomial in a Jordan matrix. Consider first a separate Jordan block of order n,

$$A = \begin{bmatrix} \rho & 1 & 0 & \cdots & 0 & 0 \\ & \rho & 1 & \cdots & 0 & 0 \\ & & \cdots & \cdots & \cdots & \cdots \\ & & & & \rho & 1 \\ & & & & & \rho \end{bmatrix} \tag{1}$$

We show that for all natural numbers m

$$A^m = \begin{bmatrix} \rho^m & \binom{m}{1}\rho^{m-1} & \cdots & \binom{m}{n-1}\rho^{m-n+1} \\ & \rho^m & \cdots & \binom{m}{n-2}\rho^{m-n+2} \\ & & \cdots & \cdots \\ & & & \rho^m \end{bmatrix}, \tag{2}$$

where

$$\binom{m}{k} = \frac{m(m-1)\cdots(m-k+1)}{1\cdot 2\cdots k}.$$

The proof is simplified by using induction on m. For $m = 1$, (2) coincides with (1). But if (2) holds for some m, then, multiplying it by A, we find, by an immediate calculation, that (2) also holds for $m + 1$.

Now let $f(\lambda)$ be a polynomial in λ,

$$f(\lambda) = \alpha_0 + \alpha_1\lambda + \cdots + \alpha_k\lambda^k .$$

By definition,

$$f(A) = \alpha_0 E + \alpha_1 A + \cdots + \alpha_k A^k .$$

Replacing the A^m by their values from (2), we see that in the ith row and $(i + s)$-th column of the matrix $f(A)$ stands the expression

$$\sum_{m=0}^{k} \alpha_m \frac{m(m-1)\cdots(m-s)}{1\cdot 2\cdots s}\rho^{m-s} = \frac{1}{1\cdot 2\cdots s} f^{(s)}(\rho) .$$

Consequently,

$$f(A) = \begin{bmatrix} f(\rho) & \frac{1}{1!}f'(\rho) & \frac{1}{2!}f''(\rho) & \cdots & \frac{1}{(n-1)!}f^{(n-1)}(\rho) \\ 0 & f(\rho) & \frac{1}{1!}f'(\rho) & \cdots & \frac{1}{(n-2)!}f^{(n-2)}(\rho) \\ & & \cdots\cdots & \cdots\cdots & \cdots\cdots \\ & & & & f(\rho) \end{bmatrix} . \qquad (3)$$

We have now computed the value of a polynomial in a Jordan block. However, a general Jordan matrix A is the direct sum of separate Jordan blocks:

$$A = A_1 \dotplus A_2 \dotplus \cdots \dotplus A_s ,$$

and, by Section 14,

$$f(A) = f(A_1) \dotplus f(A_2) \dotplus \cdots \dotplus f(A_s). \qquad (4)$$

Here $f(A_1), \cdots, f(A_s)$ are polynomials in separate Jordan blocks, whose expressions are given in (3). This result may be applied in the computation of $f(A)$ even when A is not in Jordan form. First find T such that $T^{-1}AT = B$ has Jordan normal form; then compute $f(B)$, using formulas (3) and (4), and finally, using the relation

$$f(A) = f(TBT^{-1}) = Tf(B)T^{-1}$$

(Compare Section 9), compute the value of $f(A)$.

63. Scalar Functions

A matrix function is defined in a way completely analogous to that of an ordinary numerical function. Consider some set of matrices $\mathfrak{M}$. If we place in correspondence to each matrix A from $\mathfrak{M}$ a matrix B, then we say that this correspondence is a function defined on $\mathfrak{M}$. To each ordinary numerical function $\rho = f(\lambda)$, given on some set of complex numbers and satisfying requirements to be formulated below, we associate a definite matrix function $f(A)$. This correspondence is constructed in the following way. Suppose we are given a numerical function $\rho = f(\lambda)$ and an arbitrary matrix A. Denote the distinct proper values of the matrix A by $\rho_1, \cdots, \rho_s$. Reduce A to Jordan normal form:

$$T^{-1}AT = B_1 \dotplus \cdots \dotplus B_t,$$

where $B_1, \cdots, B_t$ are Jordan blocks, and consider the block

$$B_i = \begin{bmatrix} \rho_i & 1 & 0 & \cdots & 0 \\ & \rho_i & 1 & \cdots & 0 \\ & & \cdots & \cdots & \\ & & & & \rho_i \end{bmatrix}, \tag{5}$$

which corresponds to the elementary divisor $(\lambda - \rho_i)^{n_i}$. If the function $f(\lambda)$ is defined in a neighborhood of the point ρ_i and has finite derivatives $f'(\rho_i), \cdots, f^{(n_i-1)}(\rho_i)$, then, we define

$$f(B_i) = \begin{bmatrix} f(\rho_i) & \frac{1}{1!}f'(\rho_i) & \cdots & \frac{1}{(n_i-1)!}f^{(n_i-1)}(\rho_i) \\ & f(\rho_i) & \cdots & \frac{1}{(n_i-2)!}f^{(n_i-2)}(\rho_i) \\ & \cdots & \cdots & \cdots \\ & & & f(\rho_i) \end{bmatrix}. \tag{6}$$

If $f(\lambda)$ is defined in a neighborhood of each of the points $\rho_1, \cdots, \rho_s$, and has finite derivatives of the proper orders in these neighborhoods, then also

$$f(B) = f(B_1) \dotplus \cdots \dotplus f(B_t), \tag{7}$$

$$f(A) = Tf(B)T^{-1} = Tf(B_1)T^{-1} \dotplus \cdots \dotplus Tf(B_t)T^{-1}. \tag{8}$$

The matrix $f(A)$ is called the ***value*** of the function $f(\lambda)$ at $\lambda = A$. It will be shown below that $f(A)$ does not depend on the method of reducing A to normal form,* and thus, is a matrix function of A. This function is called the ***correspondent*** of the numerical function $f(\lambda)$. It is clear that not all matrix functions have corresponding numerical functions. Those for which a corresponding numerical function exists are called ***scalar functions.***

We note some of the simplest properties of scalar functions.

1) If $f(\lambda)$ is a polynomial in λ, then the value of the scalar function $f(A)$ coincides with the value of the polynomial $f(\lambda)$ at $\lambda = A$, in the sense of Section 7.

The very definition of scalar function is chosen so that for polynomials it coincides with the old definition.

2) Let A be a matrix and $f_1(\lambda)$, $f_2(\lambda)$ be numerical functions for which the expressions $f_1(A)$, $f_2(A)$ are meaningful. If $f(\lambda) = f_1(\lambda) + f_2(\lambda)$, then $f(A)$ is also meaningful, and $f(A) = f_1(A) + f_2(A)$.

3) If A is a matrix, and $f_1(\lambda)$, $f_2(\lambda)$ are numerical functions for which $f_1(A)$, $f_2(A)$ are meaningful, and if $f(\lambda) = f_1(\lambda)f_2(\lambda)$, then $f(A)$ is meaningful

* That is, on the choice of the matrix T.

and $f(A) = f_1(A)f_2(A)$.

The proofs of properties 2) and 3) are anologous, so we confine ourselves to a consideration of property 3). To compute $f_1(A), f_2(A), f(A)$, according to the definition we must reduce A to Jordan normal form B and apply formulas (7) and (8). If we succeed in showing that $f(B) = f_1(B)f_2(B)$, then from (8) we immediately obtain $f(A) = f_1(A)f_2(A)$. On the other hand,

$$f(B) = f(B_1) \dotplus \cdots \dotplus f(B_t),$$
$$f_1(B)f_2(B) = f_1(B_1)f_2(B_1) \dotplus \cdots \dotplus f_1(B_t)f_2(B_t),$$

and the proof reduces to showing that

$$f(B_i) = f_1(B_i)f_2(B_i), \qquad (i = 1, 2, \cdots, t),$$

where B_i is a Jordan block. Taking the values of $f_1(B_i)$, $f_2(B_i)$ from (6) and multiplying, the element in the kth row and $(k+j)$th column of the matrix $f_1(B_i)f_2(B_i)$ is

$$f_1(\rho)\frac{1}{j!}f_2^{(j)}(\rho) + \frac{1}{1!}f_1'(\rho)\cdot\frac{1}{(j-1)!}f_2^{(j-1)}(\rho) + \cdots + \frac{1}{j!}f_1^{(j)}(\rho)\cdot f_2(\rho).$$

This expression may be written in the form

$$\frac{1}{j!}\left[f_1(\rho)f_2^{(j)}(\rho) + \frac{j}{1!}f_1'(\rho)f_2^{(j-1)}(\rho) + \cdots + f_1^{(j)}(\rho)f_2(\rho)\right],$$

which, by the rule for differentiating a product, equals $1/j!f^{(j)}(\rho)$. Thus,

$$f_1(B_i)f_2(B_i) = f(B_i),$$

and assertion 3 is proved.

Similarly, using the rule for differentiating a composite function, it may be shown that if the numerical functions $\varphi(\lambda)$ and $f(\lambda)$ are such that $f(\varphi(A))$ is defined, and if $\Psi(\lambda) = f(\varphi(\lambda))$, then $\Psi(A) = f(\varphi(A))$.

4) Let A be a matrix with proper values $\rho_1, \cdots, \rho_n$, each written as often as indicated by its multiplicity. If $f(\lambda)$ is a numerical function and $f(A)$ is defined, then the proper values of the matrix $f(A)$ are $f(\rho_1), \cdots, f(\rho_n)$.

The proper values of the matrices $f(A)$ and $T^{-1}f(A)T = f(T^{-1}AT)$ are respectively equal, and therefore we may assume that A has Jordan normal form. Formulas (5) and (6) show that in this case $f(A)$ has triangular form; moreover, the numbers $f(\rho_1), \cdots, f(\rho_n)$ stand on the main diagonal. Since the diagonal elements of a triangular matrix are its proper values, assertion 4 is proved.

We consider two examples.

1) Let $f(\lambda) = \lambda^{-1}$. This function is defined everywhere except at $\lambda = 0$, and has finite derivatives of all orders everywhere it is defined. Consequently, if the matrix A does not have zero as a proper value—that is, if A is nonsingular—then $f(A)$ is meaningful. But $\lambda\cdot f(\lambda) = 1$, hence $A\cdot f(A) = E$, and $f(A) = A^{-1}$. Thus, the inverse matrix corresponds to the function λ^{-1}.

2) Let $f(\lambda) = \sqrt{\lambda}$. This function, for $\lambda \neq 0$, has finite derivatives of all orders. Thus the expression $\sqrt{A}$ is meaningful for all nonsingular matrices A.* Putting $\lambda = A$ in the relation

$$f(\lambda)f(\lambda) = \lambda ,$$

we obtain

$$f(A)f(A) = A .$$

Consequently, we have shown that every nonsingular matrix has a square root.

64. Polynomial Representation of Function Values

In every course of higher algebra the problem is considered of constructing a polynomial which assumes a given set of values $\alpha_1, \cdots, \alpha_s$ at a given set of distinct points $\rho_1, \cdots, \rho_s$. The solution is given in the form of the well-known interpolation polynomial of Lagrange.

In what follows it is important to be able to construct a polynomial whose derivatives up to some order, as well as the polynomial itself, assume given values at the points $\rho_1, \cdots, \rho_s$. This problem is an immediate generalization of the preceding one. We formulate its solution in a separate lemma.

LEMMA. *Suppose we are given the distinct numbers $\rho_1, \cdots, \rho_s$ and a table of $(k+1)s$ arbitrary numbers α_{ij}. Then there exists a polynomial $p(\lambda)$ such that $p(\rho_i) = \alpha_{i0}$ and $p^{(j)}(\rho_i) = \alpha_{ij}$,* where $i = 1, \cdots, s$ and $j = 1, \cdots, k$.

It is convenient first to construct auxiliary polynomials $p_i(\lambda)$ such that $p_i(\lambda)$ and its derivatives to the kth order assume the required values at the point ρ_i and are zero at the other given points. Set

$$\begin{aligned}
\varphi_i(\lambda) &= \beta_{i0} + \beta_{i1}(\lambda - \rho_i) + \cdots + \beta_{ik}(\lambda - \rho_i)^k, \\
\Phi_i(\lambda) &= (\lambda - \rho_1)^{k+1} \cdots (\lambda - \rho_{i-1})^{k+1}(\lambda - \rho_{i+1})^{k+1} \cdots (\lambda - \rho_s)^{k+1}, \\
p_i(\lambda) &= \varphi_i(\lambda)\Phi_i(\lambda),
\end{aligned}$$

where $\beta_{i0}, \cdots, \beta_{ik}$ are certain numbers to be determined later. For arbitrary $\beta_{i0}, \cdots, \beta_{ik}$ we have

$$p_i(\rho_j) = p_i'(\rho_j) = \cdots = p_i^{(k)}(\rho_j) = 0 \qquad (j \neq i) .$$

By the rule for differentiating a product,

$$p_i^{(j)}(\rho_i) = \varphi_i^{(j)}(\rho_i)\Phi_i(\rho_i) + j\varphi_i^{(j-1)}(\rho_i)\Phi_i'(\rho_i) + \cdots + \varphi_i(\rho_i)\Phi_i^{(j)}(\rho_i)$$

or

$$\alpha_{ij} = j!\beta_{ij}\Phi_i(\rho_i) + j!\beta_{i,j-1}\Phi_i'(\rho_i) + \cdots + \beta_{i0}\Phi_i^{(j)}(\rho_i) . \tag{9}$$

---

* To remove the two-valuedness of $\sqrt{\lambda}$ and to conduct the argument rigorously, it is sufficient to slit the complex plane from the origin along a ray not containing any proper values of A, and to consider some one branch of the radical.

Since $\Phi_i(\rho_i) \neq 0$, it is possible to determine the numbers $\beta_{i0}, \beta_{i1}, \cdots, \beta_{ik}$ successively from the relations (9) for $j = 0, 1, \cdots, k$, and thus to find $p_i(\lambda)$. The polynomial

$$p(\lambda) = p_1(\lambda) + p_2(\lambda) + \cdots + p_s(\lambda)$$

evidently satisfies all the requirements of the lemma.

Consider a scalar function $f(\lambda)$ and a matrix A for which the value $f(A)$ is defined. We show that there is a polynomial $p(\lambda)$ for which $p(A)$ equals $f(A)$. Let $\rho_1, \cdots, \rho_s$ denote the distinct proper values of the matrix A, and let A have order n. Using only the proof of the lemma we can construct a polynomial $p(\lambda)$ which satisfies the requirements*

$$p(\rho_i) = f(\rho_i),\ p'(\rho_i) = f'(\rho_i),\ \cdots,\ p^{(n-1)}(\rho_i) = f^{(n-1)}(\rho_i)\,, \tag{10}$$

where $i = 1, \cdots, s$. For the determination of $f(A)$, we need the values of $f(\lambda)$ and its derivatives up to at most the $(n-1)$st order, at the points $\rho_1, \cdots, \rho_s$. Since the values of $p(\lambda)$ and $f(\lambda)$ (and their derivatives) coincide at these points, then $f(A) = p(A)$.

THEOREM 1. *The values of all scalar functions in a matrix A can be expressed by polynomials in A.*†

In particular, considering the function $f(\lambda) = \sqrt{\lambda}$, we see that *for every nonsingular matrix A there exists a polynomial $p(\lambda)$ for which*

$$p(A)p(A) = A\,.$$

With the help of Theorem 1 it is easy to decide the question left open in the preceding section, of the single-valuedness of the definition of the value $f(A)$. If we know the function $f(\lambda)$ and its derivatives at the points $\rho_1, \cdots, \rho_s$, we can construct the polynomial $p(\lambda)$, whose value, $p(A)$, does not depend on the reduction of the matrix A to Jordan normal form, and at the same time is equal to $f(A)$. Consequently, the value $f(A)$, defined in the preceding section using the reduction of A to normal form, does not depend on the way this reduction is carried out.

We make one further remark. Let $f(\lambda)$ be a numerical function, and A be a matrix for which $f(A)$ is meaningful. By Theorem 1 we can find a polynomial $p(\lambda)$ for which $p(A) = f(A)$. For a given function $f(\lambda)$, the polynomial $p(\lambda)$ depends only on the elementary divisors of the matrix A. But the elementary divisors of A and its transpose A' coincide, and hence $p(A') = f(A')$. It was shown in Section 8 that $p(A') = p(A)'$. Thus, *for all scalar functians $f(\lambda)$, we have $f(A') = f(A)'$.*

---

* If some of the derivatives $f^{(j)}(\rho_i)$ are superfluous for the determination of $f(A)$, the corresponding numbers in (10) may be replaced by zeros.

† We remark once again that the argument in the text shows that each value $f(A)$ of a given scalar function f can be represented in the form of some polynomial $p(A)$. However, this polynomial, for one and the same function f, will be different for different matrices A.

65. Elementary Divisors of a Function

We consider the question of finding the elementary divisors of the matrix $f(A)$ given the elementary divisors of the matrix A.* Reduce A to normal form:

$$T^{-1}AT = B_1 \dotplus \cdots \dotplus B_t = B, \tag{11}$$

where $B_1, \cdots, B_t$ are Jordan blocks. By definition,

$$f(A) = Tf(B)T^{-1},$$

and consequently the elementary divisors of the matrices $f(A)$ and $f(B)$ coincide. It follows from (11) that

$$f(B) = f(B_1) \dotplus \cdots \dotplus f(B_t).$$

Therefore the system of elementary divisors of $f(B)$ is the union of the systems of elementary divisors of the blocks $f(B_1), \cdots, f(B_t)$. Thus, our original question is reduced to the following; given a Jordan block B_i with elementary divisors $(\lambda - \rho_i)^{n_i}$, it is required to find the elementary divisors of $f(B_i)$.

By formulas (5), (6) we have

$$\lambda E_i - f(B_i) = \begin{bmatrix} \lambda - f(\rho_i) & -f'(\rho_i) & \cdots & -\frac{1}{(n_i-1)!}f^{(n_i-1)}(\rho_i) \\ & \lambda - f(\rho_i) & \cdots & -\frac{1}{(n_i-2)!}f^{(n_i-2)}(\rho_i) \\ & & & \cdots\cdots\cdots\cdots \\ & & & \lambda - f(\rho_i) \end{bmatrix}. \tag{12}$$

We seek the greatest common divisors $D_1(\lambda), \cdots, D_{n_i}(\lambda)$ of the 1st, 2nd, $\cdots$, n_ith order minors of this matrix. Since $D_{n_i}(\lambda)$ equals the determinant,

$$D_{n_i}(\lambda) = (\lambda - f(\rho_i))^{n_i}.$$

All the remaining $D_k(\lambda)$ are divisors of $D_{n_i}(\lambda)$, and thus have the form $(\lambda - f(\rho_i))^{\alpha}$. Consider $D_{n_i-1}(\lambda)$. This polynomial is a divisor of all the $(n_i - 1)$st order minors of the matrix (12), and among these is the minor $\Delta(\lambda)$ obtained by striking out the first column and last row. However, if λ is replaced by the number $f(\rho_i)$ in this minor, a triangular matrix with elements $-f'(\rho_i)$ on the main diagonal is obtained; this means that

$$\Delta(f(\rho_i)) = (-f'(\rho_i))^{n_i-1}. \tag{13}$$

We now assume that $f'(\rho_i) \neq 0$. Equality (*13*) then shows that $\Delta(\lambda)$ is not divisible by $\lambda - f(\rho_i)$. But the polynomial $D_{n_i-1}(\lambda)$ must be a common divisor of the polynomials $\Delta(\lambda)$ and $D_{n_i}(\lambda)$, and consequently $D_{n_i-1}(\lambda) = 1$. The remaining polynomials $D_{n_i-2}(\lambda), \cdots, D_2(\lambda), D_1(\lambda)$ are divisors of $D_{n_i-1}(\lambda)$, and therefore also equal 1. Constructing the ratios D_{k+1}/D_k, we see that the invariant factors of the matrix (12) are $1, \cdots, 1, (\lambda - f(\rho_i))^{n_i}$; as a consequence,

* In this section, by "elementary divisors of A" is meant "elementary divisors of the characteristic matrix $\lambda E - A$ of A." (*Ed.*)

the matrix (12) has only one elementary divisor, $(\lambda - f(\rho_i))^{n_i}$. Thus we have

THEOREM 2. *Let the matrix A have proper values $\rho_1, \cdots, \rho_s$, and let $f(\lambda)$ be a function for which $f'(\rho_i) \neq 0$ for $i = 1, \cdots, s$. If the matrix $f(A)$ exists, then its elementary divisors may be obtained by replacing each elementary divisor $(\lambda - \rho_i)^{n_i}$ of the matrix A by the expression $(\lambda - f(\rho_i))^{n_i}$.*

For example, if A is a nonsingular matrix and $f(\lambda) = \lambda^{-1}$, then $f(A) = A^{-1}$ and $f'(\rho_i) = -\rho_i^{-2} \neq 0$. Therefore, if each elementary divisor $(\lambda - \rho_i)^{n_i}$ is replaced by the expression $(\lambda - \rho_i^{-1})^{n_i}$, the system of elementary divisors of the inverse matrix is obtained.

* * *

Theorem 2 permits one to find the elementary divisors of $f(A)$ belonging to those proper values $f(\rho_i)$ for which $f'(\rho_i) \neq 0$. It is not difficult to give a corresponding rule for the case $f'(\rho_i) = 0$. For some proper value ρ_i of the matrix A, let

$$f'(\rho_i) = f''(\rho_i) = \cdots = f^{(k-1)}(\rho_i) = 0, \ f^{(k)}(\rho_i) \neq 0. \tag{14}$$

It is necessary to exhibit the elementary divisor of the matrix $f(A)$ into which each elementary divisor $(\lambda - \rho_i)^{n_i}$ of the matrix A is carried. This question evidently reduces to the following: to find the elementary divisors of the matrix (6) subject to condition (14). For $k \geq n_i$ the matrix (6) is diagonal, with elementary divisors $\lambda - f(\rho_i), \cdots, \lambda - f(\rho_i)$. The case $k = 1$ was examined above: the matrix (14) then has the elementary divisor $(\lambda - f(\rho_i))^{n_i}$. Therefore, we are interested only in values of k between 1 and n_i.

Consider an auxiliary linear space $\mathfrak{L}$ of dimension n_i with basis $a_1, \cdots, a_{n_i}$. For brevity, set $1/j!f^{(j)}(\rho_i) = \alpha_{j+1}$, and denote by $\mathscr{C}$ the linear transformation of the space $\mathfrak{L}$ with matrix

$$\mathscr{C} = f(B_i) - f(\rho_i) E_i .$$

Thus, we have

$$\begin{aligned} a_1\mathscr{C} &= \alpha_{k+1} a_{k+1} + \alpha_{k+2} a_{k+2} + \cdots + \alpha_n a_n , \\ a_2\mathscr{C} &= \qquad\qquad \alpha_{k+1} a_{k+2} + \cdots + \alpha_{n-1} a_n , \\ &\vdots \\ a_{n-k}\mathscr{C} &= \qquad\qquad\qquad\qquad\qquad \alpha_{k+1} a_n , \\ a_j\mathscr{C} &= \theta \qquad (j > n-k) . \end{aligned} \tag{15}$$

We are interested in the elementary divisors of the transformation $\mathscr{C}$; therefore, we take another basis in $\mathfrak{L}$, in which the matrix of the transformation $\mathscr{C}$ has a simpler form. Let

$$e_i = \beta_{ii}a_i + \beta_{i,i+1} a_{i+1} + \cdots + \beta_{in} a_n , \ (i = 1, \cdots, n);$$

then

$$e_i\mathscr{C} = \beta_{ii}\,\alpha_{k+1}\,a_{i+k} + (\beta_{ii}\,\alpha_{k+2} + \beta_{i,i+1}\,\alpha_{k+1})\,a_{i+k+1} + \cdots .$$

We impose on the numbers β_{ij} the relations

$$e_i\mathscr{C} = e_{i+k}\,, \quad e_j\mathscr{C} = \theta\,, \tag{16}$$

where $i = 1, \cdots, n-k$ and $j > n-k$. This gives the following system of equations in the β_{ij}:

$$\alpha_{k+1}\,\beta_{ii} = \beta_{i+k,i+k}\,, \qquad \alpha_{k+1}\,\beta_{i,i+1} + \alpha_{k+2}\,\beta_{ii} = \beta_{i+k,i+k+1}\,, \cdots .$$

In view of the condition $\alpha_{k+1} \neq 0$, it is possible to successively determine $\beta_{ii}, \beta_{i,i+1}, \cdots$, expressing them in terms of the β with large first index. For β_{ij} with $i \geq n-k$, no equations are in general obtained, so they may be chosen arbitrarily. In particular, setting $\beta_{n-k,n-k} = \cdots = \beta_{nn} = 1$, we obtain nonzero values for the rest of the coefficients $\beta_{11}, \cdots, \beta_{n-k+1,n-k+1}$. Thus we have obtained a new basis $e_1, \cdots, e_n$, which satisfies conditions (16). We decompose the vectors $e_1, \cdots, e_n$ into the systems

$$\begin{array}{l} e_1\,,\ e_{1+k}\,,\ e_{1+2k}\,,\ \cdots\,, \\ e_2\,,\ e_{2+k}\,,\ e_{2+2k}\,,\ \cdots\,, \\ \cdots\cdots\cdots\cdots\cdots\,, \\ e_k\,,\ e_{2k}\,,\ e_{3k}\,,\ \cdots\cdots\,, \end{array}$$

and consider the subspaces $\mathfrak{L}_1, \cdots, \mathfrak{L}_k$ spanned by these systems. Relations (16) show that $\mathfrak{L}_i$ is an invariant subspace with basis $e_{i+k}, e_{i+2k}, \cdots$; moreover,

$$\mathfrak{L} = \mathfrak{L}_1 \dotplus \cdots \dotplus \mathfrak{L}_k\,. \tag{17}$$

From the result in Section 49 it follows that the matrix of the transformation $\mathscr{C}$ decomposes into k Jordan blocks with elementary divisors $\lambda^{m_1}, \lambda^{m_2}, \cdots, \lambda^{m_k}$, where $m_1, \cdots, m_k$ are the dimensions of the subspaces $\mathfrak{L}_1, \cdots, \mathfrak{L}_k$. The matrix of the initial transformation $f(B_i)$ is related to C by the formula $f(B_i) = f(\rho_i)\,E + C$; therefore the elementary divisors of the matrix $f(B_i)$ are $(\lambda - f(\rho_i))^{m_1}, \cdots, (\lambda - f(\rho_i))^{m_k}$. If the symbol $[\alpha]$ denotes the largest integer not exceeding α, then we obtain the following expressions for $m_1, \cdots, m_k$:

$$m_1 = \left[\frac{n-1}{k}\right] + 1, \quad m_2 = \left[\frac{n-2}{k}\right] + 1, \quad \cdots, \quad m_k = \left[\frac{n-k}{k}\right] + 1 = \left[\frac{n}{k}\right].$$

Thus, if the matrix A has an elementary divisor $(\lambda - \rho)^m$, and $f'(\rho) = \cdots = f^{(k-1)}(\rho) = 0$, $f^{(k)}(\rho) \neq 0$, then, under the transition from A to $f(A)$, this elementary divisor is decomposed into the elementary divisors $(\lambda - f(\rho))^{m_1}, \cdots, (\lambda - f(\rho))^{m_k}$, where

$$m_1 = \left[\frac{m-1}{k}\right] + 1\,, \quad m_2 = \left[\frac{m-2}{k}\right] + 1\,, \quad \cdots, \quad m_k = \left[\frac{m-k}{k}\right] + 1\,.$$

We consider an example. Let A have elementary divisors $(\lambda - 1)^8$, $(\lambda + 2)^2$; it is required to find the elementary divisors of the matrix $A^6 - 3A^4 + 3A^2 - E$. Here $f(\lambda) = \lambda^6 - 3\lambda^4 + 3\lambda^2 - 1 = (\lambda - 1)^3(\lambda + 1)^3$, $f'(-2) \neq 0$, $f'(1) = f''(1) = 0$,

$f'''(1) \neq 0$. The elementary divisor $(\lambda+2)^2$ under the transition to $f(A)$ gives $(\lambda - f(-2))^2 = (\lambda - 27)^2$. The elementary divisor $(\lambda - 1)^8$ decomposes into $\lambda^3, \lambda^3, \lambda^2$. Consequently, the elementaly, divisors of the matrix $f(A)$ are $\lambda^3, \lambda^3, \lambda^2, (\lambda - 27)^2$.

66. Power Series

A sequence of square matrices

$$A_1, A_2, \cdots, A_m, A_{m+1}, \cdots, \tag{18}$$

all of the same order, is said to ***converge*** to the matrix A if the elements of the matrices (18) in a given row and column converge to the corresponding element of the matrix A. It is immediately clear from this definition that if the matrices A_m and B_m converge with increasing m to A and B respectively, then $A_m + B_m$ and $A_m B_m$ converge to $A + B$ and AB. In particular, if T is a constant matrix, and the matrices A_m converge to A, then the matrices $T^{-1}A_mT$ will have $T^{-1}AT$ as their limit. Further, if

$$A_m = A_m^{(1)} \dotplus \cdots \dotplus A_m^{(s)}, \quad (m = 1, 2, \cdots,),$$

where the orders of the blocks do not depend on m, then A_m will converge to some limit if and only if each block $A_m^{(i)}$ converges separately.

The last remark permits a completely simple solution of the question of the convergence of a so-called matrix power series. Let

$$\alpha_0 + \alpha_1\lambda + \alpha_2\lambda^2 + \cdots + \alpha_m\lambda^m + \cdots \tag{19}$$

be a formal power series in an indeterminate λ. The expression

$$\alpha_0 E + \alpha_1 A + \alpha_2 A^2 + \cdots + \alpha_m A^m + \cdots \tag{20}$$

is called the corresponding ***power series*** in the matrix A, and the polynomial

$$f_n(A) = \alpha_0 E + \alpha_1 A + \cdots + \alpha_n A^n$$

is the ***nth partial sum*** of the series. The series (20) is ***convergent*** if the sequence of partial sums $f_1(A), \cdots, f_m(A), \cdots$ has a limit; if this limit exists it is called the ***sum*** of the series (20).

We reduce the matrix A to normal form,

$$T^{-1}AT = B = B_1 \dotplus \cdots \dotplus B_t,$$

where $B_1, \cdots, B_t$ are Jordan blocks. We have seen above that convergence of the sequence $f_m(A)$ is equivalent to the convergence of the sequence $T^{-1}F_m(A)T$ $(m = 1, 2, \cdots)$. But

$$T^{-1}f_m(A)T = f_m(T^{-1}AT) = f_m(B) = f_m(B_1) \dotplus \cdots \dotplus f_m(B_t),$$

and the question of the convergence of the series (20) is equivalent to the following: under what conditions is this series convergent for the Jordan blocks $B_1, \cdots, B_t$? Consider one of these blocks, say B_i. Let it have the elementary divisor $(\lambda - \rho_i)^{n_i}$. By formula (3),

$$f_m(B_i) = \begin{bmatrix} f_m(\rho_i) & \frac{1}{1!} f_m'(\rho_i) & \cdots & \frac{1}{(n_i-1)!} f_m^{(n_i-1)}(\rho_i) \\ & f_m(\rho_i) & \cdots & \frac{1}{(n_i-2)!} f_m^{(n_i-2)}(\rho_i) \\ & & \cdots\cdots & \cdots\cdots \\ & & & f_m(\rho_i) \end{bmatrix}.$$

Consequently, $f_m(B_i)$ converges if and only if the sequences $f_m(\rho_i)$, $f_m'(\rho_i)$, $\cdots$, $f_m^{(n_i-1)}(\rho_i)$ converge—that is, if and only if the series (19) converges, and the series obtained by differentiating (19) term by term up to $(n-1)$ times, inclusive, converges. It is known from the theory of analytic functions that all these series are convergent if either ρ_i lies inside the circle of convergence of (19) or ρ_i lies on the circle of convergence and the $(n-1)$st derivative of (19) converges at ρ_i. Thus we have

THEOREM 3. *A matrix power series in A converges if and only if each proper value ρ_i of A either lies inside the circle of convergence of the corresponding power series $f(\lambda)$ or lies on the circle of convergence, and at the same time the series of* (n_i-1)st *derivatives of the terms of $f(\lambda)$ converges at ρ_i, where n_i is the highest degree of an elementary divisor belonging to ρ_i.*

* * *

67. Matrices Permutable with Given Matrices

Matrices A, B are ***permutable*** if $AB = BA$. Every matrix permutes with itself and with the identity matrix. Further, if A permutes with the matrices B, C, then the equalities

$$A \cdot BC = BAC = BC \cdot A,$$
$$A(\alpha B + \beta C) = \alpha AB + \beta AC = \alpha BA + \beta CA = (\alpha B + \beta C)A$$

show that A permutes with their product and with their linear combinations. Consequently, if B permutes with A, then B permutes with arbitrary polynomials in A. In particular, A permutes with polynomials in A, and any two polynomials in A permute with each other.

By Section 64, the value of a scalar function at a matrix A can be represented by a polynomial in A. A matrix B which permutes with A is permutable with every polynomial in A. Consequently, a matrix permutable with A permutes with the value of every scalar function at the matrix A.

The relation $\alpha E \cdot P = P \cdot \alpha E$ shows that the matrix αE is permutable with every matrix of the same order. The converse is also true:

If the square matrix A of order n permutes with every matrix of order n, then A has the form αE.

Denote the elements of the matrix A by α_{ij}. Let P be the matrix with a 1 in the pth row and qth column, and zeros elsewhere. A simple multiplication shows that

$$AP = \begin{bmatrix} 0 & \cdots & \alpha_{1p} & \cdots & 0 \\ 0 & \cdots & \alpha_{2p} & \cdots & 0 \\ \cdots & \cdots & \cdots & \cdots & \cdots \\ 0 & \cdots & \alpha_{np} & \cdots & 0 \end{bmatrix}, \qquad PA = \begin{bmatrix} 0 & 0 & \cdots & 0 \\ \cdots & \cdots & \cdots & \cdots \\ \alpha_{q1} & \alpha_{q2} & \cdots & \alpha_{qn} \\ \cdots & \cdots & \cdots & \cdots \\ 0 & 0 & \cdots & 0 \end{bmatrix},$$

where the qth column is written out in the first matrix, the pth row in the second. By assumption, $AP = PA$, and consequently, $\alpha_{pp} = \alpha_{qq}$, $\alpha_{pq} = 0$ if $p \neq q$. Since p and q are arbitrary, this means that A is diagonal, and all its diagonal elements are equal.

We now consider a more complicated problem: *to find all matrices permutable with a given matrix A.*

For its solution we reduce A to Jordan normal form:

$$T^{-1}AT = B = B_1 \dotplus \cdots \dotplus B_s \tag{21}$$

where $B_1, \cdots, B_s$ are Jordan blocks. If X permutes with B, then evidently $Y = TXT^{-1}$ will permute with A. Therefore the problem reduces to finding the matrices X which permute with B. We break the matrix X into blocks corresponding to (21):

$$X = \begin{bmatrix} X_{11} & X_{12} & \cdots & X_{1s} \\ X_{21} & X_{22} & \cdots & X_{2s} \\ \cdots & \cdots & \cdots & \cdots \\ X_{s1} & X_{s2} & \cdots & X_{ss} \end{bmatrix}.$$

The condition $BX = XB$ reduces to the equalities

$$B_pX_{pq} = X_{pq}B_q \qquad (p, q = 1, \cdots, s). \tag{22}$$

For each block X_{pq}, only one equality is obtained from which to determine the elements of X_{pq}.

Let the order of the matrices B_p, B_q be k, m respectively, and let the proper values be ρ, σ. Then X_{pq} is a rectangular matrix with k rows and m columns. Denote the elements of X_{pq} by ξ_{ij}, for $i = 1, \cdots, k$ and $j = 1, \cdots, m$, and write relation (22) in detail:

$$\begin{bmatrix} \rho & 1 & 0 & \cdots & 0 \\ & \rho & 1 & \cdots & 0 \\ & & & \cdots & \cdots \\ & & & & \rho \end{bmatrix} \begin{bmatrix} \xi_{11} & \xi_{12} & \cdots & \xi_{1m} \\ \xi_{21} & \xi_{22} & \cdots & \xi_{2m} \\ \cdots & \cdots & \cdots & \cdots \\ \xi_{k1} & \xi_{k2} & \cdots & \xi_{km} \end{bmatrix} = \begin{bmatrix} \xi_{11} & \xi_{12} & \cdots & \xi_{1m} \\ \xi_{21} & \xi_{22} & \cdots & \xi_{2m} \\ \cdots & \cdots & \cdots & \cdots \\ \xi_{k1} & \xi_{k2} & \cdots & \xi_{km} \end{bmatrix} \begin{bmatrix} \sigma & 1 & 0 & \cdots & 0 \\ & \sigma & 1 & \cdots & 0 \\ \cdots & \cdots & \cdots & \cdots & \cdots \\ & & & & \sigma \end{bmatrix}.$$

If we carry out the multiplication and compare the element in the ith row and jth column on the left with the corresponding element on the right, we obtain the equations

$$\rho\xi_{ij} + \xi_{i+1,j} = \xi_{i,j-1} + \sigma\xi_{ij} \qquad (i \neq k,\ j \neq 1), \tag{23}$$

$$\rho\xi_{kj} = \xi_{k,j-1} + \sigma\xi_{kj} \qquad (i = k,\ j \neq 1), \tag{24}$$

$$\rho\xi_{k1} = \sigma\,\xi_{k1} \qquad (i = k,\ j = 1). \tag{25}$$

If $\rho \neq \sigma$, then it follows from (25) that $\xi_{k1} = 0$; then form (24) we successively obtain $\xi_{k2} = \cdots = \xi_{km} = 0$, and finally, from (23), all remaining ξ_{ij}

are also zero. Thus, for $\rho \neq \sigma$ we have $X_{pq} = 0$.

Consider the case $\rho = \sigma$. Equations (23), (24), (25) become

$$\xi_{i+1,j} = \xi_{i,j-1} \qquad (i = 1, \cdots, k-1,\ j = 2, \cdots, m)\,. \tag{26}$$

$$\xi_{k,j-1} = 0 \qquad (j = 2, \cdots, m)\,. \tag{27}$$

If $k \geqq m$, then, setting $\xi_{11} = \xi_1,\ \xi_{12} = \xi_2, \cdots, \xi_{1m} = \xi_m$, we reduce (26) and (27) to the equations

$$\xi_{ij} = \xi_{j-i+1} \qquad (i \leqq j)\,,$$

$$\xi_{ij} = 0 \qquad (i > j)\,.$$

From this it follows that the matrix X_{pq} has the *linear triangular form*

$$X_{pq} = \begin{bmatrix} \xi_1 & \xi_2 & \xi_3 & \cdots & \xi_m \\ & \xi_1 & \xi_2 & \cdots & \xi_{m-1} \\ & & \cdots & \cdots & \cdots \\ & & & & \xi_1 \end{bmatrix} \tag{28}$$

for $k = m$, and the corresponding form

$$X_{pq} = \begin{bmatrix} \xi_1 & \xi_2 & \xi_3 & \cdots & \xi_m \\ & \xi_1 & \xi_2 & \cdots & \xi_{m-1} \\ & & \cdots & \cdots & \cdots \\ & & & & \xi_1 \\ 0 & 0 & 0 & \cdots & 0 \\ \cdots & \cdots & \cdots & \cdots & \cdots \\ 0 & 0 & 0 & \cdots & 0 \end{bmatrix}$$

for $k > m$. If $k < m$, then, setting $\xi_{1,m-k+1} = \xi_1,\ \xi_{1,m-k+2} = \xi_2, \cdots, \xi_{1m} = \xi_k$, we reduce (23), (24), (25) to the equations

$$\xi_{ij} = \xi_{j-i-m+k+1} \qquad (j - i \geqq m - k)\,,$$

$$\xi_{ij} = 0 \qquad (j - i < m - k)\,,$$

which show that the matrix X_{pq} has the form

$$X_{pq} = \begin{bmatrix} 0 & \cdots & 0 & \xi_1 & \xi_2 & \cdots & \xi_k \\ 0 & \cdots & 0 & 0 & \xi_1 & \cdots & \xi_{k-1} \\ \cdots & \cdots & \cdots & \cdots & \cdots & \cdots & \cdots \\ 0 & & 0 & \cdots & \cdots & \cdots & \xi_1 \end{bmatrix}.$$

Conversely, if the block matrix X has any of the forms indicated above, then (23), (24), (25) are satisfied, and consequently X permutes with B.

For example, if

$$B = \begin{bmatrix} \rho & 1 & 0 \\ & \rho & 1 \\ & & \rho \end{bmatrix} \dotplus \begin{bmatrix} \rho & 1 \\ & \rho \end{bmatrix} \dotplus \begin{bmatrix} \sigma & 1 & 0 \\ & \sigma & 1 \\ & & \sigma \end{bmatrix} \tag{29}$$

for $\rho \neq \sigma$, then the matrices permutable with B have the form

$$X = \left[\begin{array}{ccc:cc} \alpha_1 & \alpha_2 & \alpha_3 & \gamma_1 & \gamma_2 \\ & \alpha_1 & \alpha_2 & 0 & \gamma_1 \\ & & \alpha_1 & 0 & 0 \\ \hdashline 0 & \delta_1 & \delta_2 & \beta_1 & \beta_2 \\ 0 & 0 & \delta_1 & 0 & \beta_1 \end{array}\right] \dotplus \begin{bmatrix} \lambda_1 & \lambda_2 & \lambda_3 \\ & \lambda_1 & \lambda_2 \\ & & \lambda_1 \end{bmatrix},$$

where α_i, β_i, δ_i, γ_i, λ_i are arbitrary.

The result becomes especially simple for matrices of the form $\rho_1 E_1 \dotplus \cdots \dotplus \rho_s E_s$, where $E_1, \cdots, E_s$ are identity matrices and $\rho_1, \cdots, \rho_s$ are distinct. In this case the blocks X_{pq}, $p \neq q$, are zero, and X has block diagonal form.

In particular, if B is diagonal with distinct diagonal elements, then the matrices which permute with B are also diagonal.

68. Matrices Permutable with Permuting Matrices

Polynomials in a matrix A have the special property of permuting, not only with the matrix A, but also with any matrix X which permutes with A. As we shall see, this property is a characteristic only of polynomials in A.

THEOREM 4. *If C is permutable with every matrix which permutes with B, then C is a polynomial in B.*

Evidently we may assume that B has Jordan normal form; let

$$B = B_1 \dotplus \cdots \dotplus B_s ,$$

where $B_1, \cdots, B_s$ are Jordan blocks. The auxiliary matrices

$$X = \alpha_1 E_1 \dotplus \cdots \dotplus \alpha_s E_s ,$$

where $\alpha_1, \cdots, \alpha_s$ are arbitrary numbers and $E_1, \cdots, E_s$ are identity matrices, are known to commute with B; therefore, X also commutes with C. From the preceding section it follows that C is decomposable into blocks:

$$C = C_1 \dotplus \cdots \dotplus C_s . \tag{30}$$

Moreover, it follows from $CB = BC$ that these blocks have linear triangular form (28). Now let X be an arbitrary matrix that commutes with B. The general form of the matrix X was established in the preceding section. By assumption, C commutes with X. Representing X in block form, we see that the equality $CX = XC$ is equivalent to the relations

$$C_p X_{pq} = X_{pq} C_q \qquad (p, q = 1, \cdots, s) . \tag{31}$$

If the corresponding blocks B_p, B_q have distinct proper values, then (31) yields nothing, since then $X_{pq} = 0$. Hence we assume that B_p and B_q have the same proper values. Let

$$C_p = \begin{bmatrix} \alpha_1 & \alpha_2 & \cdots & \alpha_k \\ & \alpha_1 & \cdots & \alpha_{k-1} \\ & & \cdots\cdots & \\ & & & \alpha_1 \end{bmatrix}, \qquad C_q = \begin{bmatrix} \beta_1 & \beta_2 & \cdots & \beta_m \\ & \beta_1 & \cdots & \beta_{m-1} \\ & & \cdots\cdots & \\ & & & \beta_1 \end{bmatrix}.$$

For definiteness, suppose $k < m$. Then relation (31) becomes

$$\begin{bmatrix} \alpha_1 & \alpha_2 \cdots \alpha_k \\ & \alpha_1 \cdots \alpha_{k-1} \\ & \cdots\cdots \\ & \alpha_1 \end{bmatrix} \begin{bmatrix} 0 \cdots 0 & \xi_1 & \xi_2 \cdots \xi_k \\ 0 \cdots 0 & 0 & \xi_1 \cdots \xi_{k-1} \\ \cdots\cdots & \cdots & \cdots\cdots \\ 0 \cdots 0 & \cdots\cdots & \xi_1 \end{bmatrix}$$

$$= \begin{bmatrix} 0 \cdots 0 & \xi_1 & \xi_2 \cdots \xi_k \\ 0 \cdots 0 & 0 & \xi_1 \cdots \xi_{k-1} \\ \cdots\cdots & \cdots & \cdots\cdots \\ 0 \cdots\cdots 0 & \cdots\cdots & \xi_1 \end{bmatrix} \begin{bmatrix} \beta_1 & \beta_2 \cdots \beta_m \\ & \beta_1 \cdots \beta_{m-1} \\ & \cdots\cdots \\ & \beta_1 \end{bmatrix},$$

where $\xi_1, \cdots, \xi_k$ are arbitrary numbers. Multiplying the first row by the last column on the right and left sides, and comparing the results, we obtain

$$\alpha_1\xi_k + \alpha_2\xi_{k-1} + \cdots + \alpha_k\xi_1 = \beta_1\xi_k + \beta_2\xi_{k-1} + \cdots + \beta_k\xi_1 .$$

In view of the arbitrariness of $\xi_1, \cdots, \xi_k$ it follows that

$$\alpha_1 = \beta_1, \ \alpha_2 = \beta_2, \ \cdots, \ \alpha_k = \beta_k . \tag{32}$$

It is easy to verify that a similar equality is obtained for $k \geq m$. The matrix C is subject to all the conditions (30), (31), (32). To make these conditions somewhat more intuitive, we proceed in the following way. Suppose that the Jordan blocks of the matrix B are such that blocks with the same proper value are adjacent. For example, let

$$B = (B_1 \dotplus \cdots \dotplus B_{m_1}) \dotplus (B_{m_1+1} \dotplus \cdots \dotplus B_{m_2}) \dotplus \cdots \dotplus (B_{m_t+1} \dotplus \cdots \dotplus B_s) ,$$

where blocks with the same proper values are contained in the same set of parentheses. Denoting the sums in parentheses by $B^{(1)}, \cdots, B^{(t+1)}$ respectively, we divide the matrix B into larger blocks, which we call cells. We then divide the matrices X and C into cells in a corresponding way. The results of the preceding section show that all the nondiagonal cells of the matrix X are zero; the structure of the diagonal cells was also described there. The conditions for the matrix C obtained in the present section show that the diagonal blocks of this matrix decompose into blocks in the same way as those of B. Moreover, the blocks of the matrix C have a special triangular form. Equalities (32) mean that in the blocks of the matrix C belonging to a given cell, the elements lying on a line parallel to the main diagonal are equal.

For example, let B have the form (29). Our results show that every matrix C, permutable with each matrix which permutes with B, has the form

$$C = \left[\begin{array}{ccccc:ccc} \alpha_0 & \alpha_1 & \alpha_2 & & & & & \\ & \alpha_0 & \alpha_1 & & & & & \\ & & \alpha_0 & & & & & \\ & & & \alpha_0 & \alpha_1 & & & \\ & & & & \alpha_0 & & & \\ \hdashline & & & & & \lambda_0 & \lambda_1 & \lambda_2 \\ & & & & & & \lambda_0 & \lambda_1 \\ & & & & & & & \lambda_0 \end{array}\right] . \tag{33}$$

We now only need to prove that C can be represented as a polynomial in B. We do this only for the particular case where B has the form (29), and C, consequently, has the form (33); in the general case the argument is essentially the same. Thus, it is necessary to show that the matrix (33) is a polynomial in the matrix (29). By Section 64, there is a polynomial $f(\lambda)$ that satisfies the conditions

$$f(\rho) = \alpha_0, \qquad f'(\rho) = \alpha_1, \qquad f''(\rho) = \alpha_2,$$
$$f(\sigma) = \lambda_0, \qquad f'(\sigma) = \lambda_1, \qquad f''(\sigma) = \lambda_2.$$

Applying (3) from Section 62, it is easy to see that $f(B) = C$.

● EXAMPLES AND PROBLEMS

1. Find A^n, if

$$A = \begin{bmatrix} 1 & 4 & 2 \\ 0 & -3 & -2 \\ 0 & 4 & 3 \end{bmatrix}$$

2. Find all solutions of the equation $X^2 = A$, where A is the matrix of problem 1. Which of these solutions are polynomials in A? Also compute $\sin \pi A$, e^A, $\cos \pi A$.

3. The elementary divisors of a transformation $\mathscr{A}$ are λ^5, $(\lambda - \pi)^2$, $\lambda + (\pi/2)$. Compute the elementary divisors of the transformations $\cos \mathscr{A}$, $\sin \mathscr{A}$.

4. If A, B are parmutable matrices, the $e^A e^B = e^{A+B}$.

5. For which matrices A is the equation $A = e^x$ solvable?

6. If the sum of the power series (19) is $f(\lambda)$, then the sum of the power series (20), if it converges, is $f(A)$.

7. Write the general form of a matrix permutable with a Jordan normal matrix A, if A has elementary divisors $(\lambda - 1)^3$, $(\lambda - 1)^2$, $(\lambda - 1)$, $(\lambda + 2)^2$, $(\lambda + 2)$.

8. If the greatest common divisors $D_1(\lambda), \cdots, D_n(\lambda)$ of the minors of the matrix $\lambda E - A$ have degrees $m_1, \cdots, m_n$ respectively, then the number of linearly independent matrices X which permute with A is $n + 2\ (m_1 + \cdots + m_n)$

9. Under the conditions of the preceding problem, let $D_{n-1}(\lambda) = 1$. Then every matrix permutable with A is a polynomial in A.

5 UNITARY AND EUCLIDEAN SPACES

The linear spaces studied in the preceding chapter had less structure than the familiar space $\mathfrak{R}$. Such notions as length, angle, and inner product, which play a fundamental role in geometry, are not found in the general theory of linear spaces. Therefore, if we want a theory which embraces all of the most essential properties of the space $\mathfrak{R}$, we must introduce, besides the operations of vector addition and multiplication by a scalar, the notion of an inner product. The present chapter is devoted to the study of the properties of vectors belonging to a space with an inner product.

1. Unitary Spaces

69. Axioms and Examples

Let $\mathfrak{R}$ be the familiar space of directed line segments with origin $\mathcal{O}$. The inner product (a, b) of two vectors a, b is the length of a times the length of b times the cosine of the angle between a and b. The following properties of the inner product are immediate consequences of the definition.

a) $(a, b) = (b, a)$,

b) $(\alpha a, b) = \alpha(a, b)$,

c) $(a + b, c) = (a, c) + (b, c)$,

d) if $a \neq \theta$, then $(a, a) > 0$.

Choose three orthogonal vectors e_1, e_2, e_3, each of length 1, as a coordinate system in $\mathfrak{R}$. Then each vector a can be written uniquely in the form

$$a = \alpha_1 e_1 + \alpha_2 e_2 + \alpha_3 e_3,$$

where $\alpha_1, \alpha_2, \alpha_3$ are the lengths of the projections of a on the coordinate axes, with proper signs. If

$$b = \beta_1 e_1 + \beta_2 e_2 + \beta_3 e_3$$

is a second vector, then it follows from the definition of inner product and properties (*b*), (*c*) that

$$(a, b) = \alpha_1\beta_1 + \alpha_2\beta_2 + \alpha_3\beta_3. \qquad (1)$$

The space $\mathfrak{R}$ is real. This is seen in the fact that projections, lengths, and inner products are all real numbers. In some cases, however, it becomes necessary to consider vectors with complex projections. At first glance it seems natural to take expression (1) as the inner product of vectors with complex coordinates $\alpha_1, \alpha_2, \alpha_3$ and $\beta_1, \beta_2, \beta_3$, and in some cases this is permissible. A complex space with this inner product is called a ***complex Euclidean space.*** Unfortunately, this inner product does not possess some important properties—in particular, property (*d*). In fact, for the vector

$$a = 3e_1 + 4e_2 + 5ie_3 \qquad (i = \sqrt{-1}),$$

formula (1) gives

$$(a, a) = 9 + 16 + 25i^2 = 0,$$

violating property (*d*). To avoid this inconvenience, one takes as the definition of the inner product of complex vectors not expression (1), but the expression

$$(a, b) = \alpha_1\bar{\beta}_1 + \alpha_2\bar{\beta}_2 + \alpha_3\bar{\beta}_3, \qquad (2)$$

where the overbars denote passage to the complex conjugate. If the vectors a and b are real, then $\beta_j = \bar{\beta}_j$, and expression (2) coincides with (1). Thus the new definition is an extension of the old. On the other hand, property (*d*) is fulfilled under the new definition, since, from (2),

$$(a, a) = \alpha_1\bar{\alpha}_1 + \alpha_2\bar{\alpha}_2 + \alpha_3\bar{\alpha}_3 = |\alpha_1|^2 + |\alpha_2|^2 + |\alpha_3|^2,$$

where $|\alpha_j|$ is the modulus of α_j. Properties (*b*), (*c*) are also easily seen to be fulfilled. As for property (*a*), it has a different form for complex vectors since from (2) we have

$$(b, a) = \beta_1\bar{\alpha}_1 + \beta_2\bar{\alpha}_2 + \beta_3\bar{\alpha}_3 = \overline{\bar{\beta}_1\alpha_1 + \bar{\beta}_2\alpha_2 + \bar{\beta}_3\alpha_3},$$

or

$$a^*) \qquad (b, a) = \overline{(a, b)}.$$

A space of complex vectors in which the inner product is computed by formula (2) is called unitary. Formula a*) shows that in general the properties of a unitary space differ from the properties of the space $\mathfrak{R}$. However, in essence, these differences are small. In every case, a unitary space with its properties bears a considerably closer relationship to the space $\mathfrak{R}$ than does the complex Euclidean space mentioned above.

The arguments we have introduced here are not completely precise. Besides, the spaces considered were three-dimensional. We now give a fully rigorous definition of unitary spaces, suitable for spaces of arbitrary dimension.

In the general theory of linear spaces, almost everything was done under the assumption that the base field K was completely arbitrary. In the present chapter, only the fields of complex and of real numbers will be considered as base fields.

A linear space $\mathfrak{L}$ is called ***unitary*** if to each pair of vectors a, b in $\mathfrak{L}$, taken in a definite order, there corresponds a number from K, called the ***inner product*** (a, b) of a and b, which possesses the following properties:

1) $(a, b) = \overline{(b, a)}$,
2) $(\alpha a, b) = \alpha(a, b)$,
3) $(a + b, c) = (a, c) + (b, c)$,
4) if $a \neq \theta$, then $(a, a) > 0$.

In case the base field K is the field of real numbers, the unitary space $\mathfrak{L}$ is called a ***real unitary***, or ***real Euclidean,*** space. In this case $(a, b) = \overline{(a, b)}$, and axiom 1) has the simpler from $(a, b) = (b, a)$.

If K is the field of complex numbers, then $\mathfrak{L}$ is called a ***complex unitary*** space. In what follows, the properties of real Euclidean spaces and of complex unitary spaces will for the most part be considered jointly, and by a unitary space will be meant either a real or a complex unitary space.

We also remark that in the definition of unitary spaces it is not required that the space have finite dimension. Therefore, it is possible to speak of infinite-dimensional unitary spaces. However, even though many properties of unitary spaces do not depend on the dimension of the space, we will, unless stated to the contrary, only consider finite-dimensional spaces. The theory of infinite-dimensional spaces belongs to a special mathematical discipline—functional analysis.

It follows from properties 1) and 2) that

$$(\alpha a, \beta b) = \alpha(a, \beta b) = \alpha\overline{(\beta b, a)} = \alpha\bar{\beta}\overline{(b, a)} = \alpha\bar{\beta}(a, b) ,$$

that is,

$$(\alpha a, \beta b) = \alpha\bar{\beta}(a, b) , \tag{3}$$

Similarly, it follows from 1) to 3) that

$$(a, b + c) = \overline{(b + c, a)} = \overline{(b, a)} + \overline{(c, a)} = (a, b) + (a, c) .$$

In the usual manner, it follows that

$$(\sum \alpha_j a_j, \sum \beta_k b_k) = \sum \sum \alpha_j \bar{\beta}_k (a_j, b_k) . \tag{4}$$

Relation (3) for $\alpha = 1$, $\beta = 0$ gives

$$(a, \theta) = (\theta, a) = 0 .$$

We give two examples. Consider the linear space of rows of length n with elements from the field K. We define the inner product of the rows $a = [\alpha_1, \cdots, \alpha_n]$ and $b = [\beta_1, \cdots, \beta_n]$ by the expression

$$(a, b) = \alpha_1\bar{\beta}_1 + \cdots + \alpha_n\bar{\beta}_n . \tag{5}$$

It is evident that

$$(a, a) = \alpha_1\bar{\alpha}_1 + \cdots + \alpha_n\bar{\alpha}_n = |\alpha_1|^2 \cdots + |\alpha_n|^2 . \tag{6}$$

Since the moduli $|\alpha_j|$ are nonnegative real numbers, the sum of their squares is a nonnegative real number, equal to zero only if all the summands are zero. Thus, property 4) is fulfilled. Properties 1), 2), 3) are evidently also fulfilled, and the space of rows with inner product (5) is a unitary space of dimension n over the field K. This example is significant, since latter on it will be shown that all unitary spaces of dimension n over the field K are isomorphic.

An example of an infinite-dimensional unitary space is the space $\mathfrak{L}$ of all continuous functions $f(t)$, with complex values, defined on the interval [0, 1]. Addition and multiplication by a scalar are defined in the usual way, and the inner product of the functions $f(t)$ and $g(t)$ is defined by the formula

$$(f, g) = \int_0^1 f(t)\overline{g(t)}dt . \tag{7}$$

Properties 1) to 4) are easily demonstrated, and consequently the space $\mathfrak{L}$ is unitary. In this example the base field is the field of complex numbers. If we consider only real-valued continuous functions, then we may take the field of real numbers as the base field. Formula (7) then becomes

$$(f, g) = \int_0^1 f(t)g(t)dt .$$

70. Norm of a Vector

By axiom 4), the inner product (a, a) is a nonnegative real number. The nonnegative square root of this number is called the ***norm*** or ***length*** of the vector a, and is denoted by $||a||$. Thus, by definition,

$$||a|| = +\sqrt{(a, a)} .$$

It is immediately evident from this definition that *the zero vector is the only vector with norm zero.* Further, if α is a scalar, then

$$||\alpha a|| = \sqrt{(\alpha a, \alpha a)} = \sqrt{\alpha\bar{\alpha}(a, a)} = |\alpha|\cdot||a|| , \tag{8}$$

that is, *multiplying a vector by a scalar multiplies the norm of the vector by the modulus of the scalar.* A vector whose norm is 1 is called a ***unit vector,*** or ***normalized vector***. Equality (8) shows that a vector may be normalized by multiplying it by the reciprocal of its norm. This operation is sometimes called ***normalization.***

We now prove an important inequality which relates the inner product of two vectors with their norms.

The inequality of Cauchy-Bunyakovsky. *For any two vectors a, b of a unitary space,*

$$|(a, b)| \leqq ||a|| \, ||b||;$$

equality holds if and only if a and b are linearly dependent.

By axiom 4), for an arbitrary scalar λ,

$$(a-\lambda b, a-\lambda b) \geqq 0 , \tag{9}$$

and this yields

$$(a, a) - \bar{\lambda}(a, b) - \lambda\overline{(a, b)} + \lambda\bar{\lambda}(b, b) \geqq 0 . \tag{10}$$

If $b = \theta$, then the required inequality is satisfied trivially, since both sides are zero. Therefore, we assume that $b \neq \theta$. In inequality (10), replace λ by $(a, b)/(b, b)$ and multiply all terms by (b, b). The result is

$$(a, a)(b, b) - \overline{(a, b)}(a, b) - (a, b)\overline{(a, b)} + (a, b)\overline{(a, b)} \geqq 0 ,$$

or

$$(a, b)\overline{(a, b)} \leqq (a, a)\,(b, b) ,$$
$$|(a, b)| \leqq ||a|| \, ||b|| . \tag{11}$$

If α, b are linearly independent, then $a-\lambda b \neq 0$, and instead of (9) we have the strict inequality

$$(a - \lambda b, a - \lambda b) > 0 .$$

But then strict inequality also holds in the succeeding steps, and instead of (11) we obtain

$$|(a, b)| < ||a|| \, ||b|| . \tag{12}$$

If a, b are linearly dependent, say $a = \alpha b$, then

$$|(a, b)| = |(\alpha b, b)| = |\alpha| \, |(b, b)| = ||a|| \, ||b|| .$$

This completes the proof.

We consider the meaning of the Bunyakovsky inequality in the concrete spaces given above. Let $\mathfrak{L}$ be the unitary space of rows, and take vectors $a = [\alpha_1, \cdots, \alpha_n]$ and $b = [\beta_1, \cdots, \beta_n]$ in $\mathfrak{L}$. By (5), we have

$$|(a, b)| = |\alpha_1\bar{\beta}_1 + \cdots + \alpha_n\bar{\beta}_n| ,$$
$$||a|| = \sqrt{|\alpha_1|^2 + \cdots + |\alpha_n|^2} , \quad ||b|| = \sqrt{|\beta_1|^2 + \cdots + |\beta_n|^2} .$$

Consequently, the Cauchy-Bunyakovsky inequality yields

$$|\alpha_1\bar{\beta}_1 + \cdots + \alpha_n\bar{\beta}_n| \leqq \sqrt{|\alpha_1|^2 + \cdots + |\alpha_n|^2} \, \sqrt{|\beta_1|^2 + \cdots + |\beta_n|^2} ,$$

where α_j, β_j are arbitrary complex numbers.

Similarly, if $\mathfrak{L}$ is the space of functions mentioned earlier, then the Cauchy-Bunyakovsky inequality becomes

$$\left|\int_0^1 f(t)\overline{g(t)}dt\right|^2 \leqq \int_0^1 |f(t)|^2 dt \int_0^1 |g(t)|^2 dt .$$

We return to an arbitrary unitary space. The Cauchy-Bunyakovsky inequality permits a completely simple proof of the following proposition: *the norm of a sum of vectors does not exceed the sum of the norms of the summands.* It is evidently sufficient to examine the case of two summands; the general case follows by induction. We have

$$\begin{aligned}||a+b||^2 &= (a+b,\, a+b) = (a,\, a) + (a,\, b) + \overline{(a,\, b)} + (b,\, b)\\ &= (a,\, a) + 2\mathrm{Re}\,(a,\, b) + (b,\, b)\ ,\end{aligned}$$

where Re (a, b) denotes the real part of (a, b). Since

$$\mathrm{Re}(a,\, b) \leqq |(a,\, b)| \leqq ||a||\ ||b||\ ,$$

then

$$||a+b||^2 \leqq ||a||^2 + 2||a||\ ||b|| + ||b||^2 = (||a|| + (||b||)^2\ ,$$

or

$$||a+b|| \leqq ||a|| + ||b||\ ,$$

which was to be proved.

The expression $||a-b||$ is sometimes called the ***distance*** between the vectors a and b. Denoting this distance by the symbol $\rho(a, b)$, we obtain the following:

1) $\rho(a,\, a) = 0$; $\rho(a,\, b) > 0$ if $a \neq b$;
2) $\rho(a,\, b) = \rho(b,\, a)$;
3) $\rho(a,\, b) + \rho(b,\, c) \geq \rho(a,\, c)$.

The proofs of these are evident; for example, for the last one we have;

$$\begin{aligned}\rho(a,\, c) &= ||a-c|| = ||(a-b) + (b-c)|| \leq ||a-b|| + ||b-c||\\ &= \rho(a,\, b) + \rho(b,\, c)\ .\end{aligned}$$

71. Orthogonal Systems

Vectors a, b in a unitary space $\mathfrak{L}$ are called ***orthogonal*** if their inner product is zero. if $\mathfrak{L}$ is the space $\mathfrak{R}$, then the notion of orthogonality coincides with that of perpendicularity. Therefore, orthogonality may be considered a generalization of the notion of perpendicularity.

It follows from axiom 1) that the relation of orthogonality is symmetric: if a is orthogonal to b, then b is orthogonal to a. Evidently *the zero vector is orthogonal to every vector in the space, and is the only vector which has this property.*

A system of vectors $a_1, \cdots, a_m$ in a unitary space is called on ***orthogonal***

system if each pair of vectors a_j, a_k, $j \neq k$, are orthogonal. A system of only one vector is also called orthogonal.

THEOREM 1. *Every orthogonal system of nonzero vectors in a unitary space is linearly independent.*

Let $a_1, \cdots, a_m$ be an orthogonal system of nonzero vectors, and suppose that

$$\alpha_1 a_1 + \cdots + \alpha_m a_m = \theta .$$

Taking the inner product of both sides with a_j, we have

$$\alpha_1(a_1, a_j) + \cdots + \alpha_m(\alpha_m, a_j) = 0 ,$$

or

$$\alpha_j(a_j, a_j) = 0 , \tag{13}$$

since by the orthogonality of the system all the remaining terms are zero. But $a_j \neq \theta$ and hence $(a_j, a_j) \neq 0$, and it follows from (13) that $\alpha_j = 0$, which was to be proved.

Let the space $\mathfrak{L}$ have dimension n. Theorem 1 shows that no orthogonal system of nonzero vectors in $\mathfrak{L}$ can contain more than n vectors. If n orthogonal nonzero vectors can be found in $\mathfrak{L}$, then they constitute an ***orthogonal basis*** of $\mathfrak{L}$. We show that such a basis of $\mathfrak{L}$ always exists. More than this, we show that in a unitary space $\mathfrak{L}$, *every orthogonal system of nonzero vectors can be extended to an orthogonal basis of* $\mathfrak{L}$. Let the orthogonal system $a_1, \cdots, a_m$ be given in $\mathfrak{L}$. Extend it to a maximal orthogonal system $a_1, \cdots, a_m, a_{m+1}, \cdots, a_s$ of nonzero vectors, where $s \leqq n$. Such an extension exists, since by Theorem 1 no orthogonal system can contain more than n nonzero vectors. We show that $a_1, \cdots, a_m, a_{m+1}, \cdots, a_s$ is the desired basis of the space $\mathfrak{L}$. Consider an arbitrary vector x in $\mathfrak{L}$. We introduce the notation

$$\xi_k = \frac{(x, a_k)}{(a_k, a_k)} \qquad (k = 1, \cdots, s) ,$$

$$y = \xi_1 a_1 + \cdots + \xi_s a_s .$$

Taking the inner product of each side of the last equality with a_k, we obtain

$$(y, a_k) = (x, a_k) ,$$

and hence

$$(x-y, a_k) = (x, a_k) - (y, a_k) = 0 .$$

Thus, the vector $x - y$ turns out to be orthogonal to all the vectors $a_1, \cdots, a_s$. But by assumption the system $a_1, \cdots, a_s$ is a maximal orthogonal system of nonzero vectors in $\mathfrak{L}$; consequently, $x-y = \theta$; that is,

$$x = \xi_1 a_1 + \cdots + \xi_s a_s .$$

Therefore, the linearly independent system $a_1, \cdots, a_s$ has the property that an arbitrary vector x is a linear combination of its elements. This means that $a_1, \cdots, a_s$ is a basis of the space $\mathfrak{L}$.

An orthogonal system consisting of vectors of unit length is called an ***orthonormal*** system. It is evident that the vectors obtained by normalizing orthogonal vectors are again orthogonal. Therefore, normalizing the vectors of some orthogonal basis of a space, we obtain an orthonormal basis of the space. We have seen that every system of nonzero orthogonal vectors can be extended to an orthogonal basis. Therefore, we have

THEOREM 2. *Every orthonormal system of vectors of a space $\mathfrak{L}$ can be extended to an orthonormal basis of $\mathfrak{L}$.*

Since any system containing only one vector is orthogonal, it follows in particular that *every unitary space has an orthonormal basis.*

A system of vectors $e_1, \cdots, e_n$, considered in a definite order, has been called a coordinate system of $\mathfrak{L}$ if $e_1, \cdots, e_n$ is a basis of $\mathfrak{L}$. If $e_1, \cdots, e_n$ is an orthonormal basis, then the coordinate system is also called orthonormal. The difference between arbitrary and orthonormal coordinate systems is similar to the difference between oblique and right-angled Cartesian coordinate systems in the familiar space $\mathfrak{R}$. Any set of three arbitrary vectors a_1, a_2, a_3 in $\mathfrak{R}$ not lying in one plane constitutes a basis (compare Fig. 1, p. 40). Choose some point A and represent the vector $\overrightarrow{\mathcal{O}A}$ in terms of the coordinate vectors a_1, a_2, a_3:

$$\overrightarrow{\mathcal{O}A} = \alpha_1 a_1 + \alpha_2 a_2 + \alpha_3 a_3 .$$

By definition the numbers $\alpha_1, \alpha_2, \alpha_3$ are the coordinates of the vector $\overrightarrow{\mathcal{O}A}$. At the same time, it is evident from Fig. 1 that these numbers are the coordinates of the point A computed in the oblique Cartesian coordinate system with axes lying along the vectors a_1, a_2, a_3; the unit segments along the axes are taken to be the segments a_1, a_2, a_3 respectively.

Thus, an arbitrary coordinate system in $\mathfrak{L}$, from the point of view of analytic geometry, is equivalent to an oblique Cartesian coordinate system with distinct scales along the coordinate axes. On the other hand, an orthonormal coordinate system is equivalent in this sense to the ordinary right-angled Cartesian coordinate system with the same scale on all the axes (Fig. 4).

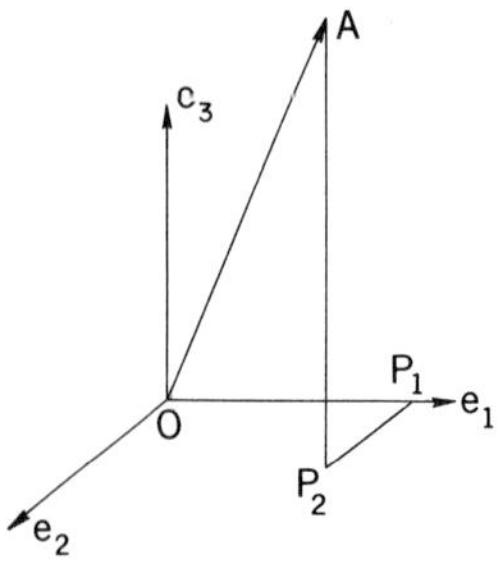

Figure 4

Orthonormal coordinate systems in unitary spaces have many special properties. We now consider some of them.

If $e_1, \cdots, e_n$ is an orthonormal coordinate system in a space $\mathfrak{L}$, then the coordinates of an arbitrary vector a equal the corresponding inner products $(a, e_1), (a, e_2), \cdots, (a, e_n)$.

Let

$$a = \alpha_1 e_1 + \cdots + \alpha_n e_n \, .$$

Taking the inner product with e_k, and using the fact that $(e_j, e_k) = 0$ for $j \neq k$, we obtain

$$(a, e_k) = \alpha_k(e_k, e_k) = \alpha_k \, .$$

If the coordinates of the vectors a, b are respectively $\alpha_1, \cdots, \alpha_n$ *and* $\beta_1, \cdots, \beta_n$ *in an orthonormal coordinate system, then*

$$(a, b) = \alpha_1\bar{\beta}_1 + \cdots + \alpha_n\bar{\beta}_n \, . \tag{14}$$

To see this let $e_1, \cdots, e_n$ be the given orthonormal coordinate system and let

$$a = \alpha_1 e_1 + \cdots + \alpha_n e_n \, ,$$
$$b = \beta_1 e_1 + \cdots + \beta_n e_n \, .$$

Then

$$(a, b) = (\sum \alpha_j e_j, \sum \beta_k e_k) = \sum \alpha_j \bar{\beta}_k (e_j, e_k) = \sum \alpha_j \bar{\beta}_j \, .$$

Bessel's inequality. *If* $e_1, \cdots e_m$ *is an arbitrary orthonormal system of vectors (not necessarily a basis) in a unitary space, and a is any vector, then, setting*

$$(a, e_k) = \alpha_k \, , \quad (k = 1, \cdots, m) \, ,$$

the following inequality holds:

$$(a, a) \geqq |\alpha_1|^2 + \cdots + |\alpha_m|^2 \, .$$

Although the inequality follows easily from the preceding proposition, we given an independent proof. Construct the auxiliary vector

$$x = \alpha_1 e_1 + \cdots + \alpha_m e_m \, .$$

We have

$$(a - x, a - x) = (a, a) - (a, x) - (x, a) + (x, x) \geqq 0 \, , \tag{15}$$
$$(x, x) = (\sum \alpha_j e_j, \sum \alpha_j e_j) = \sum \alpha_j \bar{\alpha}_j \, , \tag{16}$$
$$(a, x) = (a, \sum \alpha_j e_j) = \sum \alpha_j \bar{\alpha}_j \, , \tag{17}$$
$$(x, a) = \overline{(a, x)} = \sum \alpha_j \bar{\alpha}_j \, . \tag{18}$$

Substituting the values from (16), (17), (18) into (15), we obtain

$$(a, a) - \sum \alpha_j \bar{\alpha}_j - \sum \alpha_j \bar{\alpha}_j + \sum \alpha_j \bar{\alpha}_j \geqq 0 \, .$$

that is,

$$(a, a) \geqq \sum \alpha_j \bar{\alpha}_j \, ,$$

which was to be proved.

If the system $e_1, \cdots, e_n$ is an orthonormal basis, then instead of Bessel's inequality we have, by (14),

$$(a, a) = \alpha_1\bar{\alpha}_1 + \cdots + \alpha_n\bar{\alpha}_n ,$$

which is called ***Parseval's equality***. Parseval's equality is not only a necessary, but also a sufficient, condition, for the orthonormal system $e_1, \cdots, e_n$ to be a basis.

If $e_1, \cdots, e_n$ *is an orthonormal system of vectors in a space* $\mathfrak{L}$, *and if for each vector* a *in* $\mathfrak{L}$

$$(a, a) = \alpha_1\bar{\alpha}_1 + \cdots + \alpha_n\bar{\alpha}_n ,$$

where $\alpha_j = (a, e_j)$ *for* $j = 1, \cdots, n$, *then* $e_1, \cdots, e_n$ *is a basis of* $\mathfrak{L}$.

The proof follows easily from the preceding propositions, and is left to the reader.

* * *

The existence of an orthonormal basis for every unitary space was proved indirectly, above. However, there is a direct method, which permits one to obtain an orthonormal basis from any given basis of the space. This method is called the ***Gram-Schmidt orthogonalization process***, and is often used in considerations dealing with function spaces. Its essence lies in the following. Let $a_1, \cdots, a_m$ be some linearly independent system of vectors in the unitary space $\mathfrak{L}$. We set this goal: to construct an orthonormal sequence of vectors $e_1, \cdots, e_m$ such that the jth vector e_j is a linear combination of the first j vectors $a_1, \cdots, a_j$. The construction is carried out by induction. The vector e_1 must be a linear combination of a_1 and have norm 1. Such a vector is obtained by normalizing a_1:

$$e_1 = \frac{1}{\sqrt{(a_1, a_1)}} a_1 .$$

Now we suppose that for some j the vectors $e_1, \cdots, e_j$, with the required properties, have already been constructed. We seek e_{j+1}. First choose numbers $\alpha_1, \cdots, \alpha_j$ so that the vector

$$e'_{j+1} = a_{j+1} + \alpha_1 e_1 + \cdots + \alpha_j e_j \tag{19}$$

is orthogonal to the vectors $e_1, \cdots, e_j$. Taking the inner product of (19) with e_k for $k = 1, \cdots, j$, we see that for this it is necessary that

$$\alpha_k = -(a_{j+1}, e_k) . \tag{20}$$

Conversely, choosing for α_k the values from (20), and substituting in (19), we obtain a vector e'_{j+1} which is orthogonal to $e_1, \cdots, e_j$. But e'_{j+1} is not a linear combination of $a_1, \cdots, a_j$, and consequently cannot be a linear combination of $e_1, \cdots, e_j$; therefore e'_{j+1} is different from zero, and hence can be normalized. Set

$$e_{j+1} = \frac{1}{\| e'_{j+1} \|} e'_{j+1} . \tag{21}$$

Relations (21) and (19) show that e_{j+1} is a linear combination of $a_1, \cdots, a_{j+1}$.

In addition, e_{j+1} has norm 1 and is orthogonal to $e_1, \cdots, e_j$. This completes the induction. If the initial sequence $a_1, \cdots, a_m$ is a basis of the space $\mathfrak{L}$, then evidently the sequence $e_1, \cdots, e_m$, obtained by the orthogonalization, is also a basis of $\mathfrak{L}$.

* * *

72. Isomorphism

In Section 23 we saw that two linear spaces are isomorphic if there exists a one-to-one correspondence between their elements that preserves the operations of addition and multiplication by a scalar. In unitary spaces these operations are supplemented by the inner product, so it is natural to call unitary spaces isomorphic only if all three operations are preserved.

Definition. Two unitary spaces $\mathfrak{L}$, $\mathfrak{L}_1$ over the same field of coefficients are called isomorphic if there exists a one-to-one correspondence between their elements under which the sum of two vectors in $\mathfrak{L}$ is carried into the sum of the corresponding vectors in $\mathfrak{L}_1$, if a scalar times a vector in $\mathfrak{L}$ is carried into the same scalar times the corresponding vector in $\mathfrak{L}_1$, and if the inner products of corresponding pairs of vectors in $\mathfrak{L}$ and $\mathfrak{L}_1$ are equal.

We will be interested only in those aspects of unitary spaces that are dependent on the three fundamental operations defined in these spaces, and that do not depend on the nature of the elements constituting the space. From this point of view, isomorphic unitary spaces have identical properties, and the importance of the classification of all unitary spaces up to isomorphism is clear. This classification does not differ from the classification of linear spaces, and is given by

THEOREM 3. *Two unitary spaces over the same field of coefficients are isomorphic if and only if they have the same dimension.*

In fact, if two unitary spaces $\mathfrak{L}$ and $\mathfrak{L}_1$ are isomorphic, then they are also isomorphic as linear spaces—that is, with respect to the operations of addition and multiplication by a scalar. However, isomorphic linear spaces have the same dimension, and consequently the dimensions of $\mathfrak{L}$ and $\mathfrak{L}_1$ are equal: this proves the necessity. Conversely, suppose that $\mathfrak{L}$ and $\mathfrak{L}_1$ have the same dimension. Choose orthonormal bases $e_1, \cdots, e_n$ and $e_1', \cdots, e_n'$ in $\mathfrak{L}$ and $\mathfrak{L}_1$. Let the vectors $x \in \mathfrak{L}$ and $x' \in \mathfrak{L}_1$ be ***correspondents*** if their coordinates in these bases are identical. This correspondence is one to one and preserves the operations of addition and multiplication by a scalar (Section 23). Therefore, we need only show that the inner products of corresponding pairs of vectors are equal. Consider two arbitrary vectors

$$a = \alpha_1 e_1 + \cdots + \alpha_n e_n \,,$$
$$b = \beta_1 e_1 + \cdots + \beta_n e_n$$

in $\mathfrak{L}$. The corresponding vectors in $\mathfrak{L}_1$ are

$$a' = \alpha_1 e_1' + \cdots + \alpha_n e_n' \,,$$
$$b' = \beta_1 e_1' + \cdots + \beta_n e_n' \,.$$

Since the bases $e_1, \cdots, e_n$ and $e_1', \cdots, e_n'$ are orthonormal, by (14)

$$(a, b) = \alpha_1\bar{\beta}_1 + \cdots + \alpha_n\bar{\beta}_n = (a', b') ,$$

which was to be proved.

73. Orthogonal Sums. Projections

Two sets of vectors $\mathfrak{M}$ and $\mathfrak{N}$ in a unitary space $\mathfrak{L}$ are called ***orthogonal*** if each vector in the first set is orthogonal to each vector in the second. In particular, the vector a is orthogonal to the set $\mathfrak{M}$ if a is orthogonal to each vector in $\mathfrak{M}$. Orthogonality of $\mathfrak{M}$ and $\mathfrak{N}$ is sometimes denoted symbolically by $\mathfrak{M} \perp \mathfrak{N}$.

If the sets $\mathfrak{M}$ *and* $\mathfrak{N}$ *are orthogonal, then their intersection is either empty or contains only the zero vector.*

In fact, if the vector a is contained in $\mathfrak{M}$ and $\mathfrak{N}$, then $(a, a) = 0$; hence $a = \theta$.

A sum $\mathfrak{A}_1 + \cdots + \mathfrak{A}_m$ of linear subspaces is called an ***orthogonal sum*** if each two subspaces $\mathfrak{A}_j, \mathfrak{A}_k$, for $j \neq k$, are orthogonal.

An orthogonal sum of subspaces is a direct sum.

Indeed, if there are only two summands, then (from the preceding remark) their intersection consists only of the zero vector, and consequently the sum is direct. In the general case the proof is carried out by induction.

If the sum

$$\mathfrak{A} = \mathfrak{A}_1 + \cdots + \mathfrak{A}_s$$

is orthogonal, and

$$a = a_1 + \cdots + a_s ,$$
$$b = b_1 + \cdots + b_s ,$$

where $a_j \in \mathfrak{A}_j$ and $b_j \in \mathfrak{A}_j$, for $j = 1, \cdots, s$, *then*

$$(a, b) = (a_1, b_1) + \cdots + (a_s, b_s) . \tag{22}$$

In fact, since $\mathfrak{N}_j \perp \mathfrak{N}_k$ for $j \neq k$, then $(a_j, b_k) = 0$. Consequently,

$$(a, b) = (\sum a_j, \sum b_k) = \sum \sum (a_j, b_k) = \sum (a_j, b_j) .$$

Now consider an arbitrary nonempty set of vectors $\mathfrak{M}$ in some unitary space $\mathfrak{L}$. The set of all vectors in $\mathfrak{L}$ which are orthogonal to $\mathfrak{M}$ is called the ***orthogonal complement*** of $\mathfrak{M}$ and is denoted by $\mathfrak{M}^\perp$.

The orthogonal complement of any nonempty set $\mathfrak{M}$ *is a linear subspace.*

In fact, if a, b belong to the orthogonal complement $\mathfrak{M}^\perp$, and c is an arbitrary vector in $\mathfrak{M}$, then

$$(\alpha a + \beta b, c) = \alpha(a, c) + \beta(b, c) = 0 .$$

Consequently, for all α, β the vector $\alpha a + \beta b$ is contained in $\mathfrak{M}^\perp$, and $\mathfrak{M}^\perp$, is a linear subspace.

THEOREM 4. *A unitary space* $\mathfrak{L}$ *is the direct sum of any linear subspace* $\mathfrak{A}$ *and its orthogonal complement* $\mathfrak{A}^\perp$.

Let $e_1, \cdots, e_m$ be an orthonormal basis of the subspace $\mathfrak{A}$ and let $e_{m+1}, \cdots, e_s$ be an orthonormal basis of the subspace $\mathfrak{A}^{\perp}$. To prove the theorem it is sufficient to show that $e_1, \cdots, e_m, e_{m+1}, \cdots, e_s$ is a basis of the space $\mathfrak{L}$. Suppose, on the contrary, that the system $e_1, \cdots, e_s$ is not a basis of $\mathfrak{L}$. Then by Theorem 2 it can be supplemented to form an orthonormal basis of $\mathfrak{L}$. Let e be one of these supplementary vectors. Since e is orthogonal to all the vectors $e_1, \cdots, e_m$, then e is contained in $\mathfrak{A}^{\perp}$. Consequently, $\mathfrak{A}^{\perp}$ contains the orthogonal, and hence linearly independent, system of vectors $e_{m+1}, \cdots, e_s, e$. However, this contradicts the assumption that $e_{m+1}, \cdots, e_s$ is a basis of $\mathfrak{A}^{\perp}$, and the theorem is proved.

One special consequence of Theorem 4 is that

$$(\mathfrak{A}^{\perp})^{\perp} = \mathfrak{A} . \tag{23}$$

Indeed, $\mathfrak{A}^{\perp\perp}$ contains $\mathfrak{A}$. On the other hand, for any x in $\mathfrak{A}^{\perp\perp}$ we have, by Theorem 4,

$$x = a + b , \quad a \in \mathfrak{A}, \quad b \in \mathfrak{A}^{\perp} .$$

Taking the inner product of this equality with b, we obtain $(b, b) = 0$; that is, $b = \theta$, $x = a$. Consequently, $\mathfrak{A}^{\perp\perp} = \mathfrak{A}$.

Lastly, we define the notion of orthogonal projection of a vector on a linear subspace. Let $\mathfrak{A}$ be a linear subspace $\mathfrak{L}$. By Theorem 4, $\mathfrak{L}$ is the direct sum of $\mathfrak{A}$ and $\mathfrak{A}^{\perp}$. Consequently, every vector x in $\mathfrak{L}$ can be represented in one and only one way in the form

$$x = a + b \qquad (a \in \mathfrak{A}, b \in \mathfrak{A}^{\perp}) . \tag{24}$$

The summand a is called the ***projection** of the vector x on the subspace $\mathfrak{A}$*. Since (23) shows that $\mathfrak{A}$ is the orthogonal complement of $\mathfrak{A}^{\perp}$, the summand b in (24) is the projection of x on the subspace $\mathfrak{A}^{\perp}$.

Multiplying (24) by a scalar α we obtain

$$\alpha x = \alpha a + \alpha b, \qquad (\alpha a \in \mathfrak{A}, \ \alpha b \in \mathfrak{A}^{\perp});$$

that is, *the projection of a scalar times a vector equals the scalar times the projection of the vector.*

A similar argument shows that *the projection of the sum of vectors on a subspace equals the sum of the projections of the summands on this subspace.*

● EXAMPLES AND PROBLEMS

1. Let e_1, e_2, e_3 be an orthonormal coordinate system in a three-dimensional unitary space. Show that the system of vectors

$$a_1 = \tfrac{1}{3}(2e_1 + 2e_2 - e_3) ,$$
$$a_2 = \tfrac{1}{3}(2e_1 - e_2 + 2e_3) ,$$
$$a_3 = \tfrac{1}{3}(-e_1 + 2e_2 + 2e_3)$$

is also an orthonormal coordinate system in this space.

2. Let $e_1, \cdots, e_n$ be an orthonormal coordinate system in a unitary space $\mathfrak{L}$. Show that a system of vectors $a_1, \cdots, a_n$ is an orthonormal basis of the space $\mathfrak{L}$ if and only if the matrix constructed from the coordinate rows of these vectors is unitary (compare Section 8).
3. If $a_1, \cdots, a_m$ is an orthonormal basis of a linear subspace $\mathfrak{A}$, then the projection of a vector x on $\mathfrak{A}$ is

$$(x, a_1)a_1 + (x, a_2)a_2 + \cdots + (x, a_m)a_m .$$

4. In the space of all polynomials of degree not exceeding n, define the inner product by formula (7), Section 69. Show that this is a unitary space of dimension $n+1$. Show that applying the Gram-Schmidt process to the sequence $1, \lambda, \lambda^2$ yields the polynomials 1, $\sqrt{3}(2\lambda - 1)$, $\sqrt{5}(6\lambda^2 - 6\lambda + 1)$. λ^3
5. The determinant

$$\Delta = \begin{vmatrix} (a_1, a_1) & (a_1, a_2) & \cdots & (a_1, a_n) \\ (a_2, a_1) & (a_2, a_2) & \cdots & (a_2, a_n) \\ \cdot & \cdot & \cdot & \cdot \\ (a_n, a_1) & (a_n, a_2) & \cdots & (a_n, a_n) \end{vmatrix}$$

is called the ***Gram determinant*** of the system of vectors $a_1, \cdots, a_n$ in an n-dimensional unitary space $\mathfrak{L}$. Choose an orthonormal coordinate system in $\mathfrak{L}$. Show that the Gram determinant Δ equals the square of the modulus of the determinant consisting of the coordinate rows of the vectors $a_1, \cdots, a_n$. Show also that the vectors $a_1, \cdots, a_n$ are linearly independent if and only if their Gram determinant is different from zero.

2. *Conjugate Transformations*

74. Linear Functions

Let $\mathfrak{L}$ be an arbitrary finite-dimensional linear space over a field K. We place in correspondence to each vector x in $\mathfrak{L}$ some scalar $f(x)$ in K. In Section 19 a correspondence of this form was called a function defined on $\mathfrak{L}$ with values in K. A function $f(x)$ is called ***linear*** if, for all x, y in $\mathfrak{L}$ and α, β in K,

$$f(\alpha x + \beta y) = \alpha f(x) + \beta f(y) . \tag{1}$$

Putting $\alpha = \beta = 0$ in (1), we obtain

$$f(\theta) = 0 .$$

For this reason "linear homogeneous function" is sometimes used instead of "linear function."

It is easy to see that *the sum of linear functions, and a scalar times a linear function,* are again linear functions. We verify, for example, the first assertion. Let $f = g + h$, where g and h are linear functions. By definition,

$$f(\alpha x+\beta y)=g(\alpha x+\beta y)+h(\alpha x+\beta y)=\alpha g(x)+\beta g(y)+\alpha h(x)+\beta h(y)$$
$$=\alpha f(x)+\beta f(y)\,,$$

which was to be proved.

We already know that the operations of addition of functions and multiplication of a function by a scalar satisfy the axioms for a linear space. Since the sum of linear functions and a scalar times a linear function are again linear functions, the set of all linear functions defined on a linear space $\mathfrak{L}$ is itself a linear space. This space is called the ***conjugate space*** of $\mathfrak{L}$, and is denoted by $\mathfrak{L}'$. Its properties are considered in more detail in Section 110.

From (1), the characterization of linear functions, there easily follows the more general relation

$$f(\alpha_1 x_1+\cdots+\alpha_m x_m)=\alpha_1 f(x_1)+\cdots+\alpha_m f(x_m)\,, \tag{2}$$

the proof of which is obvious. The following theorem clarifies to a considerable extent the structure of linear functions.

THEOREM 1. *Let $e_1,\cdots,e_n$ be a coordinate system in the linear space $\mathfrak{L}$. For a completely arbitrary sequence $\alpha_1,\cdots,\alpha_n$ of numbers in* K, *there exists one and only one linear function $f(x)$ defined on $\mathfrak{L}$ which satisfies the conditions*

$$f(e_j)=\alpha_j\,,\qquad j=1,\cdots,n\,. \tag{3}$$

Let x be a vector in $\mathfrak{L}$:

$$x=\xi_1 e_1+\cdots+\xi_n e_n\,. \tag{4}$$

Let f be that function defined on $\mathfrak{L}$ such that $f(x)$ is the number $\alpha_1\xi_1+\cdots+\alpha_n\xi_n$. Thus, by definition,

$$f(x)=\alpha_1\xi_1+\cdots+\alpha_n\xi_n\,.$$

Putting $x=e_j$, we have $f(e_j)=\alpha_j$, for $j=1,\cdots,n$. But if

$$y=\eta_1 e_1+\cdots+\eta_n e_n\,, \tag{5}$$

then

$$f(y)=\alpha_1\eta_1+\cdots+\alpha_n\eta_n\,.$$

From (4) and (5), we have

$$\alpha x+\beta y=(\alpha\xi_1+\beta\eta_1)e_1+\cdots+(\alpha\xi_n+\beta\eta_n)e_n\,,$$

and hence

$$f(\alpha x+\beta y)=\alpha_1(\alpha\xi_1+\beta\eta_1)+\cdots+\alpha_n(\alpha\xi_n+\beta\eta_n)=\alpha f(x)+\beta f(x)$$

and $f(x)$ is a linear function.

We have shown that a linear function satisfying conditions (3) exists. We now show that it is unique. Let $g(x)$ be a linear function for which $g(e_j)=\alpha_j$, for $j=1,\cdots,n$. Then for an arbitrary vector x with coordinates $\xi_1,\cdots,\xi_n$ we have

$$g(x) = g(\xi_1 e_1 + \cdots + \xi_n e_n) = \xi_1 g(e_1) + \cdots + \xi_n g(e_n)$$
$$= \xi_1 \alpha_1 + \cdots + \xi_n \alpha_n ,$$

or $g(x) = f(x)$.

Theorem 1 was proved for an arbitrary linear space $\mathfrak{L}$. If the space $\mathfrak{L}$ is unitary, then the linear functions on $\mathfrak{L}$ have very simple expressions as inner products.

THEOREM 2. *In a unitary space $\mathfrak{L}$, the inner product (x, a) is a linear function of x. Thus each vector a in $\mathfrak{L}$ gives rise to a linear function $f(x) = (x, a)$. Distinct vectors give rise to distinct linear functions and every linear function on $\mathfrak{L}$ is obtained in this way.*

The first assertion is evident; for if $f(x) = (x, a)$, then

$$f(\alpha x + \beta y) = (\alpha x + \beta y, a) = \alpha(x, a) + \beta(y, a) = \alpha f(x) + \beta f(y) .$$

We prove the second assertion. Suppose on the contrary that distinct vectors a and b correspond to the same linear function—that is, that $(x, a) = (x, b)$ for all x in $\mathfrak{L}$. Transposing the right side to the left, we obtain $(x, a - b) = 0$. Setting $x = a - b$, this yields $(a - b, a - b) = 0$, which means that $a - b = \theta$ or $a = b$. This leaves only the third assertion to be proved; namely, every linear function $f(x)$ defined on $\mathfrak{L}$ can be represented in the form

$$f(x) = (x, a) \tag{6}$$

where a depends on f and x is an arbitrary vector in $\mathfrak{L}$. Denote the set of all vectors x for which $f(x) = 0$ by $\mathfrak{N}$. Since $f(\theta) = 0$, θ is in $\mathfrak{N}$. Further, if a and b are in $\mathfrak{N}$, then

$$f(\alpha a + \beta b) = \alpha f(a) + \beta f(b) = 0 ,$$

i.e. $\alpha a + \beta b$ is also in $\mathfrak{N}$. Consequently, $\mathfrak{N}$ is a linear subspace of $\mathfrak{L}$. If $\mathfrak{N} = \mathfrak{L}$, then $f(x) = 0$ for all x. In this case it is sufficient to take $a = \theta$ to satisfy requirement (6). Therefore, assume that $\mathfrak{N} \neq \mathfrak{L}$. We take some nonzero vector b in $\mathfrak{L}$ orthogonal to $\mathfrak{N}$, and endeavor to find a number α such that the vector $a = \alpha b$ satisfies relation (6). Let $f(b) = \beta$ and $f(x) = \xi$, where x is an arbitrary vector in $\mathfrak{L}$. We then have

$$f\left(x - \frac{\xi}{\beta} b\right) = f(x) - \frac{\xi}{\beta} f(b) = 0 .$$

Denoting the difference $x - (\xi/\beta)b$ by c, we see that c belongs to $\mathfrak{N}$ and $x = c + (\xi/\beta)b$. Hence

$$(x, a) = \left(\frac{\xi}{\beta} b + c, \alpha b\right) = \frac{\bar{\alpha}\xi}{\beta}(b, b) + \bar{\alpha}(c, b) .$$

Since b is orthogonal to $\mathfrak{N}$, we have $(c, b) = 0$, and

$$(x, a) = \frac{\bar{\alpha}\xi}{\beta}(b, b) . \tag{7}$$

Equality (7) shows that if we take $\alpha = \bar{\beta}(b, b)^{-1}$, then for all x we have

$$(x, a) = \xi = f(x) ,$$

which was to be proved.

75. Conjugate Transformations

We apply the results of the preceding section to construct, for each linear transformation of a unitary space, a unique new transformation called the ***conjugate*** of the old.

Let $\mathscr{A}$ be a linear transformation of a unitary space $\mathfrak{L}$. Take an arbitrary vector y in $\mathfrak{L}$ and consider the expression

$$f(x) = (x\mathscr{A}, y) , \tag{8}$$

where x is a variable vector. Since

$$f(\alpha u + \beta v) = ((\alpha u + \beta v)\mathscr{A}, y) = (\alpha \cdot u\mathscr{A} + \beta \cdot v\mathscr{A}, y) = \alpha f(u) + \beta f(v) ,$$

$f(x)$ is a linear function. Therefore, by Theorem 2, $f(x)$ can be represented in the form

$$f(x) = (x, a) , \tag{9}$$

where the vector a is uniquely determined by the function $f(x)$—that is, by the transformation $\mathscr{A}$ and the vector y. If we consider $\mathscr{A}$ as a given transformation, and the vector y as variable, then for each vector y we obtain a fully determined vector a. The transformation which carries y into a is denoted by $\mathscr{A}^*$, and is called the ***conjugate*** of $\mathscr{A}$: thus, $a = y\mathscr{A}^*$. Substituting this value in (9), and comparing with (8), we obtain the relation

$$(x\mathscr{A}, y) = (x, y\mathscr{A}^*) , \tag{10}$$

which holds for arbitrary vectors x, y in $\mathfrak{L}$.

Property (10) completely characterizes the conjugate transformation $\mathscr{A}^*$. To see this, suppose for example, that a transformation $\mathscr{B}$ also has this property—that is, for all x, y

$$(x\mathscr{A}, y) = (x, y\mathscr{B})$$

or

$$(x, y\mathscr{A}^*) - (x, y\mathscr{B}) = (x, y\mathscr{A}^* - y\mathscr{B}) = 0 .$$

This means that the vector $y\mathscr{A}^* - y\mathscr{B}$ is orthogonal to the whole space, and hence that

$$y\mathscr{A}^* = y\mathscr{B} .$$

The last equality holds for all y, and therefore $\mathscr{A}^* = \mathscr{B}$.

It is not difficult to show that *the conjugate transformation $\mathscr{A}^*$ is linear.* Indeed, from (10),

$$(x, (\alpha u + \beta v)\mathscr{A}^*) = (x\mathscr{A}, \alpha u + \beta v) = \bar{\alpha}(x\mathscr{A}, u) + \bar{\beta}(x\mathscr{A}, v)$$
$$= \bar{\alpha}(x, u\mathscr{A}^*) + \bar{\beta}(x, v\mathscr{A}^*) = (x, \alpha \cdot u\mathscr{A}^* + \beta \cdot v\mathscr{A}^*)$$

for all vectors x. By the second assertion of Theorem 2, this implies the equality

$$(\alpha u + \beta v)\mathscr{A}^* = \alpha \cdot u\mathscr{A}^* + \beta \cdot v\mathscr{A}^* ,$$

which means that $\mathscr{A}^*$ is linear.

The operation of passing to the conjugate transformation has the following properties:

a) $(\mathscr{A}^*)^* = \mathscr{A}$,

b) $(\alpha\mathscr{A})^* = \bar{\alpha}\mathscr{A}^*$,

c) $(\mathscr{A} + \mathscr{B})^* = \mathscr{A}^* + \mathscr{B}^*$,

d) $(\mathscr{A}\mathscr{B})^* = \mathscr{B}^*\mathscr{A}^*$.

All these properties are proved in the same way, so we will restrict ourselves to a proof of one of them.

For example,

$$(x\mathscr{A}\mathscr{B}, y) = (x\mathscr{A}, y\mathscr{B}^*) = (x, y\mathscr{B}^* \mathscr{A}^*) ,$$

and consequently $(\mathscr{A}\mathscr{B})^* = \mathscr{B}^* \mathscr{A}^*$.

We may also remark here that the identity and zero transformations are their own conjugates:

$$(x\mathscr{E}, y) = (x, y) = (x, y\mathscr{E}) , \quad (x\mathscr{O}, y) = 0 = (x, y\mathscr{O}) .$$

We now consider the matrix of the conjugate transformation. Take an *orthonormal* coordinate system $e_1, \cdots, e_n$ in the space $\mathfrak{L}$, and let

$$e_i\mathscr{A} = \alpha_{i1}e_1 + \cdots + \alpha_{in}e_n ,$$
$$e_i\mathscr{A}^* = \beta_{i1}e_1 + \cdots + \beta_{in}e_n .$$

Taking the inner product of these equalities with e_j, and using the orthonormality of the system $e_1, \cdots, e_n$, we obtain

$$(e_i\mathscr{A}, e_j) = \alpha_{ij} , \quad (e_i\mathscr{A}^*, e_j) = \beta_{ij} \qquad (i, j = 1, \cdots, n) .$$

Hence

$$\alpha_{ij} = (e_i\mathscr{A}, e_j) = (e_i, e_j\mathscr{A}^*) = \overline{(e_j\mathscr{A}^*, e_i)} = \bar{\beta}_{ji} .$$

Consequently, if the matrix of the transformation $\mathscr{A}$ is A, then the matrix of the conjugate transformation $\mathscr{A}^*$ is $\bar{A}'$ We have this obtained

THEOREM 3. *If a linear transformation $\mathscr{A}$ has matrix A in an orthonormal coordinate system, then the conjugate transformation $\mathscr{A}^*$ has the conjugate-transpose matrix $\bar{A}'$ in this system.*

The operation of passing to the conjugate transformation has properties (*a*), (*b*), (*c*), (*d*). By Theorem 3 we conclude that the operation of passing from a matrix to its conjugate-transpose has the same properties. This result is also easily obtained by an immediate calculation (see Section 8).

76. Normal Transformations

Linear transformations of a unitary space which permute with their conjugates possess a number of remarkable properties. For these transformations, which are called ***normal***,

$$\mathscr{A}\mathscr{A}^* = \mathscr{A}^*\mathscr{A} .$$

Recalling that, in an orthonormal coordinate system, conjugate transformations have conjugate-transpose matrices, we deduce immediately that a linear transformation of a unitary space is normal if and only if its matrix A, in an orthonormal basis, satisfies the relation

$$A\bar{A}' = \bar{A}'A .$$

The following property of normal transformations is obtained just as simply.

THEOREM 4. *Every proper vector a of a normal transformation $\mathscr{A}$, belonging to the proper value ρ, is also a proper vector of the conjugate transformation $\mathscr{A}^*$, but belonging to the complex conjugate proper value $\bar{\rho}$.*

We are given

$$\mathscr{A}\mathscr{A}^* = \mathscr{A}^*\mathscr{A}, \qquad a(\mathscr{A} - \rho\mathscr{E}) = \theta .$$

Hence

$$\begin{aligned} 0 &= (a(\mathscr{A} - \rho\mathscr{E}),\ a(\mathscr{A} - \rho\mathscr{E})) = (a(\mathscr{A} - \rho\mathscr{E})(\mathscr{A}^* - \bar{\rho}\mathscr{E}),\ a) \\ &= (a(\mathscr{A}^* - \bar{\rho}\mathscr{E})(\mathscr{A} - \rho\mathscr{E}),\ a) = (a(\mathscr{A}^* - \bar{\rho}\mathscr{E}),\ a(\mathscr{A}^* - \bar{\rho}\mathscr{E})) , \end{aligned}$$

or

$$a(\mathscr{A}^* - \bar{\rho}\mathscr{E}) = \theta ,$$

which was to be proved.

THEOREM 5. *Proper vectors belonging to distinct proper values of a normal transformation are orthogonal.*

Let

$$a\mathscr{A} = \rho a, \quad b\mathscr{A} = \sigma b \qquad (\rho \neq \sigma).$$

Then

$$\rho(a, b) = (a\mathscr{A}, b) = (a, b\mathscr{A}^*) = \sigma(a, b) ,$$

or

$$(\rho - \sigma)(a, b) = 0 , \qquad (a, b) = 0 .$$

The proof of the following fundamental theorem is only slightly more complicated.

THEOREM 6. *For each normal transformation $\mathscr{A}$ of a complex unitary space there exists an orthonormal basis of proper vectors of $\mathscr{A}$ relative to which the matrix of $\mathscr{A}$ has diagonal form.*

To prove this, take some proper vector $a_1 \neq \theta$ of the transformation $\mathscr{A}$ in the initial space $\mathfrak{L}$, and let $\mathfrak{L}_1$ denote the subspace orthogonal to a_1. If

$$a_1\mathscr{A} = \rho_1 a_1 ,\ x \in \mathfrak{L}_1 ,$$

then

$$(a_1 , x\mathscr{A}) = (a_1\mathscr{A}^*, x) = \bar{\rho}_1(a_1 , x) = 0 ,$$

which shows that the subspace $\mathfrak{L}_1$ is invariant under $\mathscr{A}$. From this invariance it follows that $\mathscr{A}$ has a proper vector a_2 in $\mathfrak{L}_1$ Denote the subspace of $\mathfrak{L}$ orthogonal to a_2 by $\mathfrak{L}_2$ and let $\mathfrak{L}_2' = \mathfrak{L}_2 \cap \mathfrak{L}_1$. Since $\mathfrak{L}_1 , \mathfrak{L}_2$ are invariant under $\mathscr{A}$, so is the subspace $\mathfrak{L}_2'$, in which, therefore, there is again some nonzero proper value a_3 of $\mathscr{A}$. Denote the subspace of $\mathfrak{L}$ orthogonal to a_3 by $\mathfrak{L}_3$; setting $\mathfrak{L}_3' = \mathfrak{L}_1 \cap \mathfrak{L}_2 \cap \mathfrak{L}_3$, we obtain an invariant subspace orthogonal to a_1 , a_2 , a_3. Continuing this process, we obtain the desired orthogonal basis $a_1 , \cdots , a_n$ of the space $\mathfrak{L}$, consisting of proper vectors of the transformation $\mathscr{A}$.

The property of normal transformations of complex spaces expressed in Theorem 6 characterizes these transformations. If the matrix A of a transformation $\mathscr{A}$ is diagonal in some orthonormal basis, then the matrix $\bar{A}'$ of the conjugate transformation is also diagonal, and hence is permutable with A.

In real unitary spaces the situation is somewhat different. To clarify it, we first prove a general proposition concerning real linear transformations,

THEOREM 7. *Every linear transformation $\mathscr{A}$ of a real nonzero space has at least one invariant subspace of dimension* 1 *or* 2.

If the characteristic polynomial $\varphi(\lambda)$ of the transformation $\mathscr{A}$ has a real zero α, then $\mathscr{A}$ has a nonzero proper vector in $\mathfrak{L}$. The subspace spanned by this vector will be a one-dimensional invariant subspace.

Suppose now that $\varphi(\lambda)$ has no real zero. In this case $\varphi(\lambda)$ has pairs of complex zeros $\alpha = \rho + i\sigma$, $\bar{\alpha} = \rho - i\sigma$, since the coefficients of the polynomial $\varphi(\lambda)$ are real. Take a coordinate system $a_1 , \cdots , a_m$ in $\mathfrak{L}$ and let A be the matrix of the transformation in this coordinate system. Consider the equation

$$[\xi_1 , \cdots , \xi_n]\, A = \alpha[\xi_1 , \cdots , \xi_n] , \tag{11}$$

where $\xi_1 , \cdots , \xi_n$ are complex-valued unknowns. Equation (11) may be written in the form

$$[\xi_1 , \cdots , \xi_n]\,(\alpha E - A) = 0 ,$$

where E is the identity matrix. This equation is equivalent to a system of linear homogeneous equations in the unknowns $\xi_1 , \cdots , \xi_n$, with matrix (αE

$-A)'$ (compare Section 46). Since the determinant of this matrix is $\varphi(\alpha)$, and consequently equals zero, equation (11) has a nonzero complex solution, which we denote by the same letters $\xi_1, \cdots, \xi_n$. For convenience let

$$[\xi_1, \cdots, \xi_n] = x ,$$

so that relation (11) assumes the form

$$xA = \alpha x . \tag{12}$$

Taking complex conjugates, we obtain $\bar{x}\bar{A} = \bar{\alpha}\bar{x}$. But the matrix A has real elements, hence $\bar{A} = A$ and

$$\bar{x}A = \bar{\alpha}\bar{x} . \tag{13}$$

Since the rows $x + \bar{x}$, $i(x - \bar{x})$ are real, there are vectors a, b in $\mathfrak{L}$ whose coordinate rows are given by

$$\begin{aligned} [a] &= \frac{1}{2}(x + \bar{x}) , \\ [b] &= \frac{1}{2i}(x - \bar{x}) . \end{aligned} \tag{14}$$

Now expressing x and $\bar{x}$ in terms of $[a]$, $[b]$ and using (12), (13), we obtain

$$\begin{aligned} [a]A &= \rho[a] - \sigma[b] , \\ [b]A &= \sigma[a] + \rho[b] , \end{aligned}$$

for $\alpha = \rho + i\sigma$. These relations are equivalent to the equalities

$$\begin{aligned} a\mathscr{A} &= \rho a - \sigma b , \\ b\mathscr{A} &= \sigma a + \rho b , \end{aligned} \tag{15}$$

which shows that the subspace spanned by the vectors a, b is invariant under $\mathscr{A}$. This proves the theorem.

Now suppose that $\mathfrak{L}$ is a real unitary space, and that $\mathscr{A}$ is a normal transformation of $\mathfrak{L}$ whose characteristic polynomial $\varphi(\lambda)$ has two nonreal conjugate zeros $\rho + i\sigma$ and $\rho - i\sigma$, where $\sigma \neq 0$. Choosing an orthonormal coordinate system $e_1, \cdots, e_n$ and repeating the preceding construction, we again obtain vectors a, b in $\mathfrak{L}$ which satisfy relation (15). We show that now the vectors a, b are *orthogonal*. Indeed, in finding these vectors it was necessary for us to consider the space of rows $\tilde{\mathfrak{L}}$ over the field of complex numbers. We may consider this space of rows to be unitary, taking the expression $\xi_1\bar{\eta}_1 + \cdots + \xi_n\bar{\eta}_n$ as the inner product of the rows $[\xi_1, \cdots, \xi_n]$ and $[\eta_1, \cdots, \eta_n]$ (compare Section 69). The rows $[e_1], \cdots, [e_n]$ constitute an orthonormal basis of $\tilde{\mathfrak{L}}$. The transformation $\tilde{\mathscr{A}}$ of $\tilde{\mathfrak{L}}$ which consists of multiplying the rows by the matrix A is a linear transformation, whose matrix in the given basis coincides with A. Since $\mathscr{A}$ is normal, $\tilde{\mathscr{A}}$ is normal, and the rows $x, \bar{x}$ constructed in the proof of Theorem 7 are proper vectors belonging to distinct proper values $\rho + i\sigma$ and $\rho - i\sigma$. By Theorem 5, $(x, \bar{x}) = 0$, and hence

$$([a], [b]) = \frac{1}{4i}(x + \bar{x}, x - \bar{x}) = 0 ,$$

or $(a, b) = 0$. Taking as x a vector of norm $\sqrt{2}$, we see from (14) that each of a and b have norm 1.

We show further that the subspace $\mathfrak{L}$ orthogonal to a and b is invariant under $\mathscr{A}$. In the space $\widetilde{\mathfrak{L}}$ of rows, the subspace orthogonal to $[a]$ and $[b]$ coincides with the subspace $\widetilde{\mathfrak{L}}_1$, which is orthogonal to x and $\bar{x}$. This last subspace is invariant under $\widetilde{\mathscr{A}}$ since it is the intersection of subspaces orthogonal to proper vectors $x, \bar{x}$ of a normal transformation. Now if $y \in \mathfrak{L}$ and $(a, y) = (b, y) = 0$, then $[y] \in \widetilde{\mathfrak{L}}_1, [y]A \in \widetilde{\mathfrak{L}}_1$ and hence

$$(y\mathscr{A}, a) = ([y]A, [a]) = 0 , \quad (y\mathscr{A}, b) = 0 ,$$

which completes the proof.

The transformation $\mathscr{A}_1$ induced by $\mathscr{A}$ in the two-dimensional subspace spanned by the vectors a, b has, from (15), the matrix

$$A_1 = \begin{bmatrix} \rho & -\sigma \\ \sigma & \rho \end{bmatrix}.$$

Writing the complex number $\rho + i\sigma$ in the form $r(\cos\varphi - i\sin\varphi)$, we may transform A_1 into the form

$$A_1 = r\begin{bmatrix} \cos\varphi & \sin\varphi \\ -\sin\varphi & \cos\varphi \end{bmatrix}.$$

Thus, A_1 is the product of a transformation with matrix rE and a transformation with matrix $\begin{bmatrix} \cos\varphi & \sin\varphi \\ -\sin\varphi & \cos\varphi \end{bmatrix}$ The first of these is a similarity transformation with center $\mathscr{O}$ and coefficient of expansion r, and the second, as is easily seen, is simply a rotation by φ of the plane a, b about $\mathscr{O}$.

THEOREM 8. *For every normal transformation $\mathscr{A}$ of a real unitary space $\mathfrak{L}$, there exists an orthonormal basis in which the matrix of A has the form*

$$A = \begin{bmatrix} \alpha_1 & & \\ & \ddots & \\ & & \alpha_k \end{bmatrix} \dotplus r_1\begin{bmatrix} \cos\varphi_1 & \sin\varphi_1 \\ -\sin\varphi_1 & \cos\varphi_1 \end{bmatrix} \dotplus \cdots \dotplus r_m\begin{bmatrix} \cos\varphi_m & \sin\varphi_m \\ -\sin\varphi_m & \cos\varphi_m \end{bmatrix}, \tag{16}$$

where k, m may be zero.

The proof coincides almost exactly with the proof of Theorem 6. The only difference is that now we can not assert that each subspace $\mathfrak{L}_i'$ invariant under $\mathscr{A}$ contains a nonzero proper value a_{i+1} of $\mathscr{A}$. However, if there is no proper vector of $\mathscr{A}$ in $\mathfrak{L}_i$, then by Theorem 7 there is a pair of orthogonal vectors a_{i+1}, b_{i+1} in $\mathfrak{L}_i$ which satisfy relations of the form (15). For the subspace $\mathfrak{L}_{i+1}$ we may take the subspace orthogonal to a_{i+1} and b_{i+1}. Then $\mathfrak{L}_{i+1}'$ will be invariant under $\mathscr{A}$, and the process may be continued, according to the scheme of the proof of Theorem 6. We finally obtain a basis $a_1, \cdots, a_k, a_{k+1}, b_{k+1}, \cdots, a_{k+m}, b_{k+m}$ satisfying relations of the form

$$a_p\mathscr{A} = \alpha_p a_p \qquad p = 1, \cdots, k,$$
$$\left.\begin{aligned} a_q\mathscr{A} &= \rho_q a_q - \sigma_q b_q, \\ b_q\mathscr{A} &= \sigma_q a_q + \rho_q b_q \end{aligned}\right. \qquad q = k+1, \cdots, k+m, \ \sigma_q \neq 0$$

which shows that the matrix of the transformation $\mathscr{A}$ in this basis has exactly the form (16).

● EXAMPLES AND PROBLEMS

1. In the usual three-dimensional Euclidean space $\mathfrak{R}$, take a directed line through the origin and denote by $f(x)$ the length of the projection of the vector x on this line, taken with the proper sign. Show that $f(x)$ is a linear function, and that every linear function on the space $\mathfrak{R}$ has the form $\alpha f(x)$ for $\alpha \geqq 0$ and a suitable axis of projection.
2. A function $f(x)$, defined on a complex linear space, is called ***skew-linear*** if $f(x + y) = f(x) + f(y)$, $f(\alpha x) = \bar{\alpha} f(x)$. Show that every skew-linear function on a unitary space has the form (a, x).
3. Show that the correspondence given by the preceding problem between vectors of a unitary space $\mathfrak{L}$ and skew-linear functions is an isomorphism between $\mathfrak{L}$ and the space of all skew-linear functions on $\mathfrak{L}$.
4. Let $\mathscr{A}$, $\mathscr{B}$ be linear transformations of a unitary space $\mathfrak{L}$ with matrices

$$A = \begin{bmatrix} 1 & 0 & 0 \\ -1 & 2 & 0 \\ 0 & 2 & -1 \end{bmatrix}. \qquad B = \begin{bmatrix} 1 & 2 & -2 \\ 2 & -1 & 0 \\ -2 & 1 & 0 \end{bmatrix}$$

in a nonorthonormal basis a_1, a_2, a_3. Find an orthonormal basis of $\mathfrak{L}$, if it is known that $\mathscr{A}$ and $\mathscr{B}$ are normal and that the vector a_1 has length 1.
5. Show that in a complex unitary space it is possible to find an mth normal root for an arbitrary normal transformation, with m a natural number —that is, that for each normal transformation $\mathscr{A}$ there exists a transformation $\mathscr{B}$, also normal, such that $\mathscr{B}^m = \mathscr{A}$. What is the maximal number of such transformations?
6. Show that if $\mathfrak{N}$ is an invariant subspace under a normal transformation $\mathscr{A}$, then the orthogonal complement $\mathfrak{N}^{\perp}$ is also invariant under $\mathscr{A}$. If the containing space is complex, then this property characterizes normal transformations.

3. *Unitary and Symmetric Transformations*

77. Unitary Transformations

An isomorphic mapping of a unitary space $\mathfrak{L}$ onto itself is called a ***unitary*** transformation of $\mathfrak{L}$. In other words, a nonsingular linear transformation

$\mathscr{U}$ of a unitary space $\mathfrak{L}$ is called unitary if it does not change the value of the inner product: for all a, b in $\mathfrak{L}$,

$$(a, b) = (a\mathscr{U}, b\mathscr{U}) . \tag{1}$$

The simplest example of a unitary transformation is a rotation of the usual three-dimensional Euclidean space about the origin $\mathscr{O}$. Another example is the reflection of this space in a plane passing through $\mathscr{O}$. It is easy to show that the combinations of these two types of transformations exhaust all the unitary transformations of this space. Therefore the unitary transformations of general unitary spaces may be considered to be in some sense analogous to the rotations and reflections of the usual Euclidean space.

From equality (1), which characterizes unitary transformations, it follows that

$$(x, y) = (x\mathscr{U}, y\mathscr{U}) = (x, y\mathscr{U}\mathscr{U}^*) ,$$

hence

$$\mathscr{U}\mathscr{U}^* = \mathscr{E}, \quad \mathscr{U}^* = \mathscr{U}^{-1} , \quad \mathscr{U}^*\mathscr{U} = \mathscr{E} . \tag{2}$$

Conversely, from (2) it follows that $\mathscr{U}$ is invertible and that

$$(x, y) = (x, y\mathscr{U}\mathscr{U}^*) = (x\mathscr{U}, y\mathscr{U}) .$$

Thus, *a linear transformation $\mathscr{U}$ is unitary if and only if the conjugate transformation $\mathscr{U}^*$ coincides with the inverse transformation $\mathscr{U}^{-1}$*.

In particular, (2) shows that *a unitary transformation is a normal transformation, in the sense of the preceding section.*

Take an orthonormal coordinate system in the space $\mathfrak{L}$ and let $\mathscr{U}$ be a unitary transformation of this space. If the matrix of the transformation $\mathscr{U}$ is U, then the matrix of the conjugate transformation, by Section 75, is $\bar{U}'$. Therefore it follows from (2) that

$$U\bar{U}' = E . \tag{3}$$

Conversely, if in some orthonormal coordinate system the matrix U of a linear transformation $\mathscr{U}$ satisfies (3), then the transformation $\mathscr{U}$ satisfies (2), and hence is unitary. Matrices U which satisfy (3) are called ***unitary*** (see Section 8), and we have the result that *every unitary transformation has, in any orthonormal coordinate system, a unitary matrix*; *conversely, if a linear transformation has a unitary matrix in some orthonormal coordinate system, then it is unitary.*

If the base field K is real, then the matrices of transformations are also real, and (3) becomes

$$UU' = E . \tag{4}$$

Matrices satisfying (4) are called ***orthogonal*** (see Section 8). Thus real unitary transformations have orthogonal matrices in an orthonormal basis. Conversely, if the matrix of a linear transformation of a real unitary space is orthogonal in an orthonormal basis, then the transformation is unitary.

By definition, unitary transformations do not change the value of the inner product. It follows that unitary transformations do not change the lengths of vectors.

This last property is another characterization of unitary transformations: *if a linear transformation $\mathscr{U}$ does not change the norms of vectors, then $\mathscr{U}$ is unitary.*

To prove this, let a, b be arbitrary vectors in $\mathfrak{L}$ and put

$$a\mathscr{U} = a', \qquad b\mathscr{U} = b'.$$

Since the transformation $\mathscr{U}$ is linear,

$$(a + \alpha b)\mathscr{U} = a' + \alpha b'$$

for all scalars α. By assumption, $\mathscr{U}$ does not affect the norm, so

$$(a + \alpha b, a + \alpha b) = (a' + \alpha b', a' + \alpha b').$$

From this it follows that

$$\alpha(b, a) + \bar{\alpha}(a, b) = \alpha(b', a') + \bar{\alpha}(a', b'). \tag{5}$$

For $\alpha = 1$ this equality becomes

$$(b, a) + (a, b) = (b', a') + (a', b'). \tag{6}$$

If the base field is real, then $(b, a) = (a, b)$ and (6) yields $(a, b) = (a', b')$. If K is not real, then, if we set $\alpha = i$ in (5) and cancel the i, (5) becomes

$$(b, a) - (a, b) = (b', a') - (a', b'),$$

which, together with (6), again yields $(a, b) = (a', b')$. Thus, in each case

$$(a, b) = (a\mathscr{U}, b\mathscr{U}),$$

that is, $\mathscr{U}$ is unitary.

We now consider the question of the transformation of coordinates in unitary spaces. Let $e_1, \cdots, e_n$ be an orthonormal basis of a unitary space $\mathfrak{L}$, and $\mathscr{U}$ be some unitary transformation of $\mathfrak{L}$. Since unitary transformations do not change the lengths of vectors, and since they carry orthogonal vectors into orthogonal vectors, the system $e_1\mathscr{U}, \cdots, e_n\mathscr{U}$ is again an orthogonal basis of $\mathfrak{L}$. Conversely, suppose that a linear transformation $\mathscr{U}$ carries an orthogonal basis $e_1, \cdots, e_n$ into an orthogonal basis $e_1\mathscr{U}, \cdots, e_n\mathscr{U}$. Take arbitary vectors a, b in $\mathfrak{L}$, with

$$a = \alpha_1 e_1 + \cdots + \alpha_n e_n, \quad b = \beta_1 e_1 + \cdots + \beta_n e_n.$$

Then

$$(a, b) = (\sum \alpha_i e_i, \sum \beta_k e_k) = \alpha_1\bar{\beta}_1 + \cdots + \alpha_n\bar{\beta}_n,$$
$$(a\mathscr{U}, b\mathscr{U}) = (\sum \alpha_i e_i\mathscr{U}, \sum \beta_k e_k\mathscr{U}) = \alpha_1\bar{\beta}_1 + \cdots + \alpha_n\bar{\beta}_n,$$

or $(a, b) = (a\mathscr{U}, b\mathscr{U})$, and the transformation $\mathscr{U}$ is unitary. Hence, *a linear transformation $\mathscr{U}$ is unitary if and only if $\mathscr{U}$ carries an orthonormal basis into an orthonormal basis.*

The following proposition is an immediate consequence: *the matrix of a transformation from one orthonormal coordinate system to another is unitary; and, conversely, if one of two coordinate systems is orthonormal and the matrix of the transformation from one system to the other is unitary, then the other coordinate system is also orthonormal.*

To prove this it is sufficient to remark that the matrix of the transformation from one system to the other coincides with the matrix of the linear transformation which carries one system into the other (compare Section 36).

We observe finally the following properties of unitary transformations, which follow easily from the definition; 1) the identity transformation is unitary; 2) the product of unitary transformations is unitary; 3) the inverse of a unitary transformation is unitary.

78. Unitary Equivalence

One of the fundamental problems of the theory of unitary spaces—the classification of the linear transformations of these spaces—may be naturally formulated in connection with the notion of unitary transformations. Let $\mathfrak{L}$ and $\mathfrak{L}_1$ be unitary spaces over a base field K. Consider linear transformations $\mathscr{A}$ of $\mathfrak{L}$ and $\mathscr{A}_1$ of $\mathfrak{L}_1$. The transformations $\mathscr{A}, \mathscr{A}_1$ are called ***similar*** if there exists an isomorphic mapping of $\mathfrak{L}$ onto $\mathfrak{L}_1$ under which the transformation $\mathscr{A}$ is carried into $\mathscr{A}_1$. Since all unitary spaces (over K) are determined up to isomorphism by their dimension, we may assume that $\mathfrak{L}_1$ coincides with $\mathfrak{L}$, and consequently that the transformations $\mathscr{A}$ and $\mathscr{A}_1$ both operate on $\mathfrak{L}$. Our definition here means that $\mathscr{A}$ and $\mathscr{A}_1$ are similar if and only if there exists an isomorphic mapping $\mathscr{U}$ of the space $\mathfrak{L}$ onto itself under which $\mathscr{A}$ is carried into $\mathscr{A}_1$. As we have seen in Section 41, this is equivalent to the condition that

$$\mathscr{A}_1 = \mathscr{U}^{-1}\mathscr{A}\mathscr{U} . \tag{7}$$

If we take an orthonormal coordinate system in $\mathfrak{L}$, (7) may be written in matrix form:

$$A_1 = U^{-1}AU , \tag{8}$$

where U is a unitary matrix and A, A_1 are the matrices of the given transformations. Matrices A, A_1 connected by a relation of the form (8) are called ***unitary-equivalent.*** Consequently, *linear transformations of a unitary space are similar if and only if their matrices, computed in an orthonormal basis, are unitary-equivalent.*

Considering the matrix U in relation (8) as the matrix of a transformation of coordinates, we obtain the following proposition; *linear transformations $\mathscr{A}, \mathscr{B}$ of a unitary space $\mathfrak{L}$ are similar if and only if there exist two orthonormal bases of $\mathfrak{L}$ such that the matrix of the transformation $\mathscr{A}$, computed in one of them, coincides with the matrix of the transformation $\mathscr{B}$, computed in the other.*

This proposition is completely analogous to the corresponding assertion for arbitrary linear spaces at the end of Section 41, where a detailed proof is given.

As an example we may take normal transformations. It is clear that for unitary similarity of linear transformations of a unitary space, it is necessary that they be linearly similar—that is, similar as linear transformations of a linear space. Therefore, the characteristic polynomials of unitary-similar linear transformations coincide. Now suppose we are given normal transformations with identical characteristic polynomials; then by Section 76, if we compute the matrices of these transformations in suitable orthonormal coordinate systems, the matrices will coincide, and hence the transformations are unitary-similar. This proves

THEOREM 1. *Normal transformations of a complex or real unitary space are unitary-similar if and only if their characteristic polynomials are identical.*

Theorem 1 may also be given in matrix form, as in

THEOREM 1a. *Matrices A, B, over the real or complex numbers, which permute with their conjugate-transposes $\bar{A}'$, $\bar{B}'$ respectively, are unitary-equivalent if and only if their characteristic polynomials are identical.*

In particular, for each complex (or real) matrix A for which $A\bar{A}' = \bar{A}'A$, there exists a complex (or real) unitary matrix U such that the matrix $UAU^{-1} = UA\bar{U}'$ is diagonal in the complex case and has the form (16) of Section 76 in the real case.

Thus, the unitary-similarity of two normal transformations turns out to be equivalent to their linear-similarity.

79. Normal Form of the Matrix of a Unitary Transformation

As has already been mentioned, unitary transformations are special cases of normal transformations. Therefore, Theorems 1 and 1a give necessary and sufficient conditions for the unitary-similarity of unitary transformations, and also given a normal form for the matrix of a unitary transformation. One difference between unitary transformations and other normal transformations is given in

THEOREM 2. *The zeros of the characteristic polynomial of a unitary transformation are all of modulus* 1.

We consider first the complex case. In this case a nonzero proper vector corresponds to each zero α of the characteristic polynomial of the unitary transformation $\mathscr{U}$. As a consequence of

$$a\mathscr{U} = \alpha a\ , \quad (a\mathscr{U}, a\mathscr{U}) = (a, a)\ ,$$

it follows that

$$(\alpha a, \alpha a) = \alpha\bar{\alpha}(a, a) = (a, a)\ ,$$

or $\alpha\bar{\alpha} = |\alpha|^2 = 1$.

In the real case, to each complex zero $\alpha = \rho + i\sigma$ there corresponds a pair of nonzero orthogonal vectors a, b for which

$$a\mathscr{U} = \rho a - \sigma b\ , \quad b\mathscr{U} = \sigma a + \rho b.$$

Hence we have

$$(a, a) + (b, b) = (a\mathscr{U}, a\mathscr{U}) + (b\mathscr{U}, b\mathscr{U}) = (\rho^2 + \sigma^2)((a, a) + (b, b))\ ,$$

or $\rho^2 + \sigma^2 = |\alpha|^2 = 1$.

Observing that the only real numbers with modulus 1 are 1 and -1, we may formulate Theorem 1a for unitary matrices:

THEOREM 3. *For every unitary matrix A there exists a complex unitary matrix U such that UAU^{-1} is diagonal with diagonal elements of modulus* 1. *For every real unitary matrix A there exists a real unitary matrix U such that*

$$UAU^{-1} = E_s \dot{+} (-E_t) \dot{+} \begin{bmatrix} \cos\varphi_1 & \sin\varphi_1 \\ -\sin\varphi_1 & \cos\varphi_1 \end{bmatrix} \dot{+} \cdots \dot{+} \begin{bmatrix} \cos\varphi_m & \sin\varphi_m \\ -\sin\varphi_m & \cos\varphi_m \end{bmatrix}, \qquad (9)$$

where E_s, E_t are identity matrices of orders s and t, and $\sin\varphi_j \neq 0$, *for* $j = 1, \cdots, m$; *moreover, the numbers s, t, m may be zero; that is, the corresponding terms may be absent from* (9).

Consider as an example the three-dimensional Euclidean space $\mathfrak{R}$. For every orthogonal transformation $\mathscr{U}$ of the space $\mathfrak{R}$ it is possible, by Theorem 3, to find an orthonormal coordinate system e_1, e_2, e_3 such that the matrix of the transformation $\mathscr{U}$ assumes one of six forms:

$$\alpha)\begin{bmatrix} 1 & & \\ & 1 & \\ & & 1 \end{bmatrix}, \qquad \beta)\begin{bmatrix} -1 & & \\ & 1 & \\ & & 1 \end{bmatrix}, \qquad \gamma)\begin{bmatrix} 1 & & \\ & -1 & \\ & & -1 \end{bmatrix},$$

$$\delta)\begin{bmatrix} -1 & & \\ & -1 & \\ & & -1 \end{bmatrix} \quad \varepsilon)\begin{bmatrix} 1 & & \\ & \cos\varphi & \sin\varphi \\ & -\sin\varphi & \cos\varphi \end{bmatrix}, \quad \kappa)\begin{bmatrix} -1 & & \\ & \cos\varphi & \sin\varphi \\ & -\sin\varphi & \cos\varphi \end{bmatrix}.$$

Evidently the transformation $\mathscr{U}$ is, in the various cases: α) the identity transformation; β) a reflection in the plane $e_1\mathscr{O}e_2$; γ) a reflection in the line $\mathscr{O}e_1$; δ) a reflection in the point $\mathscr{O}$; ε) a rotation by φ about the line $\mathscr{O}e_1$; κ) a rotation by φ about the line $\mathscr{O}e_1$, accompanied by a reflection in the plane $e_2\mathscr{O}e_3$. The first four cases may be considered as particular cases of the last two, for $\varphi = 0$ and $\varphi = \pi$.

80. Symmetric Transformations

A linear transformation $\mathscr{A}$ of a unitary space is called ***Hermitian*** or ***symmetric*** if $\mathscr{A}$ coincides with its conjugate transformation $\mathscr{A}^*$. Thus, if $\mathscr{A}$ is symmetric,

$$(x\mathscr{A}, y) = (x, y\mathscr{A})\ . \qquad (10)$$

Conversely, if for all x, y in $\mathfrak{L}$ a linear transformation $\mathscr{A}$ satisfies condition

(10), then $\mathscr{A}$ is symmetric.

From $\mathscr{A}^* = \mathscr{A}$ it evidently follows that $\mathscr{A}\mathscr{A}^* = \mathscr{A}^*\mathscr{A}$; *symmetric transformations are normal.*

Choose an orthonormal basis in $\mathfrak{L}$ and let A be the matrix of a symmetric transformation $\mathscr{A}$. The matrix of the conjugate transformation $\mathscr{A}^*$ in this basis is the conjugate-transpose matrix $\bar{A}'$. But since $\mathscr{A}^* = \mathscr{A}$,

$$\bar{A}' = A . \tag{11}$$

Conversely, it follows from (11) that $\mathscr{A}^* = \mathscr{A}$, or $\mathscr{A}$ is symmetric. Matrices satisfying relation (11) are called Hermitian (see Section 8). Thus, *in an orthonormal basis, Hermitian matrices correspond to symmetric transformations, and, conversely, symmetric transformations correspond to Hermitian matrices.*

The simplest examples of symmetric transformations are those of the form $\alpha\mathscr{E}$, where α is a real number. A more general example is a transformation whose matrix in some orthonormal basis is diagonal with real diagonal elements.

The sum of symmetric transformations, and a real number times a symmetric transformation, are again symmetric transformations.

In fact, if $\mathscr{A}$, $\mathscr{B}$ are symmetric and α is real, then

$$(\mathscr{A} + \mathscr{B})^* = \mathscr{A}^* + \mathscr{B}^* = \mathscr{A} + \mathscr{B} ,$$
$$(\alpha\mathscr{A})^* = \bar{\alpha}\mathscr{A}^* = \alpha\mathscr{A} .$$

The product of two symmetric transformations is symmetric if and only if these transformations are permutable.

Indeed, it follows from $\mathscr{A}\mathscr{B} = \mathscr{B}\mathscr{A}$, $\mathscr{A} = \mathscr{A}^*$, $\mathscr{B} = \mathscr{B}^*$, that

$$(\mathscr{A}\mathscr{B})^* = \mathscr{B}^*\mathscr{A}^* = \mathscr{B}\mathscr{A} = \mathscr{A}\mathscr{B} .$$

Conversely, if $(\mathscr{A}\mathscr{B})^* = \mathscr{A}\mathscr{B}$, $\mathscr{A} = \mathscr{A}^*$, $\mathscr{B} = \mathscr{B}^*$, then

$$\mathscr{A}\mathscr{B} = (\mathscr{A}\mathscr{B})^* = \mathscr{B}^*\mathscr{A}^* = \mathscr{B}\mathscr{A} .$$

It follows in particular that powers of a symmetric transformation, and polynomials with real coefficients in a symmetric transformation, are again symmetric transformations.

The proper values of a symmetric transformation are real.

Indeed, let $\mathscr{A}$ be a symmetric transformation, α a proper value of $\mathscr{A}$ and a a corresponding nonzero proper vector. Then

$$(a, a\mathscr{A}) = (a, \alpha a) = \bar{\alpha}(a, a) ,$$
$$(a\mathscr{A}, a) = (\alpha a, a) = \alpha(a, a) .$$

But

$$(a, a\mathscr{A}) = (a\mathscr{A}, a) .$$

Comparing these results, we see that $\bar{\alpha} = \alpha$, or that α is real.

All the zeros of the characteristic polynomial of a Hermitian matrix are real.

Indeed, each Hermitian matrix A may be considered the matrix of some symmetric transformation $\mathscr{A}$ of a unitary space. The zeros of the characteristic polynomial of the matrix A are the proper values of the transformation $\mathscr{A}$, and are therefore real.

It was remarked above that symmetric transformations are normal. Therefore, by Theorem 1, symmetric transformations are unitary-similar if and only if they have identical characteristic polynomials.

By Theorem 6 of Section 76, for each normal transformation of a complex unitary space there exists an orthonormal basis in which the matrix of the transformation has diagonal form. Since all the proper values of a symmetric transformation are real, the diagonal matrix for a symmetric transformation is real, and we have

THEOREM 4. *Every symmetric transformation of a complex unitary space has, in a suitable orthonormal basis, a real diagonal matrix.*

The converse is also true, since if the matrix of a linear transformation $\mathscr{A}$ has a real diagonal form A in some orthonormal basis, then $\bar{A}' = A$, and, consequently, $\mathscr{A}^* = \mathscr{A}$.

Theorem 4 may be formulated for matrices, as in

THEOREM 4a. *For each Hermitian matrix A there exists a complex unitary matrix U such that* UAU^{-1} *has real diagonal form.*

We now consider the case when $\mathscr{A}$ is a symmetric transformation of a real unitary space. By Theorem 8 of Section 76, the matrix of the transformation $\mathscr{A}$, in a suitable orthonormal basis, decomposes into blocks of orders 1 and 2. Blocks of order 2 appear only if the characteristic polynomial of the transformation has nonreal zeros. But the characteristic polynomial of a symmetric transformation has no nonreal zeros; consequently, in the real case also, the matrix of a symmetric transformation reduces, in a suitable orthonormal basis, to diagonal form. Clearly the converse is also true, and we have

THEOREM 5. *For each symmetric transformation of a real unitary space there exists an orthonormal basis in which the matrix of the transformation assumes diagonal form.*

The matrices of symmetric transformations, in an orthonormal basis, satisfy the relation $\bar{A}' = A$. In the real case this relation becomes $A' = A$. Matrices satisfying this equality are called ***symmetric*** (see Section 8). Thus, in an orthonormal basis, the matrices of real symmetric transformations are symmetric, and, conversely, a transformation is symmetric if its matrix is real and symmetric. This observation permits Theorem 5 to be restated:

THEOREM 5a. *For each real symmetric matrix A there exists a real unitary matrix U such that the matrix* $U^{-1}AU$ *is diagonal.*

81. Skew-symmetric Transformations

Let $\mathfrak{L}$ be a unitary space. A linear transformation $\mathscr{A}$ of $\mathfrak{L}$ is called *skew-symmetric* if it is connected to its conjugate by the relation

$$\mathscr{A}^* = -\mathscr{A} . \tag{12}$$

If a, b are arbitrary vectors in the space $\mathfrak{L}$, then from (12) it follows that

$$(a, b\mathscr{A}) = (a\mathscr{A}^*, b) = -(a\mathscr{A}, b) .$$

Conversely, if for all a, b we have

$$(a, b\mathscr{A}) = -(a\mathscr{A}, b) ,$$

then $\mathscr{A}^* = -\mathscr{A}$, and $\mathscr{A}$ is skew-symmetric.

If the base field is the field of complex numbers, skew-symmetric transformations may be very simply expressed in terms of symmetric transformations since if $\mathscr{A}$ is a symmetric transformation of $\mathfrak{L}$ then

$$(i\mathscr{A})^* = \bar{i}\mathscr{A}^* = -i\mathscr{A} ,$$

and consequently $i\mathscr{A}$ is skew-symmetric. Conversely, if $\mathscr{A}$ is skew-symmetric, then

$$(i\mathscr{A})^* = \bar{i}\mathscr{A}^* = i\mathscr{A} ,$$

and $i\mathscr{A}$ is symmetric. In real spaces this simple connection is lost.

Take an orthonormal basis in a unitary space $\mathfrak{L}$ and let A denote the matrix of a skew-symmetric transformation $\mathscr{A}$. Since the matrix of the conjugate transformation is $\bar{A}'$, condition (12) yields

$$\bar{A}' = -A . \tag{13}$$

Conversely, it is evident from (13) that $\mathscr{A}$ is skew-symmetric. Matrices which satisfy relation (13) are called ***Hermitian skew-symmetric.*** Thus, in an orthonormal basis, Hermitian skew-symmetric matrices correspond to skew-symmetric transformations, and, conversely, skew-symmetric transformations correspond to Hermitian skew-symmetric matrices.

It follows easily from (12) that the sum of skew-symmetric transformations, and a real number times a skew-symmetric transformation, are again skew-symmetric transformations.

Every proper value of a skew-symmetric transformation is either zero or a pure imaginary number.

If α is a proper value of a skew-symmetric transformation $\mathscr{A}$, and a is a corresponding nonzero proper vector, then

$$(a, a\mathscr{A}) = (a, \alpha a) = \bar{\alpha}(a, a) ,$$
$$(a\mathscr{A}, a) = (\alpha a, a) = \alpha(a, a) .$$

But $(a, a\mathscr{A}) = -(a\mathscr{A}, a)$; hence $-\alpha = \bar{\alpha}$, which was to be proved.

It follows in particular that *each zero of the characteristic polynomial of a Hermitian skew-symmetric matrix is either zero or a pure imaginary number.*

From $\mathscr{A}^* = -\mathscr{A}$ it follows immediately that $\mathscr{A}\mathscr{A}^* = \mathscr{A}^*\mathscr{A}$; hence skew-symmetric transformations are a variety of normal transformations. Therefore, to find the simplest form of the matrix of a skew-symmetric transformation it is sufficient to apply Theorem 8 of Section 76. The result is

THEOREM 6. *In a real unitary space the matrix A of a skew-symmetric transformation, in a suitable orthonormal basis, assumes the form*

$$A = O_k \dotplus \begin{bmatrix} 0 & \sigma_1 \\ -\sigma_1 & 0 \end{bmatrix} \dotplus \cdots \dotplus \begin{bmatrix} 0 & \sigma_m \\ -\sigma_m & 0 \end{bmatrix}, \tag{14}$$

where O_k is the zero matrix of order k.

Indeed, by Theorem 8 of Section 76 the matrix of the given transformation decomposes, in the proper orthonormal basis, into blocks of orders 1 and 2. It is evident that the separate blocks must satisfy relation (13). The blocks of order 1 are real numbers ρ_i, and (13) gives $\rho_i = -\bar{\rho}_i = -\rho_i$, or $\rho_i = 0$. If A_j is a block of order 2, then (13) yields

$$A_j = \begin{bmatrix} 0 & \sigma_j \\ -\sigma_j & 0 \end{bmatrix}.$$

Theorem 6 may be put in matrix form, as in

THEOREM 6a. *For each real skew-symmetric matrix A there exists a real unitary matrix U such that $U^{-1}AU$ has the form* (14).

82. Nonnegative Symmetric Transformations

A symmetric transformation $\mathscr{A}$ of a unitary space $\mathfrak{L}$ is called ***nonnegative*** if for all x in $\mathfrak{L}$

$$(x\mathscr{A}, x) \geqq 0 . \tag{15}$$

The inequality sign is meaningful, since for symmetric transformations the inner product $(x\mathscr{A}, x)$ is always real. If the equality sign in (15) holds only for the zero vector, then $\mathscr{A}$ is called a ***positive*** or ***positive-definite*** transformation.

A linear combination of nonnegative transformations with real nonnegative coefficients is a nonnegative transformation.

This is immediately apparent from the formula

$$(x(\alpha\mathscr{A} + \beta\mathscr{B}), x) = \alpha(x\mathscr{A}, x) + \beta(x\mathscr{B}, x) .$$

The product of any linear transformation with its conjugate is a nonnegative symmetric transformation.

$$(x\mathscr{A}\mathscr{A}^*, x) = (x\mathscr{A}, x\mathscr{A}) \geqq 0 ,$$
$$(x\mathscr{A}^*\mathscr{A}, x) = (x\mathscr{A}^*, x\mathscr{A}^*) \geqq 0 .$$

The square of any symmetric transformation is a nonnegative transformation.

This follows from the preceding, since a symmetric transformation is its own conjugate.

All proper values of a nonnegative transformation are real and nonnegative.

Let $\mathscr{A}$ be a nonnegative transformation, α a proper value of $\mathscr{A}$, and a a corresponding nonzero proper vector. Then

$$(a\mathscr{A}, a) = \alpha(a, a) \geqq 0 .$$

Consequently, $\alpha \geqq 0$.

If a symmetric transformation of a complex or real unitary space has only nonnegative proper values, then it is nonnegative.

By Section 80 there exists an orthonormal basis $e_1, \cdots, e_n$ of $\mathfrak{L}$ consisting of proper vectors of the transformation $\mathscr{A}$. Let $\alpha_1, \cdots, \alpha_n$ be the corresponding proper values and let

$$x = \xi_1 e_1 + \cdots + \xi_n e_n ,$$

be an arbitrary vector in $\mathfrak{L}$. Then

$$(x\mathscr{A}, x) = \alpha_1 \xi_1 \bar{\xi}_1 + \cdots + \alpha_n \xi_n \bar{\xi}_n = \alpha_1 |\xi_1|^2 + \cdots + \alpha_n |\xi_n|^2 \geqq 0 . \qquad (16)$$

This completes the proof.

The determinant of the transformation $\mathscr{A}$ is $\alpha_1 \alpha_2 \cdots \alpha_n$. If it is different from zero, then all the numbers α_j are larger than zero, and (16) is zero only for $x = \theta$. Consequently, in this case $\mathscr{A}$ is called positive definite. If $|\mathscr{A}| = 0$, then one of the proper values, say α_1, is zero. Then

$$(e_1\mathscr{A}, e_1) = 0(e_1, e_2) = 0 ,$$

and the transformation $\mathscr{A}$ is not positive-definite.

Consequently, *a nonnegative symmetric transformation is positive definite if and only if it is nonsingular.*

We now consider the operation of extracting a square root of a linear transformation. We say that a linear transformation $\mathscr{X}$ is a square root of the linear transformation $\mathscr{A}$ if

$$\mathscr{X}^2 = \mathscr{A} . \qquad (17)$$

Equation (17) may have no solution, a finite number of solutions, or an infinite number of solutions, depending on $\mathscr{A}$. However, for nonnegative symmetric transformations the situation is completely definite.

THEOREM 7. *For each nonnegative symmetric transformation $\mathscr{A}$ of a unitary space $\mathfrak{L}$ there exists one and only one nonnegative symmetric transformation $\mathscr{B}$ satisfying the relation*

$$\mathscr{B}^2 = \mathscr{A} .$$

Every linear transformation permutable with $\mathscr{A}$ is permutable with $\mathscr{B}$.

Choose an orthonormal basis of $\mathfrak{L}$ consisting of proper vectors of the transformation $\mathscr{A}$ (compare Section 80). Let $\alpha_1, \cdots, \alpha_n$ be the corresponding proper values. Let $\mathscr{B}$ be the linear transformation which carries e_j into $\sqrt{\alpha_j} e_j$, for $j = 1, \cdots, n$, where the value of the radical is taken to be nonnegative. Since $e_1, \cdots, e_n$ is an orthonormal basis of proper vectors of the transformation $\mathscr{B}$ and the corresponding proper values $\sqrt{\alpha_1}, \cdots, \sqrt{\alpha_n}$ are nonnegative, then $\mathscr{B}$ is a nonnegative symmetric transformation. But

$$e_j\mathscr{B}^2 = \alpha_j e_j = e_j\mathscr{A} \qquad (j = 1, \cdots, n)\,.$$

Therefore $\mathscr{B}^2 = \mathscr{A}$, and a square root of $\mathscr{A}$ exists.

We now prove the last assertion of the theorem. Let $\mathscr{X}$ be a linear transformation which permutes with $\mathscr{A}$. Suppose the coordinate vectors $e_1, \cdots, e_n$ are chosen in such an order that equal proper values, if there are any, correspond to adjacent coordinate vectors. Then the matrices of the transformations $\mathscr{A}$ and $\mathscr{B}$ have the form

$$A = \begin{bmatrix} \alpha_1 E_1 & & & & \\ & \alpha_2 E_2 & & & \\ & & \cdot & & \\ & & & \cdot & \\ & & & & \cdot \\ & & & & & \alpha_s E_s \end{bmatrix}, \qquad B = \begin{bmatrix} \sqrt{\alpha_1} E_1 & & & & \\ & \sqrt{\alpha_2} E_2 & & & \\ & & \cdot & & \\ & & & \cdot & \\ & & & & \cdot \\ & & & & & \sqrt{\alpha_s} E_s \end{bmatrix},$$

where $\alpha_1, \cdots, \alpha_s$ are *distinct* proper values of the transformation $\mathscr{A}$, and $E_1, \cdots, E_s$ are identity matrices. We represent the matrix of the transformation $\mathscr{X}$ in the corresponding block form,

$$X = \begin{bmatrix} X_{11} X_{12} \cdots X_{1s} \\ X_{21} X_{22} \cdots X_{2s} \\ \cdot\ \cdot\ \cdot\ \cdot\ \cdot\ \cdot\ \cdot\ \cdot\ \cdot \\ X_{s1}\, X_{s2} \cdots X_{ss} \end{bmatrix}.$$

The condition $AX = XA$ yields

$$\alpha_j X_{jk} = X_{jk} \alpha_k \qquad (j, k = 1, \cdots, s)\,,$$

or

$$(\alpha_j - \alpha_k) X_{jk} = 0\,.$$

Since $\alpha_j \neq \alpha_k$ for $j \neq k$, , $X_{jk} = 0$ for $j \neq k$. Consequently

$$X = \begin{bmatrix} X_{11} & & & & \\ & X_{22} & & & \\ & & \cdot & & \\ & & & \cdot & \\ & & & & \cdot \\ & & & & & X_{ss} \end{bmatrix},$$

but then

$$BX = \begin{bmatrix} \sqrt{\alpha_1} X_{11} & & & \\ & \cdot & & \\ & & \cdot & \\ & & & \cdot \\ & & & & \sqrt{\alpha_s} X_{ss} \end{bmatrix} = XB\,.$$

The uniqueness of $\mathscr{B}$ remains to be proved. Let $\mathscr{C}$ be another nonnegative symmetric transformation for which $\mathscr{C}^2 = \mathscr{A}$. The block decomposition of the matrix A, indicated above, decomposes the space $\mathfrak{L}$ into the direct sum of invariant subspaces $\mathfrak{L}_j$ for $j = 1, \cdots, s$. Since $\mathscr{C}\mathscr{A} = \mathscr{A}\mathscr{C}$, then, according to the proof above, the subspaces $\mathfrak{L}_j$ are also invariant under $\mathscr{C}$. Since $\mathscr{C}$ is symmetric, there exists an orthonormal basis of $\mathfrak{L}_j$ of proper vectors of $\mathscr{C}$ for $j = 1, \cdots, s$. Let $\gamma_{j1}, \cdots, \gamma_{jp}$ be the corresponding proper values. Let $\mathscr{A}_j$, $\mathscr{B}_j$, $\mathscr{C}_j$ denote the transformations induced in the subspace $\mathfrak{L}_j$ by the transformations $\mathscr{A}$, $\mathscr{B}$, $\mathscr{C}$ respectively. Then

$$A_j = \alpha_j \mathscr{E}_j , \qquad \mathscr{B}_j = \sqrt{\alpha_j}\, \mathscr{E}_j , \qquad \mathscr{C}_j^2 = \mathscr{A}_j ,$$

and hence

$$\gamma_{j1}^2 = \cdots = \gamma_{jp}^2 = \alpha_j .$$

Since $\gamma_{j1}, \cdots, \gamma_{jp}$ are all nonnegative,

$$\gamma_{j1} = \cdots = \gamma_{jp} = \sqrt{\alpha_j} ,$$

and, consequently, $\mathscr{C}_j = \sqrt{\alpha_j}\ \mathscr{E}_j = \mathscr{B}_j$, or $\mathscr{C} = \mathscr{B}$.

As an immediate corollary to Theorem 7 we prove that *the product of permutable nonnegative symmetric transformations is a nonnegative transformation.*

Let $\mathscr{A}_1, \mathscr{A}_2$ be the permutable nonnegative symmetric transformations. Let $\mathscr{B}_1, \mathscr{B}_2$ be square roots of $\mathscr{A}_1, \mathscr{A}_2$, which by Theorem 7 may be taken to be permutable, symmetric, and nonnegative. Then

$$(\mathscr{B}_1\mathscr{B}_2)^2 = \mathscr{B}_1\mathscr{B}_2\mathscr{B}_1\mathscr{B}_2 = \mathscr{B}_1^2\mathscr{B}_2^2 = \mathscr{A}_1\mathscr{A}_2 .$$

This shows that $\mathscr{A}_1\mathscr{A}_2$ is the square of the symmetric transformation $\mathscr{B}_1\mathscr{B}_2$ Consequently, $\mathscr{A}_1\mathscr{A}_2$ is nonnegative.

It follows, in particular, that polynomials with real nonnegative coefficients in symmetric nonnegative transformations are again symmetric nonnegative transformations.

• EXAMPLES AND PROBLEMS

1. Let e_1, e_2, e_3 be an orthonormal basis of a unitary space $\mathfrak{L}$. Find the matrix of a unitary transformation which carries the vectors e_1, e_2 into the vectors

$$\tfrac{2}{3}e_1 + \tfrac{2}{3}e_2 - \tfrac{1}{3}e_3 , \qquad \tfrac{2}{3}e_1 - \tfrac{1}{3}e_2 + \tfrac{2}{3}e_3 .$$

2. If $a_1, \cdots, a_m$ and $b_1, \cdots, b_m$ are two orthonormal systems of vectors in an n-dimensional unitary space $\mathfrak{L}$, where $m < n$, then there exists a unitary transformation of $\mathfrak{L}$ which carries the first system into the second.
3. A system of vectors $a_1, \cdots, a_m$ of a unitary space may be carried into a system $b_1, \cdots, b_m$ by a unitary transformation if and only if the Gram matrices of these systems coincide (compare problem 5, p. 148).

4. Using the Jordan normal form and the Gram-Schmidt orthogonalization process, show that the matrix of any linear transformation of a unitary space may be reduced to triangular form in a suitable orthonormal coordinate system (Schur's theorem).

5. Show that if an arbitrary transformation $\mathscr{A}$ of a unitary space $\mathfrak{L}$ preserves the value of the inner product, then $\mathscr{A}$ is linear and, consequently, is a unitary transformation of $\mathfrak{L}$.

6. In a linear space there exist, up to similarity, only two linear functions. In a unitary space, up to similarity, linear functions all have the form $\alpha(x, e)$, where e is a fixed unit vector.

7. Let the transformations $\mathscr{A}, \mathscr{B}, \mathscr{C}$ of a Euclidean space have the matrices

$$\begin{bmatrix} 5 & 2 & 4 \\ 2 & 2 & 2 \\ 4 & 2 & 5 \end{bmatrix}, \qquad \begin{bmatrix} 4 & 2 & 4 \\ 2 & 1 & 2 \\ 4 & 2 & 4 \end{bmatrix}, \qquad \begin{bmatrix} 1 & 3 & 1 \\ -1 & 2 & 2 \\ 1 & 0 & 2 \end{bmatrix}$$

in an orthonormal basis.

Show that $\mathscr{A}$ is positive definite, $\mathscr{B}$ is nonnegative, and, although $\mathscr{C}$ is not symmetric, that $(x\mathscr{C}, x) \geqq 0$ for all x.

8. Find the nonnegative symmetric square root of the transformation $\mathscr{A}$ of the preceding problem.

9. The matrix of a symmetric nonnegative transformation, computed in an orthonormal basis, is called ***Hermitian nonnegative***. Show that a Hermitian matrix is nonnegative if and only if the coefficients of its characteristic polynomial have alternating signs. If some coefficient is zero, then the coefficients of all the lower terms must also be zero.

10. Show that it is possible to extract a normal root of arbitrary positive order n from each normal transformation $\mathscr{A}$, or that for each normal transformation $\mathscr{A}$ there exists a normal transformation $\mathscr{B}$ such that $\mathscr{B}^n = \mathscr{A}$. What is the maximal number of such $\mathscr{B}$?

11. Choose an orthonormal basis of a unitary space $\mathfrak{L}$. Show that in this basis the matrix of every nonnegative symmetric transformation $\mathscr{A}$ of rank 1 may be represented in the form

$$A = [\bar{x}]' [x] ,$$

where $[x]$ is the coordinate row of some suitably chosen vector x.

12. Every nonnegative symmetric transformation is the sum of nonnegative symmetric transformations of rank 1.

13. If the Hermitian matrices with elements α_{ij}, β_{ij} are nonnegative, then the matrix with elements $\gamma_{ij} = \alpha_{ij}\beta_{ij}$ $(i, j = 1, \cdots, n)$ is also nonnegative.

4. *Decomposition of General Transformations*

Unitary, symmetric, and skew-symmetric transformations have a very transparent geometric structure. Therefore, in the study of general linear transformations of unitary or Euclidean spaces, the question naturally arises of the possibly of expressing these transformations in some simple way in terms of the transformations of the indicated special forms. Some of these methods of the greatest significance will now be considered.

83. Decomposition into Symmetric and Skew-symmetric Parts

Let $\mathfrak{L}$ be a complex unitary space, with $\mathscr{A}$ a linear transformation of $\mathfrak{L}$. We introduce the notation

$$\mathscr{B} = \frac{1}{2}(\mathscr{A} + \mathscr{A}^*), \qquad \mathscr{C} = \frac{1}{2i}(\mathscr{A} - \mathscr{A}^*). \tag{1}$$

We have

$$\mathscr{B}^* = \frac{1}{2}(\mathscr{A}^* + \mathscr{A}) = \mathscr{B}, \qquad \mathscr{C}^* = -\frac{1}{2i}(\mathscr{A}^* - \mathscr{A}) = \mathscr{C}.$$

Consequently, $\mathscr{B}$ and $\mathscr{C}$ are symmetric. From (1) it follows that

$$\mathscr{A} = \mathscr{B} + i\mathscr{C}. \tag{2}$$

Thus, *every linear transformation $\mathscr{A}$ of a complex unitary space may be represented in the form* (2), *where $\mathscr{B}$ and $\mathscr{C}$ are symmetric transformations.* This representation is unique, since from (2) it follows that

$$\mathscr{A}^* = \mathscr{B}^* - i\mathscr{C}^* = \mathscr{B} - i\mathscr{C},$$

which again yields expressions (1) for $\mathscr{B}$ and $\mathscr{C}$.

If the base field is real, then the decomposition (2) cannot be used. In this case we proceed in the following way. Let $\mathscr{A}$ be an arbitrary linear transformation. If we set

$$\mathscr{B} = \frac{1}{2}(\mathscr{A} + \mathscr{A}^*), \qquad \mathscr{C} = \frac{1}{2}(\mathscr{A} - \mathscr{A}^*), \tag{3}$$

then

$$\mathscr{A} = \mathscr{B} + \mathscr{C}. \tag{4}$$

Since

$$\mathscr{B}^* = \frac{1}{2}(\mathscr{A}^* + \mathscr{A}) = \mathscr{B}, \qquad \mathscr{C}^* = \frac{1}{2}(\mathscr{A}^* - \mathscr{A}) = -\mathscr{C},$$

in the decomposition (4) $\mathscr{B}$ is symmetric, $\mathscr{C}$ is skew-symmetric. Decomposition (4) is unique, since from it we have $\mathscr{A}^* = \mathscr{B} - \mathscr{C}$, from which we again obtain for $\mathscr{B}$ and $\mathscr{C}$ the expressions (3). Consequently, *every linear transformation may be represented as the sum of a symmetric and a skew-symmetric transformation. This representation is possible in only one way.*

Decomposition (4) evidently may be used for any base field. The transformation $\mathscr{B}$ is called the ***symmetric part*** of $\mathscr{A}$, and $\mathscr{C}$ is called the

skew-symmetric part of $\mathscr{A}$.

From the point of view of the matrix calculus, decomposition (2) means that every square matrix A may be represented in the form $B + iC$, where B and C are Hermitian matrices; decomposition (4) means that every square matrix A may be represented in the form $B + C$, where B is a symmetric, and C is a skew-symmetric, matrix.

84. Polar Decomposition

Much more interesting geometrically is the representation of a linear transformation as a product of a symmetric and a unitary transformation. The possibility of such a decomposition is based on

LEMMA 1. *If the linear transformations $\mathscr{A}$, $\mathscr{B}$ of a unitary space $\mathfrak{L}$ change the lengths of vectors in the same way*—that is if*

$$(a\mathscr{A}, a\mathscr{A}) = (a\mathscr{B}, a\mathscr{B}) \tag{5}$$

for all a—then there exists a unitary transformation $\mathscr{U}$ of the space $\mathfrak{L}$ such that $\mathscr{A}\mathscr{U} = \mathscr{B}$.

Consider the range of the transformation $\mathscr{A}$, or the set of vectors of the form $x\mathscr{A}$, where x runs over the space $\mathfrak{L}$. Denote this set by $\mathfrak{A}$. Analogously, denote the range of the transformation $\mathscr{B}$ by $\mathfrak{B}$. By Section 40, $\mathfrak{A}$ and $\mathfrak{B}$ are linear subspaces. We wish first of all to construct an isomorphic correspondence between $\mathfrak{A}$ and $\mathfrak{B}$. Let a be a vector in $\mathfrak{A}$. Let x be a vector in $\mathfrak{L}$ such that $x\mathscr{A} = a$, and set $x\mathscr{B} = b$. We will call b the image of a, and write $b = a\mathscr{V}$. We show that b is uniquely determined by a. In fact, nonuniqueness can arise only as a consequence of nonuniqueness of the vector x for which $x\mathscr{A} = a$. However, if x_1 is another vector satisfying the condition $x_1\mathscr{A} = a$, then $(x - x_1)\mathscr{A} = 0$. By (5), it follows that

$$((x - x_1)\mathscr{B}, (x - x_1)\mathscr{B}) = ((x - x_1)\mathscr{A}, (x - x_1)\mathscr{A}) = 0 ,$$

or $(x - x_1)\mathscr{B} = 0$ or $x_1\mathscr{B} = x\mathscr{B}$, which was to be proved. We have thus shown that $\mathscr{V}$ is a single-valued mapping of $\mathfrak{A}$ into $\mathfrak{B}$. However, it is easy to see that $\mathscr{V}$ is a *one-to-one mapping* of $\mathfrak{A}$ onto $\mathfrak{B}$. If b is a vector in $\mathfrak{B}$, then there is a vector x in $\mathfrak{L}$ for which $x\mathscr{B} = b$. Then, setting $x\mathscr{A} = a$, we have $a\mathscr{V} = b$.

From the very definition of the correspondence $\mathscr{V}$, it follows that for each vector x in $\mathfrak{L}$,

$$x\mathscr{A}\mathscr{V} = x\mathscr{B} . \tag{6}$$

Using this equality, it is possible to show that $\mathscr{V}$ is an *isomorphic mapping* of $\mathfrak{A}$ onto $\mathfrak{B}$. Let a_1, a_2 be vectors in $\mathfrak{A}$. Choose x_1, x_2 in $\mathfrak{L}$ so that $x_1\mathscr{A} = a_1$, $x_2\mathscr{A} = a_2$. Then

* Transformations $\mathscr{A}$, $\mathscr{B}$ possessing this property are called ***equimetric***.

$$(\alpha a_1 + \beta a_2)\mathscr{V} = (\alpha x_1\mathscr{A} + \mathscr{B}x_2\mathscr{A})\mathscr{V} = (\alpha x_1 + \beta x_2)\mathscr{A}\mathscr{V}$$
$$= (\alpha x_1 + \beta x_2)\mathscr{B} = \alpha(x_1\mathscr{B}) + \beta(x_2\mathscr{B})$$
$$= \alpha(x_1\mathscr{A}\mathscr{V}) + \beta(x_2\mathscr{A}\mathscr{V}) = \alpha(a_1\mathscr{V}) + \beta(a_2\mathscr{V}) . \quad (7)$$

Thus the mapping $\mathscr{V}$ preserves the operations of addition and multiplication by a scalar. Moreover,

$$(a_1\mathscr{V}, a_1\mathscr{V}) = (x_1\mathscr{A}\mathscr{V}, x_1\mathscr{A}\mathscr{V}) = (x_1\mathscr{B}, x_1\mathscr{B})$$
$$= (x_1\mathscr{A}, x_1\mathscr{A}) = (a_1, a_1) . \quad (8)$$

Thus the mapping $\mathscr{V}$ preserves the lengths of vectors. Consequently, $\mathscr{V}$ is an isomorphism.

The mapping $\mathscr{V}$ has been defined only for vectors in $\mathfrak{A}$. We now wish to extend this definition to the remaining vectors of the space $\mathfrak{L}$. To this end we consider the orthogonal subspaces $\mathfrak{A}^{\perp}$ and $\mathfrak{B}^{\perp}$. By Section 73, $\mathfrak{L}$ has the direct decompositions

$$\mathfrak{L} = \mathfrak{A} \dotplus \mathfrak{A}^{\perp} = \mathfrak{B} \dotplus \mathfrak{B}^{\perp}$$

The subspaces $\mathfrak{A}$ and $\mathfrak{B}$ are isomorphic, and therefore have the same dimension. Hence the orthogonal complements $\mathfrak{A}^{\perp}$ and $\mathfrak{B}^{\perp}$ also have the same dimension. Unitary spaces of the same dimension are isomorphic, and therefore there exists a one-to-one mapping of $\mathfrak{A}^{\perp}$ onto $\mathfrak{B}^{\perp}$, which preserves addition, multiplication by a scalar, and the lengths of vectors. We denote this mapping by $\mathscr{W}$. Consequently, if a', a'' are vectors in $\mathfrak{A}^{\perp}$, then $a'\mathscr{W}$, $a''\mathscr{W}$ are in $\mathfrak{B}^{\perp}$, and

$$(\alpha a' + \beta a'')\mathscr{W} = \alpha(a'\mathscr{W}) + \beta(a''\mathscr{W}) , \quad (9)$$
$$(a'\mathscr{W}, a''\mathscr{W}) = (a', a'') . \quad (10)$$

We now define a transformation $\mathscr{U}$ of the space $\mathfrak{L}$ in the following way. Let x be an arbitrary vector in $\mathfrak{L}$. Since $\mathfrak{L} = \mathfrak{A} \dotplus \mathfrak{A}^{\perp}$, x has a unique representation in the form

$$x = x' + x'' \qquad (x' \in \mathfrak{A} , x'' \in \mathfrak{A}^{\perp}) . \quad (11)$$

We put, by definition,

$$x\mathscr{U} = x'\mathscr{V} + x''\mathscr{W} . \quad (12)$$

The transformation $\mathscr{U}$ is linear, since, if

$$y = y' \dotplus y'' , \qquad (y' \in \mathfrak{A} , y'' \in \mathfrak{A}^{\perp}) ,$$

it follows from (7), (9), and (11) that

$$(\alpha x + \beta y)\mathscr{U} = (\alpha x' + \beta y')\mathscr{V} + (\alpha x'' + \beta y'')\mathscr{W} = \alpha(x\mathscr{U}) + \beta(y\mathscr{U}) .$$

The transformation $\mathscr{U}$ is unitary, since, from (8), (10), and (11),

$$(x\mathscr{U}, x\mathscr{U}) = (x'\mathscr{V} + x''\mathscr{W}, x'\mathscr{V} + x''\mathscr{W})$$
$$= (x'\mathscr{V}, x'\mathscr{V}) + (x''\mathscr{W}, x''\mathscr{W}) = (x', x') + (x'', x'') = (x, x) .$$

For all x in $\mathfrak{L}$,

$$x\mathscr{A}\mathscr{U} = x\mathscr{B} .$$

Indeed, $x\mathscr{A}$ belongs to $\mathfrak{A}$, and therefore in the decomposition (11) the vector x'' is zero; consequently,

$$x\mathscr{A}\mathscr{U} = x\mathscr{A}\mathscr{V} .$$

By (6), this gives $x\mathscr{A}\mathscr{U} = x\mathscr{B}$. Hence $\mathscr{A}\mathscr{U} = \mathscr{B}$, and the lemma is proved.

THEOREM 1. *Every linear transformation $\mathscr{A}$ of a unitary space $\mathfrak{L}$ admits a polar decomposition*

$$\mathscr{A} = \mathscr{D}\mathscr{U} , \tag{13}$$

where $\mathscr{D}$ is a nonnegative symmetric, and $\mathscr{U}$ is a unitary, transformation of the space $\mathfrak{L}$. The transformation $\mathscr{D}$ is uniquely determined, and if $\mathscr{A}$ is nonsingular, then $\mathscr{U}$ is also uniquely determined.

By Section 82 the transformation $\mathscr{A}\mathscr{A}^*$ is symmetric and nonnegative. Let $\mathscr{D}$ be the nonnegative symmetric square root of $\mathscr{A}\mathscr{A}^*$. Thus,

$$\mathscr{D}^2 = \mathscr{A}\mathscr{A}^* .$$

For every vector x we have

$$(x\mathscr{A}, x\mathscr{A}) = (x, x\mathscr{A}\mathscr{A}^*) = (x, x\mathscr{D}^2) = (x\mathscr{D}, x\mathscr{D}) ,$$

that is, the transformations $\mathscr{A}$ and $\mathscr{D}$ change the lengths of vectors in the same way. By Lemma 1, a unitary transformation $\mathscr{U}$ of $\mathfrak{L}$ can be found for which

$$\mathscr{D}\mathscr{U} = \mathscr{A} .$$

This proves the existence of a polar decomposition of $\mathscr{A}$. The uniqueness remains to be considered. From (13),

$$\mathscr{A}^* = \mathscr{U}^*\mathscr{D} = \mathscr{U}^{-1}\mathscr{D} , \qquad \mathscr{A}\mathscr{A}^* = \mathscr{D}\mathscr{U}\mathscr{U}^{-1}\mathscr{D} = \mathscr{D}^2 .$$

Thus, the transformation $\mathscr{D}$ is nonnegative and symmetric, and its square is the transformation $\mathscr{A}\mathscr{A}^*$. By Theorem 7 of Section 82, these conditions determine the transformation $\mathscr{D}$ uniquely. If $\mathscr{A}$ is nonsingular, then $\mathscr{D}$ is also nonsingular, and (13) yields $\mathscr{U} = \mathscr{D}^{-1}\mathscr{A}$, or $\mathscr{U}$ is also uniquely determined.

The geometric meaning of Theorem 1 is obvious. It shows that the effect of every linear transformation on a unitary space $\mathfrak{L}$ may be represented in the following way: $\mathfrak{L}$ is first expanded along n orthogonal directions by certain real nonnegative coefficients of expansion, and then is rotated about its coordinate origin.* If the transformation is nonsingular, then all the coefficients of expansion are strictly positive. In the case of a singular transformation, some of the coefficients are zero, and along these directions a projection of the space occurs, instead of an expansion.

* Rotation is understood in the sense of a unitary transformation.

We remark further that in the proof of the existence of a polar decomposition we started from the product $\mathscr{A}\mathscr{A}^*$. If the product $\mathscr{A}^*\mathscr{A}$ is taken instead, the result is a decomposition of the form

$$\mathscr{A} = \mathscr{U}\mathscr{D}_1 ,$$

where $\mathscr{U}$ is a unitary, and $\mathscr{D}_1$ is a nonnegative symmetric, transformation.

Choose an orthonormal coordinate system in the space $\mathfrak{L}$. Then unitary, Hermitian, matrices correspond to unitary, symmetric, transformations, respectively, and Theorem 1 becomes: *every square matrix may be represented as the product of a Hermitian and a unitary matrix.*

Suppose that the base field is the field of real numbers; then we obtain: *every square real matrix may be represented as the product of a real symmetric and a real orthogonal matrix.*

Theorem 1 asserts that $\mathscr{D}$ is a *nonnegative* symmetric transformation. Corresponding to this, in the last two assertions we may add, to the words *Hermitian* and *symmetric*, the words *with nonnegative proper values.*

85. Cayley's Transformation

Comparing the properties of unitary transformations with those of symmetric transformations, it may be observed that these two classes of transformations are closely connected. This connection is given explicitly by the so-called formulas of Cayley.

THEOREM 2 (Cayley's transformation). *If $\mathscr{A}$ is a symmetric transformation of a complex unitary space, then the transformations $\mathscr{A} \pm i\mathscr{E}$ are invertible; the transformation $\mathscr{U}$, given by the formula*

$$\mathscr{U} = (\mathscr{A} - i\mathscr{E})(\mathscr{A} + i\mathscr{E})^{-1} , \tag{14}$$

is unitary, and does not have 1 *as a proper value; and $\mathscr{A}$ is expressed in terms of $\mathscr{U}$ by the formula*

$$\mathscr{A} = -i(\mathscr{U} + \mathscr{E})(\mathscr{U} - \mathscr{E})^{-1} . \tag{15}$$

Conversely, if $\mathscr{U}$ is a unitary transformation which does not have 1 *as a proper value, then the transformation $\mathscr{U} - \mathscr{E}$ is invertible; the transformation $\mathscr{A}$, given by formula* (15), *is symmetric; and $\mathscr{U}$ is expressed in terms of $\mathscr{A}$ by the formula* (14).

Let $\mathscr{A}$ be a symmetric transformation of a unitary space. The numbers $\pm i$ cannot be proper values of the transformation $\mathscr{A}$, since the proper values of symmetric transformations are real (compare Section 80). This means that the transformations $\mathscr{A} \pm i\mathscr{E}$ are nonsingular. The permutability of the transformations $\mathscr{A} + i\mathscr{E}$ and $\mathscr{A} - i\mathscr{E}$, with the transformations $(\mathscr{A} + i\mathscr{E})^{-1}$, $(\mathscr{A} - i\mathscr{E})^{-1}$, follows from their permutability with each other. The transformation $\mathscr{U}$, given by formula (14), has the conjugate

$$\mathscr{U}^* = (\mathscr{A} + i\mathscr{E})^{*-1}(\mathscr{A} - i\mathscr{E})^* = (\mathscr{A} - i\mathscr{E})^{-1}(\mathscr{A} + i\mathscr{E}) .$$

Hence

$$\begin{aligned}\mathscr{U}\mathscr{U}^* &= (\mathscr{A} - i\mathscr{E})(\mathscr{A} + i\mathscr{E})^{-1}(\mathscr{A} - i\mathscr{E})^{-1}(\mathscr{A} + i\mathscr{E}) \\ &= (\mathscr{A} - i\mathscr{E})(\mathscr{A} + i\mathscr{E})^{-1}(\mathscr{A} + i\mathscr{E})(\mathscr{A} - i\mathscr{E})^{-1} = \mathscr{E},\end{aligned}$$

which shows that $\mathscr{U}$ is unitary. We show that $\mathscr{U} - \mathscr{E}$ is invertible. To do this, we subtract $\mathscr{E}$ from both sides of (14) and multiply the result by $\mathscr{A} + i\mathscr{E}$. We obtain

$$(\mathscr{U} - \mathscr{E})(\mathscr{A} + i\mathscr{E}) = -2i\mathscr{E}, \tag{16}$$

or

$$(\mathscr{U} - \mathscr{E})^{-1} = -\frac{1}{2i}(\mathscr{A} + i\mathscr{E}).$$

Thus, $\mathscr{U}$ does not have 1 as a proper value. It also follows from (16) that

$$(\mathscr{U} - \mathscr{E})\mathscr{A} = -2i\mathscr{E} - i(\mathscr{U} - \mathscr{E}) = -i(\mathscr{U} + \mathscr{E}),$$

or

$$\mathscr{A} = -i(\mathscr{U} + \mathscr{E})(\mathscr{U} - \mathscr{E})^{-1}.$$

This proves the first part of the theorem. The proof of the converse is fully analogous.

The formulas of Cayley establish a one-to-one correspondence between all symmetric transformations of a unitary space $\mathfrak{L}$ and those unitary transformations of $\mathfrak{L}$ which do not have 1 as a proper value. The analogous formulas

$$\mathscr{U} = (i\mathscr{E} + \mathscr{A})(i\mathscr{E} - \mathscr{A})^{-1} \tag{14'}$$

$$\mathscr{A} = i(\mathscr{U} - \mathscr{E})(\mathscr{U} + \mathscr{E})^{-1} \tag{15'}$$

give a one-to-one correspondence between all symmetric transformations of $\mathfrak{L}$ and those unitary transformations which do not have -1 as a proper value.

The transformations (14), (15), and also (14′), (15′), are possible because of the presence in the base field of the number i. If the base field is real, then the indicated formulas are not suitable. However, these formulas may be easily modified to make them suitable for any field. We have

THEOREM 3. *Let $\mathscr{A}$ be a skew-symmetric transformation of a unitary space $\mathfrak{L}$. Then the transformations $\mathscr{A} \pm \mathscr{E}$ are invertible, the transformation*

$$\mathscr{U} = (\mathscr{A} - \mathscr{E})(\mathscr{A} + \mathscr{E})^{-1} \tag{17}$$

is unitary and does not have 1 *as a proper value, and*

$$\mathscr{A} = -(\mathscr{U} + \mathscr{E})(\mathscr{U} - \mathscr{E})^{-1}. \tag{18}$$

Conversely, if $\mathscr{U}$ is unitary and does not have 1 *as a proper value, then the transformation $\mathscr{A}$, given by* (18), *is skew-symmetric, and $\mathscr{U}$ is expressed in terms of $\mathscr{A}$ by* (17).

Let $\mathscr{A}$ be skew-symmetric; then ± 1 are not proper values of $\mathscr{A}$, since the proper values of skew-symmetric transformations are either zero or pure imaginaries (see Section 81). Therefore, the transformations $\mathscr{A} \pm \mathscr{E}$ are nonsingular. Since $(\mathscr{A} + \mathscr{E})(\mathscr{A} - \mathscr{E}) = (\mathscr{A} - \mathscr{E})(\mathscr{A} + \mathscr{E})$ then $(\mathscr{A} - \mathscr{E})(\mathscr{A} + \mathscr{E})^{-1}(\mathscr{A} + \mathscr{E})^{-1}(\mathscr{A} - \mathscr{E})$. From (17) we have

$$\mathscr{U}^* = (\mathscr{A}^* + \mathscr{E})^{-1} = (\mathscr{A}^* - \mathscr{E}) = (-\mathscr{A} + \mathscr{E})^{-1}(-\mathscr{A} - \mathscr{E})$$
$$= (\mathscr{A} - \mathscr{E})^{-1}(\mathscr{A} + \mathscr{E}),$$

and hence

$$\mathscr{U}\mathscr{U}^* = (\mathscr{A} - \mathscr{E})(\mathscr{A} + \mathscr{E})^{-1}(\mathscr{A} - \mathscr{E})^{-1}(\mathscr{A} + \mathscr{E}) = \mathscr{E},$$

which shows that $\mathscr{U}$ is unitary. We omit the rest of the argument, since it is completely similar to that used in the proof of Theorem 2.

In conclusion we remark that the results of the last paragraph point out a resemblance between the properties of linear transformations of unitary spaces and the properties of complex numbers. Let us agree that linear transformations are in some sense analogous to complex numbers, and that conjugate transformations are analogous to conjugate complex numbers. Then symmetric transformations, characterized by the property $\mathscr{A}^* = \mathscr{A}$, are analogous to complex numbers satisfying the relation $\bar{z} = z$—that is, to real numbers; skew-symmetric transformations, characterized by the property $\mathscr{A}^* = -\mathscr{A}$, are analogous to complex numbers satisfying the relation $\bar{z} = -z$—that is, to pure imaginary numbers; unitary transformations with the property $\mathscr{U}\mathscr{U}^* = \mathscr{E}$ are analogous to complex numbers z for which $z\bar{z} = 1$; that is, $|z| = 1$. The decomposition $\mathscr{A} = \mathscr{B} + i\mathscr{C}$ in Section 83 corresponds to the representation of a complex number in the Cartesian form $z = x + iy$, and the polar decomposition $\mathscr{A} = \mathscr{D}\mathscr{U}$ corresponds to the representation of a complex number in the trigonometric form $z = \rho(\cos\varphi + i \sin\varphi)$, and so on.

* * *

86. Spectral Decomposition

From the geometric point of view, one of the simplest types of linear transformations is the projection of vectors onto a subspace. We will consider here some of the properties of these projection transformations.

Let $\mathfrak{A}$ be a linear subspace of a unitary space $\mathfrak{L}$. The set of vectors orthogonal to $\mathfrak{A}$ is the orthogonal subspace $\mathfrak{A}^\perp$; moreover, $\mathfrak{L}$ is the direct sum of $\mathfrak{A}$ and $\mathfrak{A}^\perp$. Consequently, each vector a in $\mathfrak{L}$ has a unique representation in the form

$$a = a' + a'', \tag{19}$$

where $a' \in \mathfrak{A}$ and $a'' \in \mathfrak{A}^\perp$. The vector a' is called the ***projection*** of the vector a on the subspace $\mathfrak{A}$. Placing in correspondence to each vector in $\mathfrak{L}$ its projection on $\mathfrak{A}$, we obtain a transformation of the space $\mathfrak{L}$, which is also called a ***projection***, and is denoted by $\mathscr{P}_{\mathfrak{A}}$. Thus, by definition,

$$a\mathscr{P}_{\mathfrak{A}} = a' .$$

The index $\mathfrak{A}$ is sometimes omitted for brevity.

Projection transformations are linear, since if the vector a has the decomposition (19), and b has the decomposition

$$b = b' + b'' ,$$

where $b' \in \mathfrak{A}$ and $b'' \in \mathfrak{A}^{\perp}$, then

$$\alpha a + \beta b = (\alpha a' + \beta b') + (\alpha a'' + \beta b'') ,$$

or

$$(\alpha a + \beta b)\mathscr{P} = \alpha a' + \beta b' ,$$

hence

$$(\alpha a + \beta b)\mathscr{P} = \alpha a\mathscr{P} + \beta b\mathscr{P} .$$

Projection transformations are nonnegative symmetric. Decomposition (19) yields

$$(a\mathscr{P}, a) = (a', a' + a'') = (a', a') \geqq 0 ,$$

so $\mathscr{P}$ is nonnegative. But if

$$b = b' + b'' ,$$

where $b' \in \mathfrak{A}$ and $b'' \in \mathfrak{A}^{\perp}$, then

$$(a\mathscr{P}, b) = (a', b' + b'') = (a', b') = (a' + a'', b') = (a, b\mathscr{P}) ,$$

that is, $\mathscr{P}$ is symmetric.

One further important property of projection transformations follows from (19). Evidently, for all a we have

$$a\mathscr{P}^2 = a'\mathscr{P} = a' = a\mathscr{P} ,$$

and hence

$$\mathscr{P}^2 = \mathscr{P} . \qquad (20)$$

A transformation which coincides with its square is called ***idempotent.*** Thus, (20) shows that *all projection transformations are idempotent.*

Conversely, the properties of idempotence and symmetry fully characterize projection transformations: *every symmetric idempotent transformation $\mathscr{P}$ is a projection on the range of $\mathscr{P}$.*

Let the range of $\mathscr{P}$ be $\mathfrak{A}$. Then each vector a has the decomposition

$$a = a\mathscr{P} + a(\mathscr{E} - \mathscr{P}) . \qquad (21)$$

The summand $a\mathscr{P}$, by definition, belongs to $\mathfrak{A}$. The second summand is orthogonal to $\mathfrak{A}$, since every vector in $\mathfrak{A}$ may be written $x\mathscr{P}$, where x is some vector in $\mathfrak{L}$, and, by the symmetry and idempotence of the transformation $\mathscr{P}$,

$$(x\mathscr{P}, a(\mathscr{E} - \mathscr{P})) = (x, a(\mathscr{E} - \mathscr{P})\mathscr{P}) = (x, a\mathscr{P} - a\mathscr{P}) = 0 .$$

Consequently, the decomposition (21) shows that $a\mathscr{P}$ is the projection of a on $\mathfrak{A}$, which was to be proved.

We now find the simplest form of the matrix of a projection transformation Choose orthogonal bases $e_1, \cdots, e_m$ and $e_{m+1}, \cdots, e_n$ of $\mathfrak{A}$ and $\mathfrak{A}^{\perp}$, respectively. Then the system $e_1, \cdots, e_m, e_{m+1}, \cdots, e_n$ is an orthonormal basis of the space $\mathfrak{L}$. The equalities

$$e_j\mathscr{P} = e_j\,, \qquad e_\alpha\mathscr{P} = 0 \quad (j = 1, \cdots, m,\ \alpha = m+1, \cdots, n)$$

show that in this basis the matrix of the transformation $\mathscr{P}$ has the form

$$P = \begin{bmatrix} 1 & & & & & & \\ & \cdot & & & & & \\ & & \cdot & & & & \\ & & & 1 & & & \\ & & & & 0 & & \\ & & & & & \cdot & \\ & & & & & & 0 \end{bmatrix}. \tag{22}$$

Conversely, if the matrix of some linear transformation $\mathscr{P}$ reduces to the form (22) in an orthonormal coordinate system, then $\mathscr{P}$ is evidently a projection transformation.

Let $\mathscr{P}$, $\mathscr{Q}$ be the operations of projection on subspaces $\mathfrak{A}$, $\mathfrak{B}$ of the space $\mathfrak{L}$. The question arises as to how the arrangement of the subspaces $\mathfrak{A}$, $\mathfrak{B}$ in $\mathfrak{L}$ affects the properties of the transformations $\mathscr{P}$, $\mathscr{Q}$. For example, what can be said about $\mathscr{P}$, $\mathscr{Q}$ if $\mathfrak{A}$, $\mathfrak{B}$ are orthogonal, or if $\mathfrak{A}$ is contained in $\mathfrak{B}$, and so on? To answer these questions, we first introduce a definition: *two projection transformations* $\mathscr{P}$, $\mathscr{Q}$ *are called orthogonal if* $\mathscr{P}\mathscr{Q} = \mathscr{O}$. Since projection transformations are symmetric, we have

$$\mathscr{Q}\mathscr{P} = \mathscr{Q}^*\mathscr{P}^* = (\mathscr{P}\mathscr{Q})^* = \mathscr{O}\,,$$

that is, if $\mathscr{P}$ and $\mathscr{Q}$ are orthogonal, then $\mathscr{Q}$ and $\mathscr{P}$ are orthogonal.

Projection transformations $\mathscr{P}$ *and* $\mathscr{Q}$ *are orthogonal if and only if their corresponding subspaces* $\mathfrak{A}$ *and* $\mathfrak{B}$ *are orthogonal.*

Let $\mathscr{P}\mathscr{Q} = \mathscr{O}$; then for $a \in \mathfrak{A}$, $b \in \mathfrak{B}$ we have

$$(a, b) = (a\mathscr{P}, b\mathscr{Q}) = (a\mathscr{P}\mathscr{Q}, b) = 0\,,$$

that is, $\mathfrak{A}$ is orthogonal to $\mathfrak{B}$. Conversely, if $\mathfrak{A}$ is orthogonal to $\mathfrak{B}$, then for any vector x in $\mathfrak{L}$,

$$x\mathscr{P} \in \mathfrak{A}\,, \qquad x(\mathscr{P}\mathscr{Q}) = (x\mathscr{P})\mathscr{Q} = \theta\,, \qquad \mathscr{P}\mathscr{Q} = \mathscr{O}\,.$$

For a detailed study of the properties of linear transformations it is customary to use their matrix representations. However, if for some reason the matrix representation is inconvenient, then one tries to express the given linear transformation in terms of transformations of a simpler character. In the case of normal transformations, these simpler transformations may be taken as projections.

A decomposition of the form

$$\mathscr{A} = \alpha_1 \mathscr{P}_1 + \cdots + \alpha_s \mathscr{P}_s \tag{23}$$

is called a spectral decomposition of the transformation $\mathscr{A}$, *if*

a) *the numbers* $\alpha_1, \cdots, \alpha_s$ *are distinct;*

b) $\mathscr{P}_j^* = \mathscr{P}_j \neq \mathscr{O}$, $\qquad j = 1, \cdots, s$;

c) $\mathscr{P}_j^2 = \mathscr{P}_j$, $\qquad j = 1, \cdots, s$;

d) $\mathscr{P}_j \mathscr{P}_k = \mathscr{O}$, $\qquad j \neq k, \quad j, k = 1, \cdots, s$;

e) $\mathscr{P}_1 + \cdots + \mathscr{P}_s = \mathscr{E}$.

Conditions b), c), d) mean that $\mathscr{P}_1, \cdots, \mathscr{P}_s$ are pairwise orthogonal projections.

It is clear that *spectral decompositions are admitted only by normal transformations.* It follows from (23) that

$$\mathscr{A}^* = \bar{\alpha}_1 \mathscr{P}_1 + \cdots + \bar{\alpha}_s \mathscr{P}_s,$$
$$\mathscr{A}\mathscr{A}^* = (\sum \alpha_j \mathscr{P}_j)(\sum \bar{\alpha}_k \mathscr{P}_k) = \sum \alpha_j \bar{\alpha}_j \mathscr{P}_j = \mathscr{A}^* \mathscr{A}.$$

Conversely, *every normal transformation of a complex unitary space admits a spectral decomposition.*

Let $\mathscr{A}$ be a normal transformation of a complex unitary space $\mathfrak{L}$. We have seen that $\mathfrak{L}$ has an orthonormal basis $e_1, \cdots, e_n$ of proper vectors of the transformation $\mathscr{A}$. We arrange these vectors so that those which correspond to the same proper value are adjacent. For example, let $e_1, \cdots, e_{m_1}$ correspond to the proper value α_1, let $e_{m_1+1}, \cdots, e_{m_2}$ correspond to the proper value α_2, and so on. Denote by $\mathfrak{L}_i$ the subspace spanned by the vectors $e_{m_{i-1}+1}, \cdots, e_{m_i}$ which correspond to the proper value α_i, for $i = 1, \cdots, s$. Since all the coordinate vectors of the subspace $\mathfrak{L}_i$ are proper vectors belonging to the same proper value α_j, then every vector in $\mathfrak{L}_i$ is a proper vector, with proper value α_i. We have

$$\mathfrak{L} = \mathfrak{L}_1 \dotplus \cdots \dotplus \mathfrak{L}_s. \tag{24}$$

where the subspaces $\mathfrak{L}_1, \cdots, \mathfrak{L}_s$ are pairwise orthogonal. Let $\mathscr{P}_i$ denote projection on the subspace $\mathfrak{L}_i$. It has been shown that the projections corresponding to orthogonal subspaces are orthogonal. Further, it follows from (24) that $\mathscr{P}_1 + \cdots + \mathscr{P}_s = \mathscr{P}$, where $\mathscr{P}$ is the projection on $\mathfrak{L}$. However, projection on $\mathfrak{L}$ is the identity transformation, so

$$\mathscr{P}_1 + \cdots + \mathscr{P}_s = \mathscr{E}. \tag{25}$$

Thus, the transformations $\mathscr{P}_1, \cdots, \mathscr{P}_s$ possess properties b) through e). We show finally that

$$\mathscr{A} = \alpha_1 \mathscr{P}_1 + \cdots + \alpha_s \mathscr{P}_s.$$

Let a be an arbitrary vector in $\mathfrak{L}$. Equality (25) yields

$$a = a\mathscr{P}_1 + \cdots + a\mathscr{P}_s . \tag{26}$$

The vector $a\mathscr{P}_i$ is contained in $\mathfrak{L}_i$, and all vectors in $\mathfrak{L}_i$ are proper vectors belonging to the proper value α_i; therefore, $a\mathscr{P}_i\mathscr{A} = \alpha_i a\mathscr{P}_i$. Operating on (26) by $\mathscr{A}$, we obtain

$$a\mathscr{A} = \alpha_1 a\mathscr{P}_1 + \cdots + \alpha_s a\mathscr{P}_s = a(\alpha_1\mathscr{P}_1 + \cdots + \alpha_s\mathscr{P}_s) ,$$

and hence

$$\mathscr{A} = \alpha_1\mathscr{P}_1 + \cdots + \alpha_s\mathscr{P}_s .$$

If

$$\mathscr{A} = \alpha_1\mathscr{P}_1 + \cdots + \alpha_s\mathscr{P}_s \tag{27}$$

is some spectral decomposition of the transformation $\mathscr{A}$, then $\alpha_1, \cdots, \alpha_s$ is the set of all the distinct proper values of this transformation.

Indeed, each transformation $\mathscr{P}_j$, by assumption, is different from $\mathscr{O}$. Consequently, there is a vector a in $\mathfrak{L}$ such that $a\mathscr{P}_j \neq \theta$. But then, by the orthogonality of the transformations $\mathscr{P}_1, \cdots, \mathscr{P}_j$, we obtain

$$a\mathscr{P}_j\mathscr{A} = \alpha_1 a\mathscr{P}_j\mathscr{P}_1 + \cdots + \alpha_s a\mathscr{P}_j\mathscr{P}_s = \alpha_j a\mathscr{P}_j ,$$

that is, $a\mathscr{P}_j$ is a proper vector belonging to the proper value α_j.

Conversely, let a be a nonzero proper vector of the transformation $\mathscr{A}$, which corresponds to the proper value β. It follows from property e) that

$$a = a\mathscr{P}_1 + \cdots + a\mathscr{P}_s . \tag{28}$$

Condition (27) yields

$$a\mathscr{A} = \alpha_1 a\mathscr{P}_1 + \cdots + \alpha_s a\mathscr{P}_s .$$

Since $a\mathscr{A} = \beta a$, then

$$\alpha_1 a\mathscr{P}_1 + \cdots + \alpha_s a\mathscr{P}_s = \beta a\mathscr{P}_1 + \cdots + \beta a\mathscr{P}_s .$$

Operating on this relation by $\mathscr{P}_j$ and using conditions c), d), we obtain

$$\alpha_j a\mathscr{P}_j = \beta a\mathscr{P}_j , \qquad (\alpha_j - \beta)a\mathscr{P}_j = \theta , \qquad (j = 1, \cdots, s).$$

The vector a is different from zero, and therefore at least one of the summands in (28) is different from zero. But then the equality $(\alpha_j - \beta)a\mathscr{P}_j = \theta$ gives $\beta = \alpha_j$. This completes the proof.

If

$$\mathscr{A} = \alpha_1\mathscr{P}_1 + \cdots + \alpha_s\mathscr{P}_s$$

is a spectral decomposition of the transformation $\mathscr{A}$ and

$$f(\lambda) = \beta_0 + \beta_1\lambda + \cdots + \beta_m\lambda^m$$

is a polynomial, then

$$f(\mathscr{A}) = f(\alpha_1)\mathscr{P}_1 + \cdots + f(\alpha_s)\mathscr{P}_s . \tag{29}$$

We have:

$$\mathscr{E} = \mathscr{P}_1 + \cdots + \mathscr{P}_s ,$$
$$\mathscr{A} = \alpha_1\mathscr{P}_1 + \cdots + \alpha_s\mathscr{P}_s ,$$
$$\mathscr{A}^2 = (\sum \alpha_j\mathscr{P}_j)(\sum \alpha_k\mathscr{P}_k) = \sum \alpha_j\alpha_k\mathscr{P}_j\mathscr{P}_k = \alpha_1^2\mathscr{P}_1 + \cdots + \alpha_s^2\mathscr{P}_s ,$$
$$\vdots$$
$$\mathscr{A}^m = (\sum \alpha_j^{m-1}\mathscr{P}_j)(\sum \alpha_k\mathscr{P}_k) = \sum \alpha_j^{m-1}\alpha_k\mathscr{P}_j\mathscr{P}_k = \alpha_1^m\mathscr{P}_1 + \cdots + \alpha_s^m\mathscr{P}_s .$$

If we multiply these equalities successively by the numbers $\beta_0, \cdots, \beta_m$ and add, we obtain the desired result.

If

$$\mathscr{A} = \alpha_1\mathscr{P}_1 + \cdots + \alpha_s\mathscr{P}_s$$

is some spectral decomposition of the transformation $\mathscr{A}$ *then*

$$\mathscr{P}_i = \frac{(\mathscr{A} - \alpha_1\mathscr{E})\cdots(\mathscr{A} - \alpha_{i-1}\mathscr{E})(\mathscr{A} - \alpha_{i+1}\mathscr{E})\cdots(\mathscr{A} - \alpha_s\mathscr{E})}{(\alpha_i - \alpha_1)\cdots(\alpha_i - \alpha_{i-1})(\alpha_i - \alpha_{i+1})\cdots(\alpha_i - \alpha_s)} .$$

To prove this, consider the polynomial

$$\varphi_i(\lambda) = \frac{(\lambda - \alpha_1)\cdots(\lambda - \alpha_{i-1})(\lambda - \alpha_{i+1})\cdots(\lambda - \alpha_s)}{(\alpha_i - \alpha_1)\cdots(\alpha_i - \alpha_{i-1})(\alpha_i - \alpha_{i+1})\cdots(\alpha_i - \alpha_s)} .$$

By (29),

$$\varphi_i(\mathscr{A}) = \varphi_i(\alpha_1)\mathscr{P}_1 + \cdots + \varphi_i(\alpha_s)\mathscr{P}_s .$$

But $\varphi_i(\alpha_j) = 0$, for $i \neq j$, and $\varphi_i(\alpha_i) = 1$; consequently, $\varphi_i(\mathscr{A}) = \mathscr{P}_i$.

The last property shows that *each normal transformation of a unitary space admits one and only one spectral decomposition.*

The existence of a spectral decomposition was established earlier, and we need only show its uniqueness. The coefficients $\alpha_1, \cdots, \alpha_s$ are the distinct proper values of the transformation $\mathscr{A}$, and thus are uniquely determined by $\mathscr{A}$. But, knowing these coefficients, we can write down the polynomials $\varphi_i(\lambda)$, and the projection transformations $\mathscr{P}_i$ are determined.

We note several further properties of spectral decompositions. The set of coefficients $\alpha_1, \cdots, \alpha_s$ of a spectral decomposition is called its ***spectrum.*** The *spectrum of a linear transformation* is the spectrum of its spectral decomposition. It was shown above that the spectrum of a normal transformation is the set of proper values of the transformation.

A normal transformation is i) *symmetric,* ii) *skew-symmetric, or* iii) *unitary if and only if its spectrum consists respectively, of* i) *real numbers,* ii) *pure imaginary numbers, or* iii) *numbers with modulus* 1.

Let

$$\mathscr{A} = \alpha_1\mathscr{P}_1 + \cdots + \alpha_s\mathscr{P}_s$$

be the spectral decomposition of the transformation $\mathscr{A}$. Then

$$\mathscr{A}^* = \bar{\alpha}_1\mathscr{P}_1 + \cdots + \bar{\alpha}_s\mathscr{P}_s$$

is the spectral decomposition of the conjugate transformation. Since each normal transformation admits only one spectral decomposition, the condition $\mathscr{A} = \mathscr{A}^*$ is equivalent to the equalities $\alpha_i = \bar{\alpha}_i$ for $i = 1, \cdots, s$; that is, equivalent to the condition that the spectrum be real. This proves the first assertion, and the remaining two are proved in a similar manner.

* * *

● EXAMPLES AND PROBLEMS

1. Decompose the following matrices into symmetric and skew-symmetric parts, and also find their polar decompositions:

$$\begin{bmatrix} 2 & 7 & 0 \\ 6 & 2 & 2 \\ 2 & 0 & 5 \end{bmatrix}, \qquad \begin{bmatrix} 0 & 1 & 0 \\ 4 & 0 & 0 \\ 0 & 0 & 9 \end{bmatrix}, \qquad \begin{bmatrix} -1 & 2 & -2 \\ 4 & -2 & -4 \\ 4 & 4 & 2 \end{bmatrix}.$$

2. Let $\mathfrak{L}$ be a two dimensional Euclidean space, and let $\mathscr{A}$ be a linear transformation of $\mathfrak{L}$ which has two nonorthogonal proper vectors a_1, a_2 of unit length, corresponding to the proper values α_1, α_2, where $\alpha_1 \neq \alpha_2$. Find the polar decomposition of the transformation $\mathscr{A}$, if $(a_1, a_2) = \cos\varphi$, where φ is known.

3. Give a matrix formulation of Cayley's transformation Theorems 2 and 3.

4. Show that every orthogonal matrix U of order 3, not having 1 as a proper value, has the form

$$U = \frac{1}{1 + \alpha^2 + \beta^2 + \gamma^2} \begin{bmatrix} \alpha^2 + \beta^2 - \gamma^2 - 1 & 2(\alpha + \beta\gamma) & 2(\beta - \alpha\gamma) \\ 2(-\alpha + \beta\gamma) & \alpha^2 - \beta^2 + \gamma^2 - 1 & 2(\gamma + \alpha\beta) \\ 2(-\beta - \alpha\gamma) & 2(-\gamma + \alpha\beta) & -\alpha^2 + \beta^2 + \gamma^2 - 1 \end{bmatrix}.$$

5. Let A be a row matrix, $A = [\alpha_1, \cdots, \alpha_n]$ with $|\alpha_1|^2 + \cdots + |\alpha_n|^2 = 1$. Then the matrix $B = \bar{A}'A$ is idempotent, or $B^2 = B$, and at the same time Hermitian; the matrix $C = 2B - E$ is Hermitian, unitary, and involutory—that is, $C^2 = E$.

6. The complex square matrices of order n constitute a linear space $\mathfrak{L}$ of dimension n^2, with the operations of addition and multiplication by a scalar. The matrices E_{ij}, in which all the elements are zero except for a 1 in the ith row and jth column, are a basis of the space $\mathfrak{L}$. The space $\mathfrak{L}$ is made unitary by agreeing that the E_{ij} are an orthonormal basis of $\mathfrak{L}$—that is, by defining the inner product of the matrices A, B by the formula

$$(A, B) = \sum \alpha_{ij}\bar{\beta}_{ij},$$

where α_{ij}, β_{ij} are the elements of the matrices A, B respectively. Multiplication on the right of all the matrices in $\mathfrak{L}$ by a matrix X gives a linear transformation of the space $\mathfrak{L}$. Show that

a) unitary matrices have length $\sqrt{n}$ in $\mathfrak{L}$;

b) multiplication on the right by conjugate-transpose matrices X, $\bar{X}'$ produces conjugate transformations of $\mathfrak{L}$;

c) multiplication on the right by a unitary matrix produces a unitary transformation of $\mathfrak{L}$;

d) multiplication on the right by a Hermitian matrix produces a symmetric, and multiplication on the right by a Hermitian skew-symmetric matrix produces a skew-symmetric, transformation of $\mathfrak{L}$.

7. Show that the sum of projection transformations $\mathscr{P}_{\mathfrak{A}}$, $\mathscr{P}_{\mathfrak{B}}$ is a projection transformation if and only if $\mathscr{P}_{\mathfrak{A}}\mathscr{P}_{\mathfrak{B}} = \mathscr{O}$; in this case, $\mathscr{P}_{\mathfrak{A}} + \mathscr{P}_{\mathfrak{A}} = \mathscr{P}_{\mathfrak{A}+\mathfrak{B}}$.

8. The product of projection transformations $\mathscr{P}_{\mathfrak{A}}$, $\mathscr{P}_{\mathfrak{B}}$ is a projection if and only if $\mathscr{P}_{\mathfrak{A}}$ and $\mathscr{P}_{\mathfrak{B}}$ are permutable; in this case, $\mathscr{P}_{\mathfrak{A}}\mathscr{P}_{\mathfrak{B}} = \mathscr{P}_{\mathfrak{A}\cap\mathfrak{B}}$.

9. The subspace $\mathfrak{A}$ is contained in the subspace $\mathfrak{B}$ if and only if $\mathscr{P}_{\mathfrak{A}}\mathscr{P}_{\mathfrak{B}} = \mathscr{P}_{\mathfrak{A}}$.

10. Show that

$$\mathscr{P}_{\mathfrak{A}^\perp} = \mathscr{E} - \mathscr{P}_{\mathfrak{A}}.$$

11. A subspace $\mathfrak{A}$ is invariant under a transformation $\mathscr{A}$ if and only if $\mathscr{P}\mathscr{A}\mathscr{P} = \mathscr{P}_{\mathscr{A}}$, where $\mathscr{P} = \mathscr{P}_{\mathfrak{A}}$.

12. If the transformations $\mathscr{A}$ and $\mathscr{B}$, with spectral decompositions $\mathscr{A} = \sum \alpha_j \mathscr{P}_j$, $\mathscr{B} = \sum \beta_k \mathscr{Q}_k$ are permutable, then each $\mathscr{P}_j$ permutes with each $\mathscr{Q}_k$.

13. If a normal transformation $\mathscr{A}$ permutes with the linear transformation $\mathscr{B}$, then $\mathscr{A}$ also permutes with $\mathscr{B}^*$.

14. Each unitary transformation $\mathscr{U}$ of a complex unitary space has a representation in the form $\mathscr{U} = e^{i\mathscr{A}}$, where $\mathscr{A}$ is a symmetric transformation. Conversely, the transformation $e^{i\mathscr{A}}$ is unitary for every symmetric transformation $\mathscr{A}$.

6 BILINEAR AND QUADRATIC FORMS

1. *Bilinear Forms*

87. The Transformation of Forms

A polynomial $F(\xi)$ in the indeterminates $\xi_1, \cdots, \xi_n$ with coefficients from some field K is called a ***p-th degree form*** *over* K *in* $\xi_1, \cdots, \xi_n$ if all the terms of F have degree p in the set of indeterminates. Forms of the first degree are called ***linear***, of the second degree, ***quadratic,*** of the third degree, ***cubic,*** and so on.

The fundamental problems of the theory of forms are concerned with the effects of linear transformations of the indeterminates on the coefficients of the forms, and the simplest types to which forms may be reduced by means of such transformations.

One problem is that of pairs of forms. Here one seeks a transformation of the indeterminates that will reduce two forms simultaneously to forms of the simplest type. One may also consider the problem of triples of forms, and so on.

The geometric interpretation of the transformation of forms will be given at the end of this chapter, but first the problem will be considered from a purely algebraic point of view, and will be solved for quadratic forms.

We write the formulas connecting the indeterminates $\xi_1, \cdots, \xi_n$ with the new indeterminates $\xi_1', \cdots, \xi_n'$, in accordance with Section 25:

$$\xi_j = \xi_1'\tau_{1j} + \xi_2'\tau_{2j} + \cdots + \xi_n'\tau_{nj} \qquad (j = 1, \cdots, n) . \tag{1}$$

The matrix $T = \|\tau_{ij}\|$ *will always be assumed invertible,* so that using (1) it is always possible to express the new indeterminates in terms of the old. The matrix T is called the *matrix of the transformation from the indeterminates* ξ_j *to the indeterminates* ξ'_j.

Usually it is necessary to transform the given forms sequentially: first one introduces new indeterminates ξ'_j by formulas (1), then by analogous formulas one introduces indeterminates ξ''_j from the ξ'_j, and so on. Let the matrix of the transformation from the indeterminates ξ to the indeterminates ξ' be $T = T_1$, and the matrix of the transformation from ξ' be T_2, and so on. Replacing in formulas (1) the ξ'_j by their expressions in terms of the ξ''_j, we obtain linear expressions for the ξ_j in terms of the ξ''_j. It is easily verified (see Section 25) that the matrix of the transformation from ξ to ξ'' is T_2T_1. Applying this result several times, we obtain the result: *if the transformation from the indeterminates* ξ *to the indeterminates* ξ' *has matrix* T_1, *the transformation from* ξ' *to* ξ'' *has matrix* T_2, *and so on, then the matrix of the resulting transformation from* ξ *to* $\xi^{(m)}$ *equals the product* $T_mT_{m-1}\cdots T_2T_1$ *of the matrices of all the intermediate transformations.*

For example, suppose it is required to transform the quadratic form

$$F = \xi_1^2 + \xi_3^2 - 2\xi_1\xi_2 - 2\xi_1\xi_3 + 10\xi_2\xi_3$$

to the simplest form. We have

$$F = (\xi_1 - \xi_2 - \xi_3)^2 - \xi_2^2 + 8\xi_2\xi_3 .$$

Introducing the new indeterminates

$$\xi'_1 = \xi_1 - \xi_2 - \xi_3, \quad \xi'_2 = \xi_2, \quad \xi'_3 = \xi_3 ,$$

we obtain

$$F' = \xi_1'^2 - \xi_2'^2 + 8\xi'_2\xi'_3 = \xi_1'^2 - (\xi'_2 - 4\xi'_3)^2 + 16\xi_3'^2 .$$

Now let

$$\xi''_1 = \xi'_1, \quad \xi''_2 = \xi'_2 - 4\xi'_3, \quad \xi'_3 = 4\xi'_3 .$$

This transforms F' into

$$F'' = \xi_1''^2 - \xi_2''^2 + \xi_3''^2 .$$

By the above result, the matrix of the transformation from ξ'' to ξ is

$$\begin{bmatrix} 1 & 0 & 0 \\ -1 & 1 & 0 \\ -1 & 0 & 1 \end{bmatrix} \begin{bmatrix} 1 & 0 & 0 \\ 0 & 1 & 0 \\ 0 & -4 & 4 \end{bmatrix} = \begin{bmatrix} 1 & 0 & 0 \\ -1 & 1 & 0 \\ -1 & -4 & 4 \end{bmatrix}.$$

As a second example we consider the general problem of the transformation of a system of m linear forms in n variables:

$$\begin{aligned} f_1 &= \xi_1\alpha_{11} + \xi_2\alpha_{21} + \cdots + \xi_n\alpha_{n1} , \\ &\vdots \\ f_m &= \xi_1\alpha_{1m} + \xi_2\alpha_{2m} + \cdots + \xi_n\alpha_{nm} . \end{aligned} \tag{2}$$

The matrix $A = ||\alpha_{ij}||$, rectangular for $m \neq n$, is called the matrix of this system. If in the given forms we replace the indeterminates ξ_j by their expressions in terms of the ξ'_j from (1), we obtain a system of m linear forms in the new indeterminates ξ'_j. An immediate computation shows that the matrix A_1 of the new system is given by

$$A_1 = TA\ ,$$

that is, *under a transformation to new indeterminates, the matrix of the system of linear forms is multiplied on the left by the matrix of the transformation of indeterminates.*

To reduce system (2) to simplest form, choose the first n linearly independent forms among $f_1, \cdots, f_m, \xi_1, \cdots, \xi_n$. Let these be the forms $f_{i_1}, \cdots, f_{i_r}, \xi_{i_{r+1}}, \cdots, \xi_{i_n}$. The number r is evidently the rank of the matrix A. Now introduce the indeterminates ξ'_j by the formulas

$$\xi'_1 = f_{i_1}(\xi), \cdots, \quad \xi'_r = f_{i_r}(\xi), \quad \xi'_{r+1} = \xi_{i_{r+1}}, \cdots, \quad \xi'_n = \xi_{i_n}\ ,$$

after which the given system (2) will assume the desired simpler form

$$\xi'_1, \cdots, \xi'_r, f'_{r+1}, \cdots, f'_m$$

where $f'_{r+1}, \cdots, f'_m$ are linear forms in $\xi'_1, \cdots, \xi'_n$. In particular, if all the original forms are linearly independent, then under the indicated change of indeterminates they are reduced to the canonical form $f'_1 = \xi'_1, \cdots, f_m = \xi'_m$.

88. Equivalence of Bilinear Forms

Instead of polynomials in one system of indeterminates $\xi_1, \cdots, \xi_n$, one often considers polynomials in two systems of indeterminates, say $\xi_1, \cdots, \xi_n$ and $\eta_1, \cdots, \eta_s$, and also in several systems of indeterminates. A polynomial in several systems of indeterminates is called a ***form*** if it is homogeneous in each separate system of indeterminates. Of particular interest are those forms which are linear in each system of indeterminates. If there are two systems of indeterminates, the form is ***bilinear***; if three, it is ***trilinear***; in the general case, it is called ***multilinear.***

The number of indeterminates in each system may be distinct. The meaning of the problem of the transformation of forms in several systems of indeterminates depends on whether each system of indeterminates is subjected to a linear transformation that is independent of the transformations of the other systems, or whether the same transformation operates on all the systems.

Forms that may be obtained one from the other by independent choices of the transformations of the systems of indeterminates are called ***equivalent.*** If all the systems of indeterminates are equinumerous, and if of two forms in these systems one can be obtained from the other by means of the same linear transformation operating on each of the systems, then these forms are called ***congruent.*** It is clear that congruent forms are always equivalent. The converse, of course, is not generally true. It is easy to give examples of equivalent forms that are not congruent, even among bilinear forms. In the present section we consider the simple problem of the equivalence of bilinear forms; in the next section we will consider the problem of the congruence of symmetric bilinear forms.

A bilinear form in the systems of indeterminates $\xi_1, \cdots, \xi_n$ and $\eta_1, \cdots, \eta_n$ may be written

$$F = \sum \alpha_{ij}\xi_i\eta_j \qquad (i, j = 1, \cdots, n) .$$

The matrix $A = ||\alpha_{ij}||$, consisting of the coefficients of the form, is called the ***matrix of the form,*** and the rank of the matrix A is called the ***rank of the form.***

Using the row matrices

$$X = [\xi_1, \cdots, \xi_n], \quad Y = [\eta_1, \cdots, \eta_n] ,$$

we may write the form F as

$$F = XAY' . \tag{3}$$

Suppose now that we wish to pass from the indeterminates ξ, η to new indeterminates ξ', η', connected with the old by

$$\xi_j = \sum \xi'_k\tau_{kj}, \quad \eta_j = \sum \eta'_k\sigma_{kj} ,$$

or, in matrix form,

$$X = X_1T, \quad Y = Y_1S , \tag{4}$$

where $T = ||\tau_{ij}||$, $S = ||\sigma_{ij}||$, and

$$X_1 = [\xi'_1, \cdots, \xi'_n], \quad Y_1 = [\eta'_1, \cdots, \eta'_n] .$$

Replacing in (3) the expressions of X, Y from (4), we obtain

$$F = X_1TAS'Y'_1 = X_1A_1Y'_1 ,$$

where A_1 is the matrix of the resulting form.

Consequently, if, in a bilinear form with matrix A, transformations of the systems of indeterminates are performed — on the first system by a matrix T, on the second by a matrix S — then the resulting bilinear form has the matrix

$$A_1 = TAS' . \tag{5}$$

As has already been observed, bilinear forms which can be obtained one from another by independent linear transformations of the systems of indeterminates are called equivalent. On the other hand, according to Section 51, the matrices A and A_1 are called equivalent over the field K if there exist nonsingular matrices, P, Q with elements in K such that $A_1 = PAQ$. Comparing this with (5), we see that *bilinear forms over an arbitrary field K are equivalent if and only if their matrices are equivalent over K.*

By Section 52, all square matrices of given order n and rank r are equivalent to the matrix $E_r \dotplus O_{n-r}$, where E_r is the identity matrix of order r and O_{n-r} is the zero matrix of order $n-r$. Applying this to bilinear forms, we obtain the following result, which fully solves the problem of equivalence for bilinear forms.

Bilinear forms over an arbitrary field are equivalent if and only if their matrices have the same order and the same rank.

Forms whose determinates are different from zero are called ***nonsingular***, and the remaining forms are called ***singular***. The preceding result shows that all nonsingular bilinear forms in systems of n indeterminates are equivalent to the form

$$\xi_1\eta_1 + \cdots + \xi_n\eta_n ,$$

while the singular forms are equivalent to forms

$$\xi_1\eta_1 + \cdots + \xi_r\eta_r , \qquad (r = 0, 1, \cdots, n-1) ,$$

where r is the rank of the given form.

If the base field is the field of complex numbers, then together with the customary bilinear forms one also considers ***Hermitian forms***

$$F = \sum \alpha_{ij}\xi_i\bar{\eta}_j ,$$

where the overbar denotes complex conjugation. A Hermitian bilinear form with matrix A may be written

$$F = XA\bar{Y}' ,$$

and the matrix A_1 of the Hermitian form arising from F by means of the transformations of indeterminates (4) is given by

$$A_1 = TA\bar{S}' . \tag{6}$$

As before, each Hermitian bilinear form in n indeterminates is equivalent to a form

$$\xi_1\bar{\eta}_1 + \cdots + \xi_r\bar{\eta}_r ,$$

where r is the rank of the given form.

89. Congruence of Symmetric Bilinear Forms

As defined above, two bilinear forms, each in two given systems of n indeterminates, are congruent if one can be obtained from the other by transforming both systems of indeterminates by means of the same matrix.

Setting $S = T$ in formula (5), we conclude that *if both systems of indeterminates of a bilinear form with matrix A are transformed by the matrix T, then the matrix of the resulting form is given by*

$$A_1 = TAT' . \tag{7}$$

Matrices A, A_1 that are connected by a relation of type (7), where T is a suitable nonsingular matrix, are called ***congruent***. Therefore bilinear forms are congruent if and only if their matrices are congruent.

Bilinear forms whose matrices are symmetric or skew-symmetric are called ***symmetric*** or ***skew-symmetric*** respectively.

All forms congruent to a given symmetric or skew-symmetric bilinear form are symmetric or skew-symmetric, respectively.

Indeed, if $A' = \pm A$, then from (7) we have

$$A_1' = TA'T' = \pm TAT' = \pm A_1' .$$

In a similar way, considering Hermitian bilinear forms, we see from (6) that the matrix A_1 of a Hermitian form arising from a Hermitian form with matrix A under the transformation of both systems of indeterminates by a matrix T is given by

$$A_1 = TA\bar{T}' . \tag{8}$$

Matrices A_1, A related in this way are called ***Hermitian-congruent.*** Therefore, the congruence of Hermitian bilinear forms is equivalent to the Hermitian congruence of their matrices.

A Hermitian bilinear form is called ***symmetric*** if its matrix is Hermitian-symmetric — that is, if $\bar{A}' = A$. It follows immediately from (8) that all forms congruent to a given symmetric Hermitian bilinear form are symmetric.

Since the equivalence of matrices follows from their congruence, equality of rank is a necessary condition for the congruence of forms. However, this condition is far from sufficient. Sufficient conditions under general hypotheses will be considered in Section 96; here they will be given only in the more important special cases.

First, let K be the field of real numbers, and let A be a symmetric matrix. Then, by Section 80, there is a real unitary matrix U such that the matrix $A_1 = UAU^{-1}$ is diagonal. But since U is unitary and real, $U\bar{U}' = E$, or $U^{-1} = U'$; that is, $A_1 = UAU'$. Thus, A is congruent to the diagonal matrix A_1, and we have proved

THEOREM 1. *Every real symmetric bilinear form can be reduced, by means of a suitable real unitary transformation of the indeterminates, to the form*

$$\alpha_1\xi_1\eta_1 + \cdots + \alpha_r\xi_r\eta_r , \tag{9}$$

where r is the rank of the form and $\alpha_1, \cdots, \alpha_r$ are the nonzero characteristic numbers of the matrix of the form. In particular, for unitary congruence of real symmetric bilinear forms it is necessary and sufficient that the matrices of the forms have identical characteristic polynomials.

This theorem gives more than was originally required. It asserts that the reduction to diagonal form is realized by means of a *unitary transformation* of indeterminates. If a unitary transformation of indeterminates is not needed, then the reduction may be continued to an even simpler form. Let the given form be already reduced to the form (9). We reorder the indeterminates so all the terms of (9) with positive coefficients come first: $\alpha_1, \cdots, \alpha_s$ positive, and $\alpha_{s+1}, \cdots, \alpha_r$ negative. Then, setting

$$\xi_j' = \sqrt{\alpha_j}\,\xi_j\,,\ \eta_j' = \sqrt{\alpha_j}\,\eta_j \qquad (j = 1, \cdots, s)\,,$$
$$\xi_k' = \sqrt{-\alpha_k}\,\xi_k\,,\ \eta_k = \sqrt{-\alpha_k}\,\eta_k \qquad (k = s+1, \cdots, r)\,,$$

we obtain a reduction to the form

$$\xi_1'\eta_1' + \cdots + \xi_s'\eta_s' - \xi_{s+1}'\eta_{s+1}' - \cdots - \xi_r'\eta_r'\,. \tag{10}$$

The difference

$$\sigma = s - (r - s) = 2s - r$$

is called the ***signature*** of the form (10). Evidently the form (10) is completely determined by its rank and signature, since $s = (\sigma + r)/2$. That the signature does not depend on the method of reducing the given form to (10), and thus is uniquely determined by the given form, is expressed by the so-called ***law of inertia,*** which will be considered in detail in Section 92.

The situation is completely analogous for Hermitian symmetric forms. Let F be a Hermitian form with Hermitian-symmetric matrix A. By Theorem 4a of Section 80 there exists a unitary matrix U such that the matrix $A_1 = UAU^{-1}$ is real and diagonal. Since U is unitary, $U^{-1} = \bar{U}'$, hence $A_1 = UA\bar{U}'$, and we have proved

THEOREM 2. *Every Hermitian symmetric bilinear form may be reduced, by means of a unitary transformation of indeterminates, to the diagonal form*

$$\alpha_1\xi_1\bar{\eta}_1 + \cdots + \alpha_r\xi_r\bar{\eta}_r$$

with real coefficients. The numbers $\alpha_1, \cdots, \alpha_r$ are the non-zero zeros of the characteristic polynomial of the matrix of the given form; therefore, for the unitary congruence of Hermitian-symmetric bilinear forms it is necessary and sufficient that the matrices of these forms have identical characteristic polynomials.

If we consider not unitary congruence, but congruence under arbitrary linear transformations, then the reduction process may be continued in the way indicated above, resulting in a form

$$\xi_1\bar{\eta}_1 + \cdots + \xi_s\bar{\eta}_s - \xi_{s+1}\bar{\eta}_{s+1} - \cdots - \xi_r\bar{\eta}_r\,. \tag{11}$$

Consequently, any Hermitian-symmetric form can be reduced to one of these $n+1$ types of forms for $r = 0, 1, \cdots, n$. The noncongruence of forms (11) for distinct s again follows from the law of inertia.

● EXAMPLES AND PROBLEMS

1. Show that the system of linear forms

$$\xi_1 + \xi_2,\quad \xi_2 + \xi_3,\quad \xi_3 + \xi_4,\quad \xi_4 + \xi_1$$

is equivalent to the system

$$\xi_1 + \xi_2 + \xi_3,\quad \xi_2 + \xi_3 + \xi_4,\quad \xi_1 + \xi_3 + \xi_4,\quad 2\xi_1 + \xi_3$$

and is not equivalent to the system

$$\xi_1 - \xi_2 + \xi_3, \quad \xi_2 + \xi_3 - \xi_4, \quad \xi_1 + \xi_3, \quad 2\xi_1 + 3\xi_3 - \xi_4 .$$

2. Show that the system of linear forms

$$f_i = \xi_1\alpha_{1i} + \xi_2\alpha_{2i} + \cdots + \xi_n\alpha_{ni} \qquad (i = 1, \cdots, m) \tag{12}$$

is equivalent to the system

$$g_i = \xi_1\beta_{1i} + \xi_2\beta_{2i} + \cdots + \xi_n\beta_{ni} \qquad (i = 1, \cdots, m) \tag{13}$$

if and only if the system of vectors

$$a_i = [\alpha_{1i}, \alpha_{2i}, \cdots, \alpha_{ni}] \qquad (i = 1, \cdots, m) \tag{14}$$

is carried by a nonsingular linear transformation of the space of row-vectors into the system

$$b_i = [\beta_{1i}, \beta_{2i}, \cdots, \beta_{ni}] \qquad (i = 1, \cdots, m) . \tag{15}$$

3. Show that the system of linear forms (12) can be reduced, by means of a unitary transformation of indeterminates, to the system (13) if and only if the system (14) of vectors of the unitary space of rows can be carried by a unitary transformation of this space into the system of vectors (15).
4. Show that for the equivalence of bilinear forms in systems containing different numbers of indeterminates, it is necessary and sufficient that the matrices of the forms have the same dimensions (numbers of rows and columns) and the same rank. In particular, bilinear forms in the systems $\xi_1, \cdots, \xi_n$ and $\eta_1, \cdots, \eta_m$ $(n>m)$ having rank r are equivalent to the form $\xi_1\eta_1 + \cdots + \xi_r\eta_r$.

2. Quadratic Forms

90. Congruence

According to the general definition, a quadratic form in the indeterminates $\xi_1, \cdots, \xi_n$ is a second-degree homogeneous polynomial in these indeterminates. Each quadratic form in these indeterminates admits a unique symmetric representation:

$$F(\xi) = \sum \alpha_{ij}\xi_i\xi_j \qquad (\alpha_{ij} = \alpha_{ji}) . \tag{1}$$

The matrix $A = ||\alpha_{ij}||$ is the matrix of the quadratic form, and the symmetric bilinear form

$$F(\xi, \eta) = \sum \alpha_{ij}\xi_i\eta_j$$

in two systems of indeterminates, having the same matrix as the quadratic form, is called the ***polar form*** of the quadratic form. Identifying the second system of indeterminates with the first in the polar form, we obtain the initial quadratic form. At the same time, this establishes a one-to-one correspondence between quadratic forms and symmetric bilinear forms. For example, let

$$F(\xi) = \xi_1^2 - \xi_3^2 + 3\xi_1\xi_2 - 6\xi_2\xi_3 .$$

Written symmetrically, this becomes

$$F(\xi) = \xi_1^2 - \xi_3^2 + \frac{3}{2}\xi_1\xi_2 + \frac{3}{2}\xi_2\xi_1 - 3\xi_2\xi_3 - 3\xi_3\xi_2 ,$$

and the corresponding polar form is

$$F(\xi, \eta) = \xi_1\eta_1 - \xi_3\eta_3 + \frac{3}{2}\xi_1\eta_2 + \frac{3}{2}\xi_2\eta_1 - 3\xi_2\eta_3 - 3\xi_3\eta_2$$

We say that a quadratic form is diagonal if its matrix is diagonal— that is, if the form contains only terms with squared indeterminates.

By performing a linear change of indeterminates with matrix T on the form (1), we obtain a new form (see Section 87)

$$F(\xi) = XAX' = X_1TAT'X_1' ,$$

where $X = [\xi_1, \cdots, \xi_n]$, $X_1 = [\xi_1', \cdots, \xi_n']$, with matrix

$$A_1 = TAT' .$$

Thus, the matrix of a quadratic form changes in the same way as the matrix of the corresponding polar form. It follows that quadratic forms are congruent if and only if the corresponding polar forms are congruent, and from Theorem 1 of the preceding paragraph we immediately obtain

THEOREM 1. *Each real quadratic form, under a suitable orthogonal transformation of indeterminates, reduces to the diagonal form*

$$\alpha_1\xi_1^2 + \cdots + \alpha_r\xi_r^2 ,$$

where r is the rank of the original form, and $\alpha_1, \cdots, \alpha_r$ are the nonzero characteristic numbers of the matrix of the form. In particular, for orthogonal congruence of real quadratic forms it is necessary and sufficient that the matrices of the given forms have identical characteristic polynomials.

If nonorthogonal transformations of indeterminates are also admitted, then further reduction is possible. If $\alpha_1, \cdots, \alpha_s$ are positive, $\alpha_{s+1}, \cdots, \alpha_r$ negative, then the substitution

$$\xi_i' = \sqrt{\alpha_i}\,\xi_i, \quad \xi_j' = \sqrt{-\alpha_j}\,\xi_j \qquad (i = 1, \cdots, s,\ j = s+1, \cdots, r) \qquad (2)$$

reduces (2) to the form

$$\xi_1'^2 + \cdots + \xi_s'^2 - \xi_{s+1}'^2 - \cdots - \xi_r'^2 .$$

Consequently, every quadratic form over the real field can be reduced to such a form. Other fields will be considered in the next section.

An expression

$$F(\xi) = \sum \alpha_{ij}\xi_i\bar{\xi}_j = XA\bar{X}' \qquad (X = [\xi_1, \cdots, \xi_n]) ,$$

in which $\alpha_{ij} = \alpha_{ji}$, for $i, j = 1, \cdots, n$ is called a ***Hermitian quadratic form*** in the indeterminates $\xi_1, \cdots, \xi_n$ with matrix $A = ||\alpha_{ij}||$. The Hermitian symmetric bilinear form $F(\xi, \eta) = \sum \alpha_{ij}\xi_i\bar{\eta}_j$ is called the ***polar form*** of $F(\xi)$. The matrix of a Hermitian quadratic form changes in the same way as the matrix of the corresponding polar form. Therefore, congruence of the corresponding polar forms, and the theorem in Section 89 on the reduction of Hermitian symmetric bilinear forms yields

THEOREM 2. *Each Hermitian quadratic form, by means of a unitary transformation of indeterminates, can be reduced to the form*

$$\alpha_1\xi_1\bar{\xi}_1 + \cdots + \alpha_r\xi_r\bar{\xi}_r \,, \tag{3}$$

where r is the rank, and $\alpha_1, \cdots, \alpha_r$ are the nonzero characteristic numbers, of the matrix of the given form. For the unitary congruence of Hermitian quadratic forms it is necessary and sufficient that the matrices of the given forms have identical characteristic polynomials.

Applying the transformation (2), the form (3) may be reduced to

$$\xi_1'\bar{\xi}_1' + \cdots + \xi_s'\bar{\xi}_s' - \xi_{s+1}'\bar{\xi}_{s+1}' - \cdots - \xi_r'\bar{\xi}_r' \,.$$

91. Lagrange's Algorithm

One of the simplest methods of reducing a quadratic form to diagonal form is the so-called method of Lagrange, which will be considered here. We assume that the base field is an arbitrary field of characteristic different from 2.

Suppose we wish to reduce (1) to diagonal form. Two cases are possible: a) the form contains at least one squared indeterminate; b) the form does not contain a squared indeterminate.

a) Suppose, for example, that $\alpha_{11} \neq 0$. If we represent (1) in the form

$$\begin{aligned} F &= \alpha_{11}\xi_1^2 + 2\alpha_{12}\xi_1\xi_2 + \cdots + 2\alpha_{1n}\xi_1\xi_n + \sum_{\lambda,\mu>1} \alpha_{\lambda\mu}\xi_\lambda\xi_\mu \\ &= \alpha_{11}^{-1}(\alpha_{11}\xi_1 + \alpha_{12}\xi_2 + \cdots + \alpha_{1n}\xi_n)^2 \\ &\qquad - \alpha_{11}^{-1}(\alpha_{12}^2\xi_2^2 + 2\alpha_{12}\alpha_{13}\xi_2\xi_3 + \cdots + \alpha_{1n}^2\xi_n^2) + \sum_{\lambda,\mu>1} \alpha_{\lambda\mu}\xi_\lambda\xi_\mu \\ &= \alpha_{11}^{-1}(\alpha_{11}\xi_1 + \alpha_{12}\xi_2 + \cdots + \alpha_{1n}\xi_n)^2 + F_1(\xi_2, \cdots, \xi_n) \,, \end{aligned}$$

where F_1 is a quadratic form in $\xi_2, \cdots, \xi_n$, and apply the substitution

$$\begin{aligned} \xi_1' &= \alpha_{11}\xi_1 + \alpha_{12}\xi_2 + \cdots + \alpha_{1n}\xi_n \,, \\ \xi_i' &= \xi_i \qquad (i = 2, \cdots, n) \,, \end{aligned}$$

we transform F into the form

$$F = \alpha_{11}^{-1}\xi_1'^2 + F_1 \,,$$

where F_1 does not depend on ξ_1'.

b) Let $\alpha_{11} = \cdots = \alpha_{nn} = 0$, but, say, $\alpha_{12} \neq 0$. Write F in the form

$$F = 2\xi_1(\alpha_{12}\xi_2 + \cdots + \alpha_{1n}\xi_n) + F_1(\xi_2, \cdots, \xi_n)$$

and set

$$\xi_2' = \alpha_{12}\xi_2 + \cdots + \alpha_{1n}\xi_n - \xi_1 ,$$
$$\xi_i' = \xi_i \qquad (i = 1, 3, 4, \cdots, n) .$$

We then obtain the form

$$F = 2\xi_1'(\xi_1' + \xi_2') + F_1 = 2\xi_1'^2 + 2\xi_1'\xi_2' + 2\alpha_{12}^{-1}\alpha_{23}\xi_1'\xi_3' + \cdots ,$$

which contains the square of the indeterminate ξ_1'.

Thus, applying process a) and supplementing it when necessary with process b), we may reduce the given form to diagonal form.

* * *

Example. Reduce the following quadratic form to diagonal form:

$$F = \xi_1^2 + 4\xi_2^2 + 8\xi_3^2 - \xi_4^2 - 4\xi_1\xi_2 + 6\xi_1\xi_3 - 12\xi_2\xi_3 + 2\xi_3\xi_4 + \xi_2\xi_5 - \xi_4\xi_5 \cdot$$

We have

$$F = (\xi_1 - 2\xi_2 + 3\xi_3)^2 - \xi_3^2 - \xi_4^2 + 2\xi_3\xi_4 + \xi_2\xi_5 - \xi_4\xi_5 .$$

Using the substitution

$$\xi_1' = \xi_1 - 2\xi_2 + 3\xi_3 , \quad \xi_i' = \xi_i \qquad (i > 1) ,$$

we obtain the form

$$F_1 = \xi_1'^2 - \xi_3'^2 + 2\xi_3'\xi_4' - \xi_4'^2 + \xi_2'\xi_5' - \xi_4'\xi_5' = \xi_1'^2 - (\xi_3' - \xi_4')^2 + \xi_2'\xi_5' - \xi_4'\xi_5' ,$$

which under the transformation

$$\eta_3 = \xi_3' - \xi_4' , \quad \eta_i = \xi_i' \qquad (i \neq 3)$$

becomes

$$F_2 = \eta_1^2 - \eta_3^2 + \eta_2\eta_5 - \eta_4\eta_5 ,$$

Now, according to b), we perform the substitution

$$\eta_4' = \eta_2 - \eta_4 - \eta_5 , \quad \eta_i' = \eta_i \qquad (i \neq 4) ,$$

and obtain the form

$$F_3 = \eta_1'^2 - \eta_3'^2 + (\eta_4' + \eta_5')\eta_5' = \eta_1'^2 - \eta_3'^2 + \left(\eta_5' + \frac{1}{2}\eta_4'\right)^2 - \frac{1}{4}\eta_4'^2 ,$$

The substitution

$$\zeta_2 = \eta_5' + \frac{1}{2}\eta_4' , \quad \zeta_5 = \eta_2' , \quad \zeta_i = \eta_i' \qquad (i = 1, 3, 4) ,$$

reduces this form to the diagonal form

$$F_4 = \zeta_1^2 + \zeta_2^2 - \zeta_2^2 - \frac{1}{4}\zeta_4^2 .$$

To find the matrix T of the transformation from the indeterminates ζ_i to the initial indeterminates ξ_i, it is sufficient, by Section 87, to multiply together the matrices of the intermediate transformations.

* * *

If instead of a quadratic form it is required to reduce a symmetric bilinear form to diagonal form, then we change the bilinear form to the corresponding quadratic form, reduce the latter to diagonal form and compute the matrix of the transformation of indeterminates. Because of the connection between quadratic and bilinear forms, this same transformation of indeterminates will also reduce the bilinear form to diagonal form.

We consider finally the problem of the reduction of skew-symmetric bilinear forms

$$F = \sum \alpha_{ij}\xi_i\eta_j \qquad (\alpha_{ij} = -\alpha_{ji}) ,$$

with coefficients from a completely arbitrary field.

If all the coefficients are zero, the form is already reduced. In the contrary case, suppose that $\alpha_{12} \neq 0$. Rewriting the form, we have

$$F = \xi_1(\alpha_{12}\eta_2 + \cdots + \alpha_{1n}\eta_n) - \eta_1(\alpha_{12}\xi_2 + \cdots + \alpha_{1n}\xi_n) + R(\xi_2, \cdots, \xi_n, \eta_2, \cdots, \eta_n) .$$

Applying the transformation

$$\xi_2' = \alpha_{12}\xi_2 + \cdots + \alpha_{1n}\xi_n, \quad \eta_2' = \alpha_{12}\eta_2 + \cdots + \alpha_{1n}\eta_n ,$$
$$\xi_i' = \xi_i, \quad \eta_i' = \eta_i \qquad (i = 1, 3, 4, \cdots, n) ,$$

we obtain the form

$$F_1 = \xi_1'\eta_2' - \xi_2'\eta_1' + R_1(\xi_2', \cdots, \xi_n', \eta_2', \cdots, \eta_n') .$$

Now there are two possible cases: a) the remainder R_1 does not involve ξ_2', and consequently does not involve η_2'; b) the remainder involves ξ_2'. In case a) the process is continued only with the remainder, since it does not depend on the excluded terms $\xi_1'\eta_2' - \xi_2'\eta_1'$. In case b) we write F_1 in the form

$$\begin{aligned} F_1 &= \xi_1'\eta_2' - \xi_2'\eta_1' + \xi_2'(\alpha_{23}'\eta_3' + \cdots + \alpha_{2n}'\eta_n') - \eta_2'(\alpha_{23}'\xi_3' + \cdots + \alpha_{2n}'\xi_n') + R_2(\xi_3', \cdots) \\ &= (\xi_1' - \alpha_{23}'\xi_3' - \cdots - \alpha_{2n}'\xi_n')\eta_2' - (\eta_1' - \alpha_{23}'\eta_3' - \cdots - \alpha_{2n}'\eta_n')\xi_2' + R_2(\xi_3', \cdots) \end{aligned}$$

and perform the transformation

$$\xi_1'' = \xi_1' - \alpha_{23}'\xi_3' - \cdots - \alpha_{2n}'\xi_n', \quad \eta_1'' = \eta_1' - \alpha_{23}'\eta_3' - \cdots - \alpha_{2n}'\eta_n')$$
$$\xi_i'' = \xi_i', \quad \eta_i'' = \eta_i' \qquad (i = 2, \cdots, n) .$$

The result is the form

$$\xi_1''\eta_2'' - \xi_2''\eta_1'' + R_2(\xi_3'', \cdots, \eta_3'', \cdots) .$$

Repeating the process on the remainder, and then on the new remainder, and so on, we reduce the given form to the form

$$\xi_1\eta_2 - \xi_2\eta_1 + \xi_3\eta_4 - \xi_4\eta_3 + \cdots + \xi_{2r-1}\eta_{2r} - \xi_{2r}\eta_{2r-1} ,$$

where $2r$ is the rank of the reduced form and consequently also of the original form. In particular, we again find that *the rank of a skew-symmetric matrix is always an even number.*

* * *

Example. Reduce the form

$$F = \xi_1\eta_2 - \xi_2\eta_1 + \xi_1\eta_3 - \xi_3\eta_1 + 2\xi_4\eta_1 - 2\xi_1\eta_4 + 3\xi_2\eta_3 - 3\xi_3\eta_2 + \xi_2\eta_4 - \xi_4\eta_2 - 4\xi_3\eta_4 + 4\xi_4\eta_3 .$$

In agreement with the above method, we first apply the substitution

$$\xi_2' = \xi_2 + \xi_3 - 2\xi_4 , \quad \eta_2' = \eta_2 + \eta_3 - 2\eta_4 , \quad \xi_i' = \xi_i , \quad \eta_i' = \eta_i \qquad (i = 1, 3, 4) ,$$

after which the form becomes

$$F_1 = \xi_1'\eta_2' - \xi_2'\eta_1' + 3\xi_2'\eta_3' - 3\xi_3'\eta_2' + \xi_2'\eta_4' - \xi_4'\eta_2' - 4\xi_3'\eta_4' + 4\xi_4'\eta_3' .$$

We now perform the transformation

$$\xi_1'' = \xi_1' - 3\xi_3' - \xi_4' , \quad \eta_1'' = \eta_1' - 3\eta_3' - \eta_4' , \quad \xi_i'' = \xi_i' , \quad \eta_i'' = \eta_i' \qquad (i = 2, 3, 4) ,$$

and we obtain the simple form

$$F_2 = \xi_1''\eta_2'' - \xi_2''\eta_1'' - 4\xi_3''\eta_4'' + 4\xi_4''\eta_3'' .$$

* * *

From a practical point of view the problem of the reduction of quadratic forms to simpler forms falls into two parts: the determination of the final simplest type of form, and the finding of the matrix of the transformation of indeterminates necessary for reducing a given form to the simplest type. In the case of reduction by means of arbitrary linear transformations, both parts of the problem are solved by the algorithm of Lagrange.

The situation is more complicated in the case of the reduction of forms by means of *unitary* transformations of indeterminates. Let A be the matrix of a given Hermitian form. In the auxiliary unitary space of vector rows, multiplication of rows by the matrix A will yield a unitary linear transformation $\mathscr{A}$ with matrix A in the simplest basis (see Section 22). It is necessary to find a new orthonormal basis, in which the matrix of the transformation $\mathscr{A}$ will assume diagonal form. To do this, we find the characteristic numbers $\alpha_1, \cdots, \alpha_n$ of the matrix A by solving the characteristic equation of A. Then, solving the system of linear equations

$$[\xi_1, \cdots, \xi_n]A = \alpha_i[\xi_1, \cdots, \xi_n]$$

for the unknowns $\xi_1, \cdots \xi_n$, we find orthogonal (compare Section 76) proper vectors

$$X_i = [\xi_1^{(i)}, \cdots, \xi_n^{(i)}] \qquad (i = 1, \cdots, n)$$

of the transformation $\mathscr{A}$. Normalizing these vectors, we obtain an orthonormal basis in which the matrix A, and, consequently, the initial Hermitian form, has diagonal form, with diagonal elements $\alpha_1, \cdots, \alpha_n$. If the vectors X_i already have unit length, then the desired matrix of the transformation of indeterminates is $T = \| \xi_i^{(j)} \|$.

92. The Law of Inertia for Quadratic Forms

There is a gap in the results of Section 90 — on the reduction of real quadratic and complex Hermitian forms to diagonal form: it was not established whether or not it is possible for forms with distinct signatures to be congruent. This gap is filled by

THEOREM 3 (Law of inertia). *Each real quadratic form can be reduced, by a finite number of substitutions of the indeterminates, to a diagonal form* $\alpha_1\xi_1^2 + \cdots + \alpha_r\xi_r^2$. *However, although the coefficients* $\alpha_1, \cdots, \alpha_n$ *themselves may depend on the substitutions used, the number of positive, and the number of negative, numbers among them do not depend on the substitutions, and thus are uniquely determined by the original form.*

Suppose, on the contrary, that the real quadratic form

$$\alpha_1\xi_1^2 + \cdots + \alpha_s\xi_s^2 - \alpha_{s+1}\xi_{s+1}^2 - \cdots - \alpha_r\xi_r^2 \qquad (\alpha_i > 0)$$

is carried, under the substitution of indeterminates $\xi_i = \sum \xi'_\lambda \tau_{\lambda i}$ into the diagonal form

$$\beta_1\xi_1'^2 + \cdots + \beta_t\xi_t'^2 - \beta_{t+1}\xi_{t+1}'^2 - \cdots - \beta_r\xi_r'^2 \qquad (\beta_i > 0)\,,$$

with $s < t$. This means that if the indeterminates ξ_i in the equality

$$\alpha_1\xi_1^2 + \cdots + \alpha_s\xi_s^2 - \alpha_{s+1}\xi_{s+1}^2 - \cdots - \alpha_r\xi_r^2 = \beta_1\xi_1'^2 + \cdots + \beta_t\xi_t'^2 - \beta_{t+1}\xi_{t+1}'^2 - \cdots - \beta_r\xi_r'^2$$

are replaced by their expressions in terms of the ξ'_i, the equality becomes an identity. We rewrite this identity in the form

$$\begin{aligned} \alpha_1\xi_1^2 + \cdots + \alpha_s\xi_s^2 + \beta_{t+1}\xi_{t+1}'^2 + \cdots + \beta_r\xi_r'^2 \\ = \beta_1\xi_1'^2 + \cdots + \beta_t\xi_t'^2 + \alpha_{s+1}\xi_{s+1}^2 + \cdots + \alpha_r\xi_r^2\,, \end{aligned} \tag{4}$$

and consider the system of equations

$$\xi_1 = 0, \cdots, \quad \xi_s = 0, \quad \xi'_{t+1} = 0, \cdots, \quad \xi'_r = 0, \tag{5}$$

where by $\xi_1, \cdots, \xi_s$ are understood their expressions in terms of $\xi'_1, \cdots, \xi'_r$. The system (5) is a system of linear homogeneous equations in the unknowns $\xi'_1, \cdots, \xi'_r$; moreover, the number of equations, $s + (r - t) = r-(t-s)$, is less than the number of unknowns, since $t > s$. Therefore, system (5) has at least one nontrivial solution

$$\xi'_1 = \gamma_1, \cdots, \quad \xi'_t = \gamma_t, \quad \xi'_{t+1} = 0, \cdots, \quad \xi'_r = 0\,. \tag{6}$$

Substituting in (4), we obtain

$$0 = \beta_1\gamma_1^2 + \cdots + \beta_t\gamma_t^2 + \alpha_{s+1}\xi_{s+1}^2 + \cdots + \alpha_r\xi_r^2 , \tag{7}$$

The numbers β_i, α_j are positive and γ_i^2, ξ_j^2 are nonnegative; therefore it follows from (7) that $\gamma_1 = \cdots = \gamma_t = 0$, which contradicts the choice of the solution (6).

The law of inertia in the same form holds also for Hermitian quadratic forms. The proof is the same as that already given.

93. Forms of Constant Sign

A real quadratic form $F(\xi) = \sum \alpha_{ij}\xi_i\xi_j$ is called ***nonnegative*** if for all real values of the indeterminates ξ_i the value of the form is nonnegative. A form is called ***positive definite*** if for every nonzero system of values of the indeterminates the value of the form is strictly positive. The notions of ***nonpositive*** and ***negative definite*** forms are defined analogously. Nonnegative and nonpositive forms are sometimes called ***forms of constant sign.***

It is easy to see that a diagonal form

$$\alpha_1\xi_1^2 + \cdots + \alpha_s\xi_s^2 - \alpha_{s+1}\xi_{s+1}^2 - \cdots - \alpha_r\xi_r^2 \qquad (\alpha_i > 0)$$

in indeterminates $\xi_1, \cdots, \xi_n$, is positive definite in case $s = n$, nonnegative for $s = r \leqq n$, nonpositive for $s = 0$, and negative definite for $s = 0$, $r = n$. For $0 < s < r$ the form can take on both positive and negative values. Since the sign of a form of constant sign is not changed by a transformation of indeterminates, we may say that positive definite forms are those forms which reduce to a sum of n positive squares, nonnegative forms are those which reduce to a sum of positive squares, with possibly fewer summands than the number of indeterminates; similarly for nonnegative and negative definite forms. In particular, a nonnegative form is positive definite if it is nonsingular.

If the indeterminates of a general quadratic form are allowed to take on complex as well as real values, then these notions lose their meaning, since the form may take on nonreal values. However, the situation is different in the case of Hermitian quadratic forms, since for both real and complex values of the indeterminates a Hermitian form assumes real values. It follows from the condition $\alpha_{ij} = \alpha_{ji}$ that

$$\bar{F} = \sum \overline{\alpha_{ij}\xi_i\bar{\xi}_j} = \sum \bar{\alpha}_{ij}\bar{\xi}_i\xi_j = \sum \alpha_{ji}\xi_j\bar{\xi}_i = F ,$$

that is, F is real. Thus, the notions of nonnegative, positive definiteness, and so on, extend immediately to Hermitian quadratic forms.

The positive definiteness of forms, as well as their signatures, are easily established in general through a reduction to diagonal form by the method of Lagrange. However, in certain cases immediate criteria for positive definiteness are of more interest. Of these, we consider only the so-called

Jacobi criterion. *A quadratic or Hermitian quadratic form in n indeterminates with matrix A is nonnegative if and only if the coefficients of the*

characteristic polynomial of A have alternating signs. If some coefficient turns out to be zero, then the coefficients of all lower terms must also be zero.

Indeed, by Section 90 the given form may be reduced, by means of a transformation of indeterminates with unitary matrix U, to a diagonal form with a real diagonal matrix $A_1 = U A \bar{U}' = U A U^{-1}$. Since A is not only congruent, but similar, to A_1, A and A_1 have identical characteristic polynomials, and it is only necessary to verify the criterion for real diagonal forms of $\alpha_1\xi_1\bar{\xi}_1 + \cdots + \alpha_r\xi_r\bar{\xi}_r$. The characteristic polynomial of the matrix of the latter form is

$$\varphi(\lambda) = (\lambda - \alpha_1)\cdots(\lambda - \alpha_r)\lambda^{n-r} = \lambda^n - \sigma_1\lambda^{n-1} + \sigma_2\lambda^{n-2} - \cdots .$$

If all the α_i are positive, then the formulas of Vieta

$$\sigma_i = \sum \alpha_{n_1}\alpha_{n_2}\cdots\alpha_{n_i} \qquad (n_1 < n_2 < \cdots < n_i)$$

show that the coefficients of $\varphi(\lambda)$ have the required properties. Conversely, suppose that the coefficients of some nonzero polynomial with real zeros have alternating signs. It is necessary to show that all the zeros are positive. Suppose this has been established for all polynomials of degree less than the degree of the polynomial under consideration, $\varphi(\lambda)$. Then $\varphi'(\lambda)$ has $n-1$ positive zeros — since, if all the hypotheses are satisfied for $\varphi(\lambda)$, they are also satisfied for $\varphi'(\lambda)$. This means that $\varphi(\lambda)$, by Rolle's theorem, has not less than $n-1$ positive zeros, and the nth zero of $\varphi(\lambda)$ will also be positive, since, by hypothesis, the product of all the zeros of $\varphi(\lambda)$ is positive.

● EXAMPLES AND PROBLEMS

1. Find the matrix of the linear transformation of indeterminates which reduces the bilinear from

$$\xi_1\eta_2 - \xi_2\eta_1 + \xi_3\eta_2 - \xi_2\eta_3 + 2\xi_4\eta_1 - 2\xi_1\eta_4$$

to the simplest type of form

2. Show that in a real unitary space each real skew-symmetric bilinear form may be reduced by means of a real unitary transformation of indeterminates to the form

$$\alpha_1(\xi_1\eta_2 - \xi_2\eta_1) + \cdots + \alpha_r(\xi_{2r-1}\eta_{2r} - \xi_{2r}\eta_{2r-1}) .$$

(Compare Section 81.)

3. Find the matrices of the real orthogonal transformations of indeterminates which reduce to diagonal form the forms:

a) $\xi_1^2 + \xi_1\xi_2 + \xi_2^2$;
b) $99\xi_1^2 - 12\xi_1\xi_2 + 48\xi_1\xi_3 + 130\xi_2^2 - 60\xi_2\xi_3 + 71\xi_3^2$;
c) $10\xi_1\eta_1 + 4\xi_1\eta_2 + 4\xi_2\eta_1 + 12\xi_1\eta_3 + 12\xi_3\eta_1 - 2\xi_2\eta_2 - 14\xi_2\eta_3 - 14\xi_3\eta_2 + \xi_3\eta_3$,

and write out these diagonal forms.

4. Find the matrix of a unitary transformation which reduces the form

$$6\xi_1\eta_2 - 6\xi_2\eta_1 + 2\xi_1\eta_4 - 2\xi_4\eta_1 + 2\xi_2\eta_3 - 2\xi_3\eta_2 - 6\xi_3\eta_4 + 6\xi_4\eta_3 .$$

5. Find a transformation of indeterminates which reduces the form

$$\xi_1\eta_n + \xi_2\eta_{n-1} + \cdots + \xi_s\eta_{n-s+1} \qquad \left(s = \left[\frac{n}{2}\right]\right)$$

to a sum of squares.

3. *Pairs of Forms*

94. Equivalence of Pairs of Forms

In the preceding sections we considered the problem of reducing a single quadratic form to the simplest possible form. In the present paragraph we consider the important problem of the simultaneous reduction of two quadratic forms.

We recall that a sequence of bilinear forms $F_1, \cdots, F_k$, in indeterminates $\xi_1, \cdots, \xi_n$ and $\eta_1, \cdots, \eta_n$, is called ***equivalent*** to the sequence of bilinear forms $G_1, \cdots, G_k$, in indeterminates $\xi_1', \cdots, \xi_n'$ and $\eta_1', \cdots, \eta_n'$, if the forms of the first sequence can be reduced to the corresponding forms of the second sequence by means of invertible linear transformations of the indeterminates

$$[\xi] = [\xi']T, \quad [\eta] = [\eta']S \qquad ([\xi] = [\xi_1, \cdots, \xi_n]) .$$

It follows from the results of Section 87 that a sequence of bilinear forms with matrices $A_1, \cdots, A_k$ is equivalent to a sequence of bilinear forms with matrices $B_1, \cdots, B_k$ if and only if there exist nonsingular matrices P, Q, with elements from the base field, such that

$$PA_jQ = B_j \qquad (j = 1, \cdots, k) . \tag{1}$$

Two sequences of matrices $A_1, \cdots, A_k$ and $B_1, \cdots, B_k$ are called ***equivalent*** if they are connected by relations (1) for some nonsingular matrices P and Q. Thus, equivalence of sequences of forms is equivalent to the equivalence of the corresponding sequences of matrices.

Let λ be an indeterminate, and let F, G be a pair of square matrices of order n. The invariant factors of the λ-matrix $\lambda F - G$ (see Section 52) are called the ***invariant factors of the pair*** F, G. If the pair F, G is equivalent to the pair F_1, G_1, then it follows from (1) that

$$\lambda F_1 - G_1 = U(\lambda F - G)V' .$$

By Section 53, this shows that the invariant factors of the λ-matrices $\lambda F_1 - G_1$ and $\lambda F - G$ coincide. Thus, *for the equivalence of two pairs of matrices it is necessary that these pairs have the same invariant factors.* In general this condition is not sufficient.* However, if the first matrix of each pair is nonsingular, then the coincidence of the invariant factors of the pairs is sufficient for their equivalence.

* In general it is necessary to consider the so-called minimal indices, in addition to the invariant factors.

THEOREM 1. *Let F, G and F_1, G_1 be two pairs of square matrices, all of the same order, and let F and F_1 be nonsingular. Then the pairs F, G and F_1, G_1 are equivalent if and only if the invariant factors of the matrix $\lambda F - G$ coincide with the invariant factors of the matrix $\lambda F_1 - G_1$.*

The necessity of the condition has already been shown; there remains only the sufficiency. Let the matrices $\lambda F - G$ and $\lambda F_1 - G_1$ have identical invariant factors. From the relations

$$F^{-1}(\lambda F - G) = \lambda E - F^{-1}G\,,$$
$$F_1^{-1}(\lambda F_1 - G_1) = \lambda E - F_1^{-1}G_1\,,$$

it follows that the invariant factors of the matrices $\lambda E - F^{-1}G$ and $\lambda E - F_1^{-1}G_1$ are also identical. Since these are the characteristic matrices of $F^{-1}G$ and $F_1^{-1}G_1$, then $F^{-1}G$ and $F_1^{-1}G_1$ are similar, by Section 58 — that is, there exists a nonsingular matrix T such that

$$F_1^{-1}G_1 = T^{-1}F^{-1}GT\,.$$

We now have

$$\lambda E - F_1^{-1}G_1 = T^{-1}(\lambda E - F^{-1}G)T = T^{-1}F^{-1}(\lambda F - G)T\,,$$
$$\lambda F_1 - G_1 = F_1T^{-1}F^{-1}(\lambda F - G)T\,,$$

and hence

$$F_1 = UFV', \quad G_1 = UGV'\,,$$

where $U = F_1T^{-1}F^{-1}$, $V = T'$. Thus, the pairs F, G and F_1, G_1 are equivalent.

95. Congruence of Pairs of Forms

A sequence of bilinear forms in the indeterminates $\xi_1, \cdots, \xi_n$ and $\eta_1, \cdots, \eta_n$ with matrices $A_1, \cdots, A_k$ is called ***congruent*** to a sequence of bilinear forms with matrices $B_1, \cdots, B_k$ if the forms of the first sequence can be reduced to the forms of the second sequence by means of a single transformation operating on both systems of indeterminates.

Denoting the matrix of the transformation of indeterminates by T, we have

$$B_j = TA_jT' \qquad (j = 1, \cdots, k)\,. \tag{2}$$

Two sequences of matrices $A_1, \cdots, A_k$ are called ***congruent*** if there exists a nonsingular matrix T for which conditions (2) are fulfilled.

Analogously, we say that one sequence of quadratic or Hermitian quadratic forms is congruent to another sequence if the forms of the first sequence can be simultaneously reduced to the corresponding forms of the second sequence by means of a suitable invertible transformation of indeterminates.

Condition (2) is evidently necessary and sufficient for the congruence of sequences of quadratic forms with matrices $A_1, \cdots, A_k$ and $B_1, \cdots, B_k$. For Hermitian forms this condition becomes

$$B_j = TA_j\bar{T}' \qquad (j = 1, \cdots, k) .$$

The conditions under which sequences of bilinear forms are congruent are extremely complicated, even for pairs of forms. In the case when both forms of each pair are symmetric, and in particular for quadratic forms with one nonsingular form in each pair, necessary and sufficient conditions for congruence were obtained by Weierstrass in the second half of the last century. These will be given at the end of this section. The general case of the congruence of pairs of quadratic forms was studied by Kronecker. In view of a certain cumbersomeness of Kronecker's conditions, they are usually presented in more specialized texts. These and other conditions are concerned with forms over the field of complex numbers. The case of other fields has been considered by Dickson and other authors.

We first consider the most important case of pairs of real quadratic forms, when one form of the pair is positive definite.

THEOREM 2. *Each pair of real quadratic forms in n indeterminates, where the first form is positive definite, can be reduced to the pair*

$$\xi_1^2 + \cdots + \xi_n^2, \quad \alpha_1\xi_1^2 + \cdots + \alpha_n\xi_n^2 \tag{3}$$

by means of a suitable real transformation of indeterminates. The numbers $\alpha_1, \cdots, \alpha_n$ *are uniquely determined up to their order by the original forms, and do not depend on the method of reduction.*

Indeed, let the given quadratic forms be $F(\xi)$ and $G(\xi)$. By means of a proper linear transformation of indeterminates the first of these forms reduces to a sum of squares, since it is positive definite. We thus obtain the pair of forms

$$\xi_1^2 + \cdots + \xi_n^2, \quad \sum \alpha_{ij}\xi_i\xi_j .$$

We now find a transformation of indeterminates with a real orthogonal matrix U which diagonalizes the second form. The matrix of the first form under this transformation will be

$$UEU' = UU' = E$$

in the new indeterminates; thus after the indicated transformations the given forms will assume the required forms (3).

Finally, let us suppose that the forms F, G are reduced to (3) under one transformation, and are reduced to

$$\xi_1^2 + \cdots + \xi_n^2, \quad \beta_1\xi_1^2 + \cdots + \beta_n\xi_n^2 \tag{4}$$

under some other transformation. Then a suitable transformation of indeterminates with matrix T will transform the pair (3) into the pair (4), and consequently the matrices of these forms will satisfy the relations

$$E = TET', \quad B = TAT', \tag{5}$$

where A is the diagonal matrix with elements $\alpha_1, \cdots, \alpha_n$ and B is the diagonal matrix with elements $\beta_1, \cdots, \beta_n$ on the main diagonal. The first of relations (5) yields $TT' = E$ and hence $B = TAT^{-1}$—that is, the matrices A and B are similar; thus the characteristic numbers $\alpha_1, \cdots, \alpha_n$ of A must coincide with the characteristic numbers $\beta_1, \cdots, \beta_n$ of B.

For Hermitian duadratic forms we have the completely analogous

THEOREM 2a. *Each pair of Hermitian quadratic forms, where the first is positive definite, can be reduced to the pair*

$$\xi_1\bar{\xi}_1 + \cdots + \xi_n\bar{\xi}_n, \quad \alpha_1\xi_1\bar{\xi}_1 + \cdots + \alpha_n\xi_n\bar{\xi}_n$$

by means of a suitable complex linear transformation of indeterminates. The numbers $\alpha_1, \cdots, \alpha_n$ are uniquely determined by the original forms and do not depend on the method of reduction.

The proof is analogous to the preceding.

Passing to a consideration of the general case, we remark first of all that the congruence of pairs of forms implies their equivalence. Surprisingly, it turns out that under some conditions the converse is also true.

THEOREM 3. *Let two pairs F, G and F_1, G_1 of square matrices be given, and suppose that F and F_1 are either both symmetric or both skew-symmetric, and also that G and G_1 are either both symmetric or both skew-symmetric. Then, over the field of complex numbers, the congruence of the pairs follows from their equivalence.*

By assumption, there exist nonsingular matrices U, V such that

$$F_1 = UFV', \quad G_1 = UGV'. \tag{6}$$

Taking the transposed matrices, we obtain $F_1' = VF'U'$, $G_1' = VG'U'$. Since F and F_1 are symmetric or skew-symmetric, this yields

$$F_1 = VFU', \tag{7}$$

and a similar equality holds for G_1. Comparing (7) with (6), we obtain

$$UFV' = VFU', \quad V^{-1}U\cdot F = F\cdot(V^{-1}U)'. \tag{8}$$

Let $V^{-1}U = T$. The second equality of (8) now gives

$$\begin{aligned} TF &= FT', \\ T^2F &= FT'^2, \\ &\vdots \\ T^kF &= FT'^k, \end{aligned}$$

hence

$$(\alpha_0 E + \alpha_1 T + \cdots + \alpha^k T^k)F = F(\alpha_0 E + \alpha_1 T_1' + \cdots + \alpha_k T'^k),$$

where $\alpha_0, \cdots, \alpha_k$ are arbitrary. It was shown in Chapter IV (Section 64) that $\alpha_0, \cdots, \alpha_k$ may be chosen so the polynomial

$$\varphi(T) = \alpha_0 E + \alpha_1 T + \cdots + \alpha_k T^k$$

is a square root of T, or $\varphi(T)\varphi(T) = T$. Setting $P = V\varphi(T)$, we have

$$PFP' = V\varphi(T)F\varphi(T')V' = V\varphi(T)\varphi(T)FV' = VTFV' = UFV' ,$$

or

$$PFP' = F_1 .$$

Repeating the argument for the matrix G, we obtain

$$PGP' = G_1 .$$

Consequently, the pair F, G is congruent to the pair F_1, G_1; this completes the proof.

Theorems 1 and 3 permit the following formulation of conditions for the congruence of pairs of matrices.

Let two pairs of matrices F, G and F_1, G_1 be given. If F, F_1 are nonsingular and either both are symmetric or both are skew-symmetric, and if G, G_1 are also either both symmetric or both skew-symmetric, then a necessary and sufficient condition for the congruence of the pairs F, G and F_1, G_1 over the field of complex numbers is that the matrices $\lambda F - G$ and $\lambda F_1 - G_1$ have identical invariant factors.

Indeed, if $\lambda F - G$ and $\lambda F_1 - G_1$ have identical invariant factors, then by Theorem 1 the pairs F, G and F_1, G_1 are equivalent. But then by Theorem 3 these pairs are congruent. Conversely, if F, G and F_1, G_1 are congruent, then they are also equivalent, and this means that the invariant factors of $\lambda F - G$ coincide with the invariant factors of $\lambda F_1 - G_1$.

The actual application of Theorem 3 in finding the simplest form for pairs of complex forms will be considered later, in Chapter VII. In the following section the question of the congruence of nonsymmetric bilinear forms will be solved with the help of this theorem.

We also remark that, although up to Theorem 3 real quadratic forms and Hermitian forms have behaved identically, Theorem 3 fails for Hermitian forms. An example will be considered at the beginning of paragraph 4, Chapter VII.

96. Congruence of Nonsymmetric Bilinear Forms

As said before, the results of the preceding section permit the formulation of necessary and sufficient conditions for the congruence of arbitrary complex nonsingular bilinear forms and the essential completion of the results of Section 89.

THEOREM 4. *Two nonsingular complex bilinear forms with matrices G and G_1 are congruent if and only if the elementary divisors of the λ-matrices $\lambda G - G'$ and $\lambda G_1 - G_1'$ coincide.*

Suppose the forms are congruent. Then the matrices G and G_1 are connected by a relation

$$G_1 = UGU' ,$$

and hence

$$G_1' = UG'U' .$$

Consequently, the pair of matrices G, G' is congruent to the pair G_1, G_1', and the elementary divisors of $\lambda G - G'$ coincide with the elementary divisors of $\lambda G_1 - G_1'$.

Conversely, let the elementary divisors of the matrices $\lambda G - G'$ and $\lambda G_1 - G_1'$ coincide. Then from Theorem 1 the pair G, G' is equivalent to the pair G_1, G_1', or

$$G_1 = UGV', \quad G_1' = UG'V' . \tag{9}$$

Set

$$G + G' = S, \quad G - G' = T, \quad G_1 + G_1' = S_1, \quad G_1 - G_1' = T_1 .$$

It follows from (9) that

$$S_1 = USV', \quad T_1 = UTV' ,$$

that is, the pair S, T is equivalent to the pair S_1, T_1. Since the matrices S, S_1 are symmetric, and T, T_1 are skew-symmetric, then by Theorem 3 the pairs S, T and S_1, T_1 are congruent, or

$$S_1 = PSP', \quad T_1 = PTP' . \tag{10}$$

But $G = \dfrac{S+T}{2}$, $G_1 = \dfrac{S_1 + T_1}{2}$; therefore it follows from (10) that

$$G_1 = PGP' .$$

Thus, the matrices G and G_1 are congruent.

Theorem 4 shows that nonsingular bilinear forms over the field of complex numbers are determined up to congruence by the elementary divisors of the matrix $\lambda G - G'$. Therefore, to solve the problem of the classification of such forms, it is sufficient to show which systems of expressions of the form $(\lambda - \alpha)^m$ can serve as the systems of elementary divisors of matrices of the type $\lambda G - G'$. It is easy to see that these systems cannot be arbitrary. Indeed, let $(\lambda - \alpha)^m$ occur k times in the system of elementary divisors of some matrix $\lambda G - G'$. Then $(\lambda - \alpha)^m$ will also occur k times in the system of elementary divisors of the transposed matrix $\lambda G' - G$. But $\lambda G' - G$ is equivalent to $G'^{-1}(\lambda G' - G) = \lambda E - G'^{-1}G$; consequently, $(\lambda - \alpha)^m$ occurs k times in the system of elementary divisors of the matrix $\lambda E - G'^{-1}G$. The theorem on the elementary divisors of functions (Section 65) asserts that each elementary divisor $(\lambda - \alpha)^m$ of the matrix $\lambda E - G'^{-1}G$ is carried into an elementary divisor $(\lambda - \alpha^{-1})^m$ of the matrix $\lambda E - (G'^{-1}G)^{-1}$. Since the latter matrix is equivalent to $\lambda G - G'$, then $(\lambda - \alpha^{-1})^m$ occurs k times in the system of elementary divisors of the matrix $\lambda G - G'$. Consequently, *if* $(\lambda - \alpha)^m$ *is an elementary divisor of multiplicity k of the matrix* $\lambda G - G'$, *then* $(\lambda - \alpha^{-1})^m$ *is also an elementary divisor of multiplicity k of this matrix.* For $\alpha = \pm 1$ the assertion is trivial. With the help of an additional argument it is possible to show that an elementary divisor of the form $(\lambda - 1)^{2m}$ or $(\lambda + 1)^{2m+1}$ occurs with even multiplicity, whereas an elementary divisor of the form $(\lambda - 1)^{2m+1}$ or $(\lambda + 1)^{2m}$ may occur with arbitrary multiplicity. These conditions, for α equal or unequal to ± 1, are not only necessary, but sufficient, for a system of expressions of the form $(\lambda - \alpha)^m$ to be the system of elementary divisors of some matrix $\lambda G - G'$.

● EXAMPLES AND PROBLEMS

1. By means of real transformations of the indeterminates, reduce the pairs of forms

   a) $x^2 + 2xy + 2y^2, \quad 2x^2 - xy$;

   b) $2x^2 + 2xy + 2xz + 2y^2 + 2yz + 2z^2, \quad -9x^2 + 36xy + 18xz + 15y^2 + 18yz + 18z^2$

   to the simplest possible form.
2. By means of real transformations of the indeterminates, a pair consisting of a symmetric positive definite, and a skew-symmetric, real bilinear form, can be reduced to the form

$$\xi_1\eta_1 + \cdots + \xi_n\eta_n, \quad \alpha_1(\xi_1\eta_2 - \xi_2\eta_1) + \cdots + \alpha_r(\xi_{2r-1}\eta_{2r} - \xi_{2r}\eta_{2r-1}) .$$

3. Show that the pair of forms with matrices $\begin{bmatrix} -2 & -6 \\ 1 & 3 \end{bmatrix}, \begin{bmatrix} -6 & 6 \\ 1 & -1 \end{bmatrix}$ is equivalent to the pair with matrices $\begin{bmatrix} 2 & -3 \\ -2 & 3 \end{bmatrix}, \begin{bmatrix} -10 & 5 \\ 2 & -1 \end{bmatrix}$. To do this, generalize Theorem 1, Section 94, to pairs A, B for which $|\lambda A + \mu B| \neq 0$, by considering the invariant factors as homogeneous polynomials in λ and μ.
4. Prove the last assertion of Section 96.

4. *Bilinear Functions*

The theory of bilinear forms may be interpreted geometrically as the theory of bilinear functions on linear spaces. This interpretation also permits a deeper understanding of the fundamental facts of the theory of forms. The present paragraph is devoted to its exposition.

97. Fundamental Definitions

We say that a function $\varphi(x, y)$ of two variable vectors x, y is given on a linear space $\mathfrak{L}$ if to each pair of vectors in the space $\mathfrak{L}$ there corresponds a definite element $\varphi(x, y)$ of the base field K of $\mathfrak{L}$. The function $\varphi(x, y)$ is called ***bilinear*** if it is linear with respect to each variable separately— that is, if it satisfies the identities

$$\varphi(\alpha_1 x_1 + \alpha_2 x_2, y) = \alpha_1\varphi(x_1, y) + \alpha_2\varphi(x_2, y) , \tag{1}$$

$$\varphi(x, \beta_1 y_1 + \beta_2 y_2) = \beta_1\varphi(x, y_1) + \beta_2\varphi(x, y_2) . \tag{2}$$

A function of two variables on a complex linear space is called ***Hermitian bilinear*** if it is linear in the first variable and skew-linear in the second —that is, if it satisfies 1 and the identity

$$\varphi(x, \beta_1 y_1 + \beta_2 y_2) = \bar{\beta}_1\varphi(x, y_1) + \bar{\beta}_2\varphi(x, y_2) . \tag{3}$$

The more general distributive law

$$\varphi(x_1 + \cdots + x_m, y_1 + \cdots + y_s) = \sum \varphi(x_i, y_j) \tag{4}$$

follows immediately from (1), (2), (3); this law holds for bilinear and Hermitian bilinear functions.

Choose an arbitrary coordinate basis $a_1, \cdots, a_n$ in $\mathfrak{L}$, and let

$$x = \xi_1 a_1 + \cdots + \xi_n a_n ,$$

$$y = \eta_1 a_1 + \cdots + \eta_n a_n .$$

Formulas (2) and (4) yield

$$\varphi(x, y) = \sum \varphi(a_i, a_j)\xi_i\eta_j = \sum \alpha_{ij}\xi_i\eta_j ; \quad \alpha_{ij} = \varphi(a_i, a_j) . \tag{5}$$

The matrix $A = ||\alpha_{ij}||$ is called the ***matrix of the function*** $\varphi(x, y)$ in the given basis. Knowing the matrix A, we evidently also know the function $\varphi(x, y)$, since (5) permits the finding of the value $\varphi(x, y)$ for any pair of vectors x, y.

The correspondence between matrices and bilinear functions is one to one, since for an arbitrary matrix A the function $\varphi(x, y)$, computed by means of (5), is bilinear and has matrix A.

Denoting by $[x]$ and $[y]$ the coordinate rows of the vectors x, y in the given coordinate system, formula (5) may be written in the shorter matrix form

$$\varphi(x, y) = [x]A[y]' , \tag{6}$$

which allows the immediate deduction of the following *rule for the transformation* of the matrix of a bilinear function: *if in some basis the matrix of a bilinear function is A, then in a new basis the matrix of the function will be*

$$A_1 = TAT' , \tag{7}$$

where T is the matrix of the transformation of coordinates from the old basis to the new.

Indeed, applying (6) in the old and new bases, we obtain

$$\varphi(x, y) = [x]A[y]' = [x]_1 TAT'[y]_1' = [x]_1 A_1 [y]_1' ,$$

where A_1 is the matrix of the function $\varphi(x, y)$, and $[x]_1, [y]_1$ are the coordinate rows of the vectors x, y, in the new basis. Therefore $A_1 = TAT'$.

Regarding the coordinates of the vectors x, y as independent variables in formula (5), we see that *the value of a bilinear function is expressed in each coordinate basis by a bilinear form, the matrix of which coincides with the matrix of the function in this basis.*

By (7), a transition to a new basis has as a consequence a change from one bilinear form to a corresponding congruent form, and hence *congruent bilinear forms may be regarded as bilinear forms of the same bilinear function, computed in different coordinate bases.*

The bilinear function $\varphi(x, y)$ is called ***symmetric*** if

$$\varphi(x, y) = \varphi(y, x) ,$$

and ***skew-symmetric*** if

$$\varphi(x, y) = -\varphi(y, x) .$$

Evidently *symmetric and skew-symmetric bilinear functions are those functions whose bilinear forms are respectively symmetric or skew-symmetric.*

If $\varphi(x, y)$ is an arbitrary bilinear function, then the functions

$$\varphi_1(x, y) = \frac{1}{2}[\varphi(x, y) + \varphi(y, x)], \quad \varphi_2(x, y) = \frac{1}{2}[\varphi(x, y) - \varphi(y, x)] \tag{8}$$

are bilinear and symmetric and skew-symmetric respectively. It follows from (8) that

$$\varphi(x, y) = \varphi_1(x, y) + \varphi_2(x, y) ,$$

hence every bilinear function may be represented as the sum of a symmetric and a skew-symmetric function; moreover, it is easy to see that this representation is possible in only one way.

A function of the form $\psi(x) = \varphi(x, x)$, where $\varphi(x, y)$ is some bilinear function, is called a ***quadratic function.*** Thus, quadratic functions are those functions of one variable vector which arise from bilinear functions by identifying the two variable vectors. But if the quadratic function $\psi(x)$ arises in this way from the bilinear function $\varphi(x, y)$, then $\psi(x)$ also arises by identifying the variables in the symmetric bilinear function $\varphi_1(x, y)$:

$$\varphi_1(x, x) = \frac{1}{2}[\varphi(x, x) + \varphi(x, x)] = \varphi(x, x) .$$

Therefore, for the consideration of quadratic functions it is sufficient to take only symmetric bilinear functions as generators.

On the other hand, if $\varphi(x, y)$ is symmetric and $\psi(x) = \varphi(x, x)$, then

$$\psi(x+y) = \varphi(x+y, x+y) = \varphi(x, x) + 2\varphi(x, y) + \varphi(y, y) ,$$

or

$$\varphi(x, y) = \frac{1}{2}[\psi(x + y) - \psi(x) - \psi(y)] ,$$

that is, *each quadratic function arises from one and only one symmetric bilinear function*, called the ***palar form*** *of the corresponding quadratic func-*

tion.

Let $a_1, \cdots, a_n$ be some basis of the space $\mathfrak{L}$ and let $\psi(x) = \varphi(x, x)$, where $\varphi(x, y)$ is a symmetric bilinear function. Then for $x = \xi_1 a_1 + \cdots + \xi_n a_n$ we have

$$\psi(x) = \varphi(x, x) = \sum \varphi(a_i, a_j)\xi_i\xi_j ,$$

that is *the value of a quadratic function is expressed by a quadratic form in the coordinates of the variable vector; the matrix of the form coincides with the matrix of the corresponding polar bilinear form.*

By a similar argument, the value of a *Hermitian* bilinear function $\varphi(x, y)$ is expressed, not by (5), but by the formula

$$\varphi(x, y) = \sum \varphi(a_i, a_j)\xi_i\bar{\eta}_j ,$$

that is by a Hermitian bilinear form. Under a transformation of coordinates the matrix of a Hermitian function is changed according to the law

$$A = TA\bar{T}' .$$

A Hermitian function $\varphi(x, y)$ is called symmetric if

$$\varphi(x, y) = \overline{\varphi(y, x)} .$$

The value of a Hermitian symmetric bilinear function is expressed by a Hermitian symmetric bilinear form.

Functions of one variable vector which arise from Hermitian symmetric bilinear functions by identifying the variables are called ***Hermitian quadratic functions.*** The connection between Hermitian quadratic functions and the corresponding Hermitian symmetric bilinear functions is established by the formulas

$$\begin{aligned} \psi(x + iy) &= \varphi(x + iy, x + iy) = \varphi(x, x) + i[\overline{\varphi(x, y)} - \varphi(x, y)] + \varphi(y, y) , \\ \psi(x + y) &= \varphi(x, x) + \overline{\varphi(x, y)} + \varphi(x, y) + \varphi(y, y) , \qquad (9) \\ 2\varphi(x, y) &= \psi(x + y) + i\psi(x + iy) - (1 + i)[\psi(x) + \psi(y)] . \end{aligned}$$

Computing the value of a Hermitian quadratic function $\psi(x)$ for a vector $x = \xi_1 a_1 + \cdots + \xi_n a_n$, where the system $a_1, \cdots, a_n$ is a basis of the space, we obtain

$$\psi(x) = \sum \varphi(a_i, a_j)\xi_i\bar{\xi}_j ,$$

that is, *the value of a Hermitian quadratic function is expressed by a Hermitian quadratic form in the coordinates of the variable vector*; the matrix of the form coincides with the matrix of the corresponding Hermitian symmetric bilinear function computed from formula (9).

We remark further that the quadratic forms of constant sign discussed in Section 93 correspond to those quadratic functions in real spaces and Hermitian quadratic functions in complex spaces whose values are all of one sign.

98. Spaces with Bilinear Metrics

According to Section 69, a real or complex linear space is called unitary if there is defined on it some function of two variable vectors whose values are called the inner products of these vectors. The axioms formulated there mean simply that the inner product is a Hermitian symmetric positive definite bilinear function. The study of the properties of unitary spaces is therefore the study of the properties of positive definite bilinear functions from a particular point of view.

By analogy with this we call a linear space $\mathfrak{L}$ ***bilinear-metric*** if there is defined on it some bilinear function; this function $\varphi(x, y)$ will again be called an inner product, and we will write $\varphi(x, y)=(x, y)$. If the inner product is a Hermitian symmetric bilinear function, then the space will be called a space with a Hermitian bilinear metric.

If the matrix of the inner product — that is, of the bilinear function — is nonsingular, then the space is called ***nondegenerate.*** In the opposite case the space is called ***degenerate.***

The matrix

$$G = \begin{bmatrix} (a_1, a_1) \cdots (a_1, a_m) \\ (a_2, a_1) \cdots (a_2, a_m) \\ \cdot \quad \cdot \quad \cdot \quad \cdot \quad \cdot \quad \cdot \quad \cdot \quad \cdot \quad \cdot \\ (a_m, a_1) \cdots (a_m, a_m) \end{bmatrix},$$

constructed from the inner products of vectors $a_1, \cdots, a_m$ of a bilinear-metric space $\mathfrak{L}$, is called the ***Gram matrix*** of the system $a_1, \cdots, a_m$. The Gram matrix constructed for a basis $a_1, \cdots, a_n$ of $\mathfrak{L}$ is simply the matrix of the fundamental bilinear function $\varphi(x, y) = (x, y)$, computed in this basis. It follows that the Gram matrices constructed for different bases of the space are congruent to each other, and therefore have the same rank.

The notion of the orthogonality of vectors plays an important role in the theory of unitary spaces. This notion carries over immediately to bilinear-metric spaces.

Let $\mathfrak{L}$ be an ordinary or Hermitian bilinear-metric space. A vector a in $\mathfrak{L}$ is said to be ***orthogonal*** to b if $(a, b)= 0$. It no longer follows that if a is orthogonal to b, then b is orthogonal to a, since in general $(a, b) \neq (b, a)$. Therefore, for definiteness one sometimes says that a is ***left orthogonal*** to b, and b is ***right-orthogonal*** to a, if $(a, b)= 0$. It follows from the distributive laws (1) and (2) that if a is orthogonal to vectors $a_1, \cdots, a_m$, then a is also orthogonal to all of their linear combinations. From this it follows in turn that *the set of all vectors of a space $\mathfrak{L}$ which are right-orthogonal to the vectors of some system $\mathfrak{M}$ is a linear subspace of $\mathfrak{L}$.* This subspace is denoted by $\mathfrak{M}^{\perp}$. The set of vectors in $\mathfrak{L}$ which are left-orthogonal to $\mathfrak{M}$ is also a linear subspace, which is denoted by ${}^{\perp}\mathfrak{M}$.

A vector x is ***left-isotropic*** in a space $\mathfrak{L}$ if it is left-orthogonal to all vectors in $\mathfrak{L}$. The subspace ${}^{\perp}\mathfrak{L}$, consisting of all the left-isotropic vectors of $\mathfrak{L}$, is called the *left-isotropic subspace* of $\mathfrak{L}$. Right-isotropic vectors and the right-isotropic subspace are defined similarly.

THEOREM 1. *The dimensions of the left- and right-isotropic subspaces are equal to each other and to the nullity of the matrix of the metric form* (x, y), *computed in an arbitrary basis. Thus, the difference between the dimension of the space and the dimension of an isotropic subspace equals the rank of the metric bilinear form; a bilinear-metric space is nondegenerate if and only if it contains no nonzero isotropic vectors.*

To prove this, choose a basis of $\mathfrak{L}$. Then the left-isotropic vectors x must satisfy the relation

$$(x, y) = [x]A[y]' = 0 \tag{10}$$

for arbitrary y in $\mathfrak{L}$, where A is the Gram matrix of the chosen basis. But from (10) it follows that

$$[x]A = 0 ,$$

that is, the left-isotropic vectors constitute the kernel of the linear transformation with matrix A (see Section 40), and the dimension of the kernel of a linear transformation equals the nullity of the matrix of the transformation. Similarly, the dimension of the right-isotropic subspace equals the dimension of the kernel of the linear transformation with matrix A', and, consequently, equals the nullity of the matrix A; this completes the proof. Every linear subspace $\mathfrak{N}$ or $\mathfrak{L}$ may itself be considered as an ordinary or Hermitian bilinear-metric space with respect to the inner product already given in $\mathfrak{L}$. In general, the nondegeneracy of $\mathfrak{L}$ does not imply nondegeneracy of its subspaces, and, conversely, the nondegeneracy of subspaces $\mathfrak{N}$ does not imply the nondegeneracy of the whole space $\mathfrak{L}$.

THEOREM 2. *If* $\mathfrak{N}$ *is a nondegenerate subspace of a space* $\mathfrak{L}$, *then* $\mathfrak{L}$ *has the direct decompositions*

$$\mathfrak{L} = \mathfrak{A} \dotplus \mathfrak{A}^{\perp} = {}^{\perp}\mathfrak{A} \dotplus \mathfrak{A} . \tag{11}$$

Conversely, if at least one of the decompositions (*11*) *is valid, then the subspace* $\mathfrak{N}$ *is nondegenerate.*

Indeed, the intersection $\mathfrak{A} \cap \mathfrak{A}^{\perp}$ is the right-isotropic subspace of $\mathfrak{A}$. Since $\mathfrak{A}$ is nondegenerate, then $\mathfrak{A} \cap \mathfrak{A}^{\perp} = 0$; consequently, the sum $\mathfrak{A} \dotplus \mathfrak{A}^{\perp}$ is direct.

Now let c be an arbitrary vector in $\mathfrak{L}$. Let

$$(\alpha_j, c) = \gamma_j , \quad j = 1, \cdots, m ,$$

where the system $a_1, \cdots, a_m$ is a basis of $\mathfrak{A}$. The system of equations

$$(a_j, a_1)\xi_1 + (a_j, a_2)\xi_2 + \cdots + (a_j, a_m)\xi_m = \gamma_j \qquad (j = 1, \cdots, m)$$

is solvable for $\xi_1, \cdots, \xi_m$, since its determinant is the determinant of the Gram matrix for the system $a_1, \cdots, a_m$, which is different from zero by the nondegeneracy of $\mathfrak{A}$. The vector $a = \xi_1 a_1 + \cdots + \xi_m a_m$ belongs to $\mathfrak{A}$, and

$$(a_j, c - a) = 0, \quad j = 1, \cdots, m,$$

that is, $c - a \in \mathfrak{A}^{\perp}$. Since every vector c has the decomposition

$$c = a + (c - a) \qquad (a \in \mathfrak{A}, c - a \in \mathfrak{A}^{\perp}),$$

$\mathfrak{L}$ is the sum of $\mathfrak{A}$ and $\mathfrak{A}^{\perp}$, this completes the proof.

Bilinear-metric spaces over the same field of coefficients are ***isomorphic*** if it is possible to establish a one-to-one correspondence between their elements under which sums and multiplication by scalars are preserved and the inner products of pairs of corresponding vectors are equal.

From the last condition it is evident in particular that under an isomorphism the Gram matrices of systems of corresponding vectors coincide. Conversely, if there exist bases of two bilinear-metric spaces over the same field which have identical Gram matrices, then the spaces are isomorphic.

It was shown earlier for ordinary and unitary linear spaces that up to isomorphism there exists only one space of each dimension n. For bilinear-metric spaces the situation is more complicated.

First of all we prove the following obvious assertion.

THEOREM 3. *Bilinear-metric spaces over the same field are isomorphic if and only if the Gram matrices for arbitrary bases of these spaces are congruent.*

The necessity is clear, since the Gram matrices for all bases of a given space are congruent, and the Gram matrices for corresponding bases of isomorphic spaces are identical. But if A and B are the Gram matrices for given bases of the spaces $\mathfrak{L}$ and $\mathfrak{L}_1$, and A is congruent to B, then by the fundamental results of the preceding section a basis of $\mathfrak{L}$ can be found which has Gram matrix B.

Theorem 3 shows that the problem of the classification of nonisomorphic bilinear-metric spaces is identical with the problem of the classification of bilinear forms up to congruence, which has already been considered in Section 96. We formulate here in the terminology of the theory of bilinear-metric spaces only a few of the consequences of the results of Section 96.

A real nondegenerate bilinear-metric space with a symmetric metric $(x, y) = (y, x)$ is called ***pseudo-Euclidean.***

The Gram matrix A for an arbitrary basis of a pseudo-Euclidean space is real and symmetric. By a theorem in Section 89 the matrix A is congruent to a diagonal matrix with the numbers $+1$ and -1 on the main diagonal. In other words, each pseudo-Euclidean space of dimension n has a basis in which the inner product of vectors with coordinates $\xi_1, \cdots, \xi_n$ and $\eta_1, \cdots, \eta_n$ is

$$(x, y) = \xi_1\eta_1 + \cdots + \xi_s\eta_s - \xi_{s+1}\eta_{s+1} - \cdots - \xi_n\eta_n.$$

The number $\sigma = s - (n - s)$ is the ***signature*** of the space.

Thus, *pseudo-Euclidean spaces are determined up to isomorphism by their dimension and signature.* For any $n > 0$ and any s, where $0 \leqq s \leqq n$, there exists a pseudo-Euclidean space with dimension n and signature $s - (n - s)$.

A nondegenerate bilinear-metric space with a skew-symmetric metric $(x, y) = -(y, x)$ is called ***symplectic.***

The Gram matrix for any basis of a symplectic space is skew-symmetric, and therefore, by Section 81, is congruent to a block diagonal matrix with blocks of the form $\begin{bmatrix} 0 & 1 \\ -1 & 0 \end{bmatrix}$ on the main diagonal. Thus, *the dimension of a symplectic space is always an even number, and for each n there exists, up to isomorphism, only one symplectic space of dimension 2n. In each symplectic space of dimension 2n there exists a basis in which the inner product has the form*

$$(x, y) = \xi_1\eta_2 - \xi_2\eta_1 + \cdots + \xi_{2n-1}\eta_{2n} - \xi_{2n}\eta_{2n-1} ,$$

where $\xi_1, \cdots, \xi_n$ and $\eta_1, \cdots \eta_n$ are the coordinates of the vectors x and y.

A nondegenerate complex bilinear-metric space with a symmetric metric is called ***complex Euclidean.*** Since every nonsingular symmetric bilinear form reduces over the field of complex numbers to a form with the identity matrix, there exists, up to isomorphism, only one complex Euclidean space of each dimension n. *In each Euclidean space of dimension n there exists a basis in which the inner product has the form*

$$(x, y) = \xi_1\eta_1 + \cdots + \xi_n\eta_n .$$

Finally, a nondegenerate complex space with a Hermitian symmetric metric $(x, y) = \overline{(y, x)}$ is called ***pseudo-unitary.*** It follows from a theorem of Section 89 that *in each pseudo-unitary space of dimension n there exists a basis in which the inner product has the form*

$$(x, y) = \xi_1\bar{\eta}_1 + \cdots + \xi_s\bar{\eta}_s - \xi_{s+1}\bar{\eta}_{s+1} - \cdots - \xi_n\bar{\eta}_n .$$

The number $\sigma = s - (n - s)$ is the ***signature*** of the pseudo-unitary space. Evidently, together with the dimension n, it determines a pseudo-unitary space up to isomorphism.

The classification of arbitrary nondegenerate complex bilinear-metric spaces is carried out by means of the fundamental Theorem 4 of Section 96. To characterize these spaces it is now necessary to write out sets of elementary divisors, subject to the conditions formulated at the end of Section 96.

99. Bilinear Functions on Bilinear-metric Spaces

In the preceding section the geometrical theory of one bilinear function given on a linear space $\mathfrak{L}$ was achieved by regarding the values of the bilinear function as the inner products of vectors, thus imposing a particular metric on $\mathfrak{L}$. Similarly, for the geometrical theory of pairs of bilinear functions given on a linear space $\mathfrak{L}$, one of them is understood to be a metric function, and the second is regarded as a bilinear function given on a bilinear-metric space. It is clear now that the pair $\varphi(x, y)$, $\varphi_1(x, y)$ and the pair $\varphi(x, y)$, $\varphi_2(x, y)$ are similar under an automorphism of the *linear* space $\mathfrak{L}$ if and only if the function $\varphi_1(x, y)$ is carried into the function $\varphi_2(x, y)$ by an automorphism of the *bilinear-metric* space $\mathfrak{L}$ with the fundamental metric function $\varphi(x, y)$.

More than this, in a nondegenerate bilinear-metric space it turns out to be possible to connect, one to one, a linear transformation of the space with each bilinear function. Since this connection does not depend on the choice of basis, then at the same time the study of bilinear functions becomes equivalent to the study of linear transformations of a bilinear-metric space. From the point of view of the theory of linear spaces, this means that the study of pairs of bilinear functions, of which one is nondegenerate, is equivalent to the study of pairs consisting of a nondegenerate bilinear function and a linear transformation.

Thus, let $\mathfrak{L}$ be a nondegenerate ordinary or Hermitian bilinear-metric space.

THEOREM 4. *Every linear function $f(x)$ defined on $\mathfrak{L}$ may be represented in one and only way in the form (x, a).*

Indeed, the condition $f(x)=(x, a)$ is equivalent to the system of relations

$$(a_j, a)=f(a_j), \qquad j=1, \cdots, n, \tag{12}$$

where the system $a_1, \cdots, a_n$ is some basis of $\mathfrak{L}$. Setting $a=\xi_1 a_1+\cdots+\xi_n a_n$ and regarding (12) as a system of equations in $\xi_1, \cdots, \xi_n$, we see that this is a system of n equations in n unknowns, the determinant of which is different form zero, since $\mathfrak{L}$ is nondegenerate. Consequently, the equations (12) have a unique solution.

Theorem 4 may be used to introduce the notion of the conjugate transformation, as was done in Section 75 for unitary spaces.

Consider an arbitrary linear transformation $\mathscr{A}$ of the space $\mathfrak{L}$. For each given vector a the expression $(x\mathscr{A}, a)$ represents a linear function in x. By Theorem 4, there is a unique vector b in $\mathfrak{L}$ for which

$$(x\mathscr{A}, a)=(x, b) \tag{13}$$

for all x. Denote by $\mathscr{A}^*$ the transformation which carries a into b. Then $b=a\mathscr{A}^*$, and equality (13) may be written in the form

$$(x\mathscr{A}, a)=(x, a\mathscr{A}^*). \tag{14}$$

The transformation $\mathscr{A}^*$ is called the ***right conjugate*** of $\mathscr{A}$. The right conjugate transformation is fully characterized by property (14). Indeed, if for some transformation $\mathscr{B}$

$$(x\mathscr{A}, a)=(x, a\mathscr{B})$$

for all a, x, then, comparing this equality with (14), we obtain

$$(x, a\mathscr{A}^*-a\mathscr{B})=0,$$

which shows that $a\mathscr{A}^* - a\mathscr{B}$ is an isotropic vector of the space $\mathfrak{L}$. Since $\mathfrak{L}$ contains no nonzero isotropic vectors, $a\mathscr{A}^* - a\mathscr{B} = 0$ and $\mathscr{A}^* = \mathscr{B}$.

Repeating the arguments of Section 75, it is easy to show the linearity of $\mathscr{A}^*$ and to verify the formulas

$$(\mathscr{A} + \mathscr{B})^* = \mathscr{A}^* + \mathscr{B}^*, \tag{15}$$

$$(\mathscr{A}\mathscr{B})^* = \mathscr{B}^*\mathscr{A}^*, \tag{16}$$

$$(\alpha\mathscr{A})^* = \alpha\mathscr{A}^* \tag{17}$$

for ordinary bilinear-metric spaces, and (15), (16) and

$$(\alpha\mathscr{A})^* = \bar{\alpha}\mathscr{A}^* \tag{18}$$

for Hermitian bilinear-metric spaces.

We now give the connection between the matrix of the transformation $\mathscr{A}$ and the matrix of the right conjugate $\mathscr{A}^*$. To do this, we choose a basis of $\mathfrak{L}$ and denote the matrices of the transformations $\mathscr{A}, \mathscr{A}^*$ by A, B, respectively. Let $\mathfrak{L}$ be an ordinary space. On the basis of formula (6) of Section 97, we have

$$(x\mathscr{A}, a) = [x\mathscr{A}]G[a]' = [x]AG[a]',$$

$$(x, a\mathscr{A}^*) = [x]G[a\mathscr{A}^*]' = [x]GB'[a]',$$

where G is the Gram matrix for the chosen basis of $\mathfrak{L}$. Hence

$$AG = GB', \quad B' = G^{-1}AG. \tag{19}$$

In a Hermitian bilinear-metric space, formula (19) becomes

$$AG = G\bar{B}', \quad \bar{B}' = G^{-1}AG. \tag{20}$$

We have seen that in unitary spaces there exist orthonormal coordinate systems. The Gram matrix for these systems is the identity matrix, and relation (20) gives the known result (Section 75): $\bar{B}' = A$.

Up to now we have defined only the right conjugate transformation. Evidently the same method may be used to introduce the left conjugate. Let $\mathscr{A}$ be a given linear transformation of $\mathfrak{L}$; repeating the argument above, we see that there exists a unique transformation $\mathscr{C}$ of $\mathfrak{L}$ such that for all x and a in $\mathfrak{L}$,

$$(x, a\mathscr{A}) = (x\mathscr{C}, a)$$

The transformation $\mathscr{C}$, which is linear, is called the *left conjugate* of $\mathscr{A}$ and is denoted by ${}^*\mathscr{A}$.

If the metric in $\mathfrak{L}$ is symmetric or skew-symmetric, then the right and left conjugates of any linear transformation coincide, since

$$(x\mathscr{A}^*, y) = \pm(y, x\mathscr{A}^*) = \pm(y\mathscr{A}, x) = (x, y\mathscr{A}) = (x\,{}^*\mathscr{A}, y).$$

Passing to a consideration of bilinear functions on $\mathfrak{L}$, we observe first of all that the expression $(x\mathscr{A}, y)$, where $\mathscr{A}$ is some linear transformation of $\mathfrak{L}$, represents a bilinear function on $\mathfrak{L}$.

If the linear transformations $\mathscr{A}, \mathscr{B}$ are distinct, then the corresponding bilinear functions $(x\mathscr{A}, y)$, $(x\mathscr{B}, y)$ are also distinct.

Indeed, the contrary means that $(x\mathscr{A}, y)=(x\mathscr{B}, y)$ for all x, y in $\mathfrak{L}$. Then $(x\mathscr{A} - x\mathscr{B}, y)= 0$ for all values of y — that is, $x\mathscr{A} - x\mathscr{B}$ is a left isotropic vector. Since $\mathfrak{L}$ has no nonzero isotropic vectors, $x\mathscr{A} = x\mathscr{B}$ or $\mathscr{A} = \mathscr{B}$.

We now show that *every bilinear function $f(x, y)$ defined on $\mathfrak{L}$ may be represented in the form $(x\mathscr{A}, y)$, where $\mathscr{A}$ is a linear transformation of the space $\mathfrak{L}$.* In this proposition $f(x, y)$ is understood to be an ordinary function if $\mathfrak{L}$ is an ordinary bilinear-metric space, and a Hermitian function if $\mathfrak{L}$ is a Hermitian bilinear-metric space.

Indeed, for each given value of y, $f(x, y)$ is a linear function in x. By Theorem 4 this means that for each y there is a unique vector z such that

$$f(x, y)=(x, z)$$

holds for all values of x. Let $\mathscr{B}$ denote the transformation which carries y into z; then.

$$f(x, y)=(x, y\mathscr{B}) . \tag{21}$$

In the case of a Hermitian bilinear-metric space we have

$$\begin{aligned} f(x, \alpha y_1 + \beta y_2) &= \bar{\alpha} f(x, y_1)+\bar{\beta} f(x, y_2) \\ &= \bar{\alpha}(x, y_1\mathscr{B})+ \bar{\beta}(x, y_2\mathscr{B})=(x, \alpha\cdot y_1\mathscr{B}+\beta\cdot y_2\mathscr{B}) . \end{aligned}$$

But from (21),

$$f(x, \alpha y_1 + \beta y_2)=(x, (\alpha y_1+\beta y_2)\mathscr{B}) .$$

Hence

$$(\alpha y_1 + \beta y_2)\mathscr{B} = \alpha\cdot y_1\mathscr{B} + \beta\cdot y_2\mathscr{B} ,$$

that is, $\mathscr{B}$ is a linear transformation. The same thing is true for an ordinary bilinear-metric space. Denoting the left conjugate transformation of $\mathscr{B}$ by $\mathscr{A}$, we may rewrite (21) in the form

$$f(x, y)=(x\mathscr{A}, y) ,$$

which was to be proved. Thus, we have obtained

THEOREM 5. *If $\mathfrak{L}$ is a nondegenerate ordinary or Hermitian bilinear-metric space, then the expression $(x\mathscr{A}, y)$, where $\mathscr{A}$ is a linear transformation of the space $\mathfrak{L}$, is an ordinary or, respectively, Hermitian, bilinear function on $\mathfrak{L}$. Conversely, for each ordinary* or, *respectively, Hermitian, bilinear, function $f(x, y)$ given on $\mathfrak{L}$, there exists a uniquely determined linear transformation $\mathscr{A}$ of $\mathfrak{L}$ for which $(x\mathscr{A}, y)= f(x, y)$ for all x, y in $\mathfrak{L}$.*

Theorem 5 establishes a one-to-one correspondence between bilinear functions and linear transformations of a nondegenerate bilinear-metric space, which permits the reduction of the study of bilinear functions to the study of the linear transformations of these spaces. From the point of view of the theory of pairs, Theorem 5 means that the study of pairs of bilinear functions, one of which is nonsingular, may be reduced to the study of mixed pairs, consisting of a nonsingular bilinear function and a linear transformation.

We now consider the connection between the matrix of a bilinear function $f(x, y)$ and its corresponding linear transformation $\mathscr{A}$. Choose a basis of $\mathfrak{L}$, and let F, A be the matrices of the function $f(x, y)$ and the transformation $\mathscr{A}$. By formula Section 97,

$$f(x, y) = [x]F[y]' ,$$

$$(x\mathscr{A}, y) = [x\mathscr{A}]G[y]' = [x]AG[y]' ,$$

and hence

$$F = AG , \tag{22}$$

where G is the Gram matrix of the space $\mathfrak{L}$ in the chosen basis. It is easy to verify that this formula also holds in the case of a Hermitian bilinear-metric space. A linear transformation $\mathscr{A}$ of a bilinear-metric space is called ***symmetric*** if

$$(x\mathscr{A}, y) = (x, y\mathscr{A}) \tag{23}$$

for all x, y in $\mathfrak{L}$. It is called ***skew-symmetric*** if

$$(x\mathscr{A}, y) = -(x, y\mathscr{A}) . \tag{24}$$

Comparing (23) and (24) with the formulas which defined the right and left conjugate transformations, we obtain the relations, equivalent to (23) and (24),

$$\mathscr{A} = \mathscr{A}^* = {}^*\mathscr{A} , \tag{25}$$

$$\mathscr{A} = -\mathscr{A}^* = -{}^*\mathscr{A} . \tag{26}$$

Let $\mathfrak{L}$ be a space with a symmetric metric, and let $\mathscr{A}$ be a symmetric linear transformation of the space $\mathfrak{L}$. The bilinear function which corresponds to the transformation $\mathscr{A}$ has the form

$$f(x, y) = (x\mathscr{A}, y) .$$

If $\mathfrak{L}$ is an ordinary space, then

$$f(x, y) = (x\mathscr{A}, y) = (y, x\mathscr{A}) = (y\mathscr{A}, x) = f(y, x) .$$

If $\mathfrak{L}$ is Hermitian, then

$$f(x, y) = (x\mathscr{A}, y) = \overline{(y, x\mathscr{A})} = \overline{(y\mathscr{A}, x)} = \overline{f(y, x)} .$$

Thus, in each case $f(x, y)$ is a symmetric function. The same argument shows that symmetry of a function $f(x, y)$ implies the symmetry of the corresponding linear transformation $\mathscr{A}$. Similarly, skew-symmetry of a transformation $\mathscr{A}$ is equivalent to skew-symmetry of the corresponding function $f(x, y)$.

If the metric of the space $\mathfrak{L}$ is skew-symmetric, then the relations between symmetric and skew-symmetric linear transformations and bilinear functions are reversed: symmetric transformations correspond to skew-symmetric functions, and skew-symmetric transformations correspond to symmetric functions. If $\mathscr{A}$ is a symmetric transformation of an ordinary bilinear-metric space $\mathfrak{L}$ with a skew-symmetric metric, then

$$f(x, y)=(x\mathscr{A}, y)=-(y, x\mathscr{A})=-(y\mathscr{A}, x)=-f(y, x) .$$

The remaining assertions are proved similarly. We thus have

THEOREM 6. *If $\mathfrak{L}$ is a nondegenerate ordinary or Hermitian space with a symmetric metric, then symmetric and skew-symmetric bilinear functions correspond respectively to symmetric and skew-symmetric linear transformations of $\mathfrak{L}$. If the metric of the space $\mathfrak{L}$ is skew-symmetic, then symmetric and skew-symmetric functions correspond respectively to skew-symmetric and symmetric transformations.*

Returning to the theory of pairs, we see by Theorem 6 that the study of pairs of symmetric or skew-symmetric bilinear functions is equivalent to the study of symmetric and skew-symmetric linear transformations of spaces with symmetric or skew-symmetric metrics.

● EXAMPLES AND PROBLEMS

1. The Gram matrix of a bilinear-metric space $\mathfrak{L}$ in the basis a_1, a_2, a_3, a_4 is

$$\begin{bmatrix} 1 & -3 & -7 & -2 \\ 2 & 1 & 7 & 3 \\ 3 & -2 & 0 & 1 \\ 4 & -1 & 5 & 3 \end{bmatrix}$$

Show that the left and right isotropic subspaces of $\mathfrak{L}$ have the respective bases $a_1 + a_2 - a_3$, $5a_2 + 6a_3 - 7a_4$ and $2a_1 + 3a_2 - a_3$, $a_1 + a_2 - a_4$.

2. In order that a bilinear-metric space be decomposable into a direct sum of two-sided orthogonal subspaces, it is necessary and sufficient that the Gram matrix be decomposable in some basis.
3. If the Gram matrix of a nondegenerate bilinear-metric space $\mathfrak{L}$ is G, then the linear transformation of $\mathfrak{L}$ which has matrix $G'G^{-1}$ is an automorphism of $\mathfrak{L}$.
4. Show that for an arbitrary nondegenerate subspace $\mathfrak{N}$ of a bilinear-metric space $\mathfrak{L}$ the dimension of $\mathfrak{N}^{\perp}$ and of ${}^{\perp}\mathfrak{N}$ equals the difference between the dimensions of $\mathfrak{L}$ and $\mathfrak{N}$. In particular, show that ${}^{\perp}(\mathfrak{N}^{\perp}) = ({}^{\perp}\mathfrak{N})^{\perp} = \mathfrak{N}$.
5. A subspace of a Hermitian real or complex bilinear-metric space $\mathfrak{L}$ is called ***maximal positive definite*** if it is unitary under the metric of $\mathfrak{L}$ and if it is contained in no larger subspace with this property. Maximal negative definite subspaces are similarly defined. Show that the dimension of every maximal positive definite subspace is equal to some fixed number s, and that the dimension t of every maximal negative definite

subspace satisfies the equality $s+t=r$, where r is the rank of $\mathfrak{L}$.

6. Every space with a symmetric or skew-symmetric metric is the direct sum of isotropic and nondegenerate subspaces.
7. If right and left orthogonality of vectors are equivalent in a bilinear-metric space $\mathfrak{L}$, then $\mathfrak{L}$ is the direct sum of two-sided orthogonal subspaces with symmetric and skew-symmetric metrics.
8. A function ψ is a quadratic function on a linear space if and only if it satisfies the identity

$$\beta\psi(\alpha x+y)+\alpha\psi(x-\beta y)=(1+\alpha\beta)(\alpha\psi(x)+\beta\psi(y)) .$$

9. Let I be a fixed square matrix. A matrix A is called ***I-orthogonal*** if $AIA'=I$, ***I-symmetric*** if $AI=IA$, and ***I-skew-symmetric*** if $AI=-IA$. Show that if the Gram matrix of a bilinear-metric space in some basis is I, then in this basis isometric linear transformations have I-orthogonal matrices, and symmetric and skew-symmetric transformations have I-symmetric and I skew-symmetric matrices, respectively.

7 LINEAR TRANSFORMATIONS OF BILINEAR-METRIC SPACES

In the present chapter we consider the classification of the fundamental types of linear transformations (symmetric, skew-symmetric, and isometric) of spaces with bilinear metrics. The connection of this classification with the classification of pairs of bilinear forms was studied in paragraph 4, Chapter VI, the results of which, for the present chapter, are assumed known to the reader.

1. The Fundamental Types of Linear Transformations

100. Automorphisms

According to Section 99, a nonsingular linear transformation $\mathscr{U}$ of a bilinear-metric space $\mathfrak{L}$ is an *automorphism* of the space $\mathfrak{L}$ if $\mathscr{U}$ does not change the value of the inner product, or if

$$(x\mathscr{U}, y\mathscr{U}) = (x, y) \tag{1}$$

for all x, y in $\mathfrak{L}$. Automorphisms of a space $\mathfrak{L}$ are sometimes also called ***isometric transformations.*** Using the notions of right and left conjugate transformations, relation (1) may be written in the form

$$(x, y) = (x\mathscr{U}, y\mathscr{U}) = (x, y\mathscr{U}\mathscr{U}^*) = (x\mathscr{U}^*\mathscr{U}, y)\,,$$

hence

$$\mathscr{U}\mathscr{U}^* = \mathscr{U}^*\mathscr{U} = \mathscr{E}\,. \tag{2}$$

It is clear that, conversely, (1) follows from (2). Thus, *in order that a linear transformation $\mathscr{U}$ of a nondegenerate bilinear-metric space be an auto-*

morphism, it is necessary and sufficient that both conjugate transformations of $\mathscr{U}$ coincide with the inverse of $\mathscr{U}$.

Choose a basis of $\mathfrak{L}$ and let U denote the matrix of the transformation $\mathscr{U}$. If $\mathfrak{L}$ is an ordinary space, then relation (1) becomes

$$[x]UGU'[y]' = [x]G[y]' ,$$

where G is the Gram matrix. Hence

$$UGU' = G . \tag{3}$$

If $\mathfrak{L}$ is a Hermitian space, then (1) yields

$$[x]UG\bar{U}'[\bar{y}]' = [x]G[\bar{y}]'$$

or

$$UG\bar{U}' = G . \tag{4}$$

(3) and (4) represent conditions which are satisfied by the *matrices of isometric transformations* of a nondegenerate ordinary or respectively Hermitian bilinear-metric space.

Two linear transformations $\mathscr{A}_1$, $\mathscr{A}_2$ of a bilinear-metric space $\mathfrak{L}$ are called ***similar*** if there exists an isomorphic mapping $\mathscr{U}$ of the space $\mathfrak{L}$ onto itself which carries $\mathscr{A}_1$ into $\mathscr{A}_2$. By Section 41 we have

$$\mathscr{A}_2 = \mathscr{U}^{-1}\mathscr{A}_1\mathscr{U} . \tag{5}$$

The transformation $\mathscr{U}$ is an automorphism of the space $\mathfrak{L}$, and therefore relation (5) shows that *similarity of linear transformations of a bilinear-metric space is equivalent to their similarity under an isometric transformation.* It follows from the results of Section 58 that similar linear transformations have identical invariant factors. In general this criterion is not sufficient for the similarity of transformations. However, the situation is different if the transformations considered are symmetric, skew-symmetric, or isometric.

THEOREM 1. *Let $\mathfrak{L}$ be a nondegenerate ordinary space over the field of complex numbers, with symmetric or skew-symmetric metric. Then symmetric, skew-symmetric, or isometric transformations of the space $\mathfrak{L}$ are similar if and only if their invariant factors coincide.*

The necessity of the condition was established above; therefore we consider only the sufficiency. Let $\mathscr{A}_1$, $\mathscr{A}_2$ be given linear transformations. By assumption, the invariant factors of $\mathscr{A}_1$ and $\mathscr{A}_2$ coincide, and consequently

$$\mathscr{A}_2 = \mathscr{T}^{-1}\mathscr{A}_1\mathscr{T} , \tag{6}$$

where $\mathscr{T}$ is some nonsingular linear transformation of the space $\mathfrak{L}$. Taking the conjugate transformations on both sides,* we obtain

$$\mathscr{A}_2^* = \mathscr{T}^*\mathscr{A}_1^*\mathscr{T}^{*-1} . \tag{7}$$

* The metric in $\mathfrak{L}$ is either symmetric or skew-symmetric, and therefore the right and left conjugate transformations are equal.

If $\mathscr{A}_1, \mathscr{A}_2$ are both symmetric or skew-symmetric, then $\mathscr{A}_1^* = \pm \mathscr{A}_1$, $\mathscr{A}_2^* = \pm \mathscr{A}_2$, and (7) becomes

$$\mathscr{A}_2 = \mathscr{T}^* \mathscr{A}_1 \mathscr{T}^{*-1} . \tag{8}$$

If $\mathscr{A}_1, \mathscr{A}_2$ are isometric, then $\mathscr{A}_1^* = \mathscr{A}_1^{-1}$, $\mathscr{A}_2^* = \mathscr{A}_2^{-1}$. Substituting these values into (7) and raising both sides of the result to the -1 power, we again obtain (8). From (6) and (8) we have $\mathscr{T}^{-1}\mathscr{A}_1\mathscr{T} = \mathscr{T}^*\mathscr{A}_1\mathscr{T}^{*-1}$, hence

$$\mathscr{A}_1 \cdot \mathscr{T}\mathscr{T}^* = \mathscr{T}\mathscr{T}^* \cdot \mathscr{A}_1 . \tag{9}$$

It immediately follows from (9) that

$$\mathscr{A}_1 \cdot (\mathscr{T}\mathscr{T}^*)^k = (\mathscr{T}\mathscr{T}^*)^k \cdot \mathscr{A}_1 \quad (k = 1, 2, \cdots) ,$$

and, in general,

$$\mathscr{A}_1 \cdot f(\mathscr{T}\mathscr{T}^*) = f(\mathscr{T}\mathscr{T}^*) \cdot \mathscr{A}_1 ,$$

where $f(\lambda)$ is an arbitrary polynomial (see Section 95). By the theorem on the extraction of square roots (Section 64), the polynomial $f(\lambda)$ may be chosen so that

$$f(\mathscr{T}\mathscr{T}^*) \cdot f(\mathscr{T}\mathscr{T}^*) = \mathscr{T}\mathscr{T}^* .$$

Setting

$$\mathscr{D} = f(\mathscr{T}\mathscr{T}^*), \quad \mathscr{U} = \mathscr{D}^{-1}\mathscr{T} ,$$

we obtain

$$\begin{aligned} \mathscr{D}^* &= [f(\mathscr{T}\mathscr{T}^*)]^* = f(\mathscr{T}\mathscr{T}^*) = \mathscr{D} , \\ \mathscr{U}^* &= \mathscr{T}^*\mathscr{D}^{*-1} = \mathscr{T}^*\mathscr{D}^{-1} , \\ \mathscr{U}\mathscr{U}^* &= \mathscr{D}^{-1}\mathscr{T}\mathscr{T}^*\mathscr{D}^{-1} = \mathscr{D}^{-1} f(\mathscr{T}\mathscr{T}^*) f(\mathscr{T}\mathscr{T}^*) \mathscr{D}^{-1} \\ &= \mathscr{D}^{-1}\mathscr{D}^2\mathscr{D}^{-1} = \mathscr{E} . \end{aligned}$$

Thus, $\mathscr{U}$ is an isometric transformation. At the same time, it follows from $\mathscr{A}_1\mathscr{D} = \mathscr{D}\mathscr{A}_1$ that

$$\begin{aligned} \mathscr{U}^{-1}\mathscr{A}_1\mathscr{U} &= \mathscr{T}^{-1}\mathscr{D}\mathscr{A}_1\mathscr{D}^{-1}\mathscr{T} = \mathscr{T}^{-1}\mathscr{A}_1\mathscr{D}\mathscr{D}^{-1}\mathscr{T} \\ &= \mathscr{T}^{-1}\mathscr{A}_1\mathscr{T} = \mathscr{A}_2 , \end{aligned}$$

which was to be proved.

Theorem 1 shows that for the classification up to similarity of symmetric, skew-symmetric, and isometric transformations of complex Euclidean, and also complex symplectic, spaces, it is sufficient to show which sets of elementary divisors these transformations can have.

THEOREM 2. *If an isometric transformation $\mathscr{U}$ of a nondegenerate ordinary bilinear-metric space $\mathfrak{L}$ contains the elementary divisor $(\lambda - \alpha)^m$ with multiplicity k, then $\mathscr{U}$ also contains the elementary divisor $(\lambda - \alpha^{-1})^m$ with multiplicity k.*

For $\alpha = \pm 1$ the theorem has no content. Therefore, suppose that $\alpha \neq \pm 1$.

Choose a basis of $\mathfrak{L}$ and denote the matrix of the transformation $\mathscr{U}$ by U. From (3), $UGU' = G$, where G is the Gram matrix. Hence

$$U' = G^{-1}U^{-1}G\,. \tag{10}$$

The elementary divisors of the matrix U coincide with the elementary divisors of the matrix U'. Formula (10) shows that, in turn, the elementary divisors of U' coincide with the elementary divisors of U^{-1} (compare Section 58). Thus, the elementary divisors of the matrix U must be exactly those of the matrix U^{-1}. However, by the theorem on the elementary divisors of functions (see Section 65) the elementary divisors of the matrix U^{-1} are obtained from the elementary divisors $(\lambda - \alpha)^m$ of the matrix U by replacing α by α^{-1}. Consequently, if α is replaced by α^{-1} in each elementary divisor of the matrix U of the form $(\lambda - \alpha)^m$, another elementary divisor of the matrix U is obtained. This completes the proof.

For Hermitian bilinear-metric spaces, relation (10) becomes

$$\bar{U}' = G^{-1}UG\,.$$

Corresponding to this, the assertion about the elementary divisors becomes: *if* $(\lambda - \alpha)^m$ *occurs* k *times as an elementary divisor of an isometric transformation of a Hermitian bilinear-metric space, then* $(\lambda - \bar{\alpha}^{-1})^m$ *also occurs* k *times as an elementary divisor of this transformation.* The proof is exactly the same.

THEOREM 3. *Let* a, b *be two root vectors of some isometric transformation* $\mathscr{U}$ *of an ordinary bilinear-metric space* $\mathfrak{L}$. *If* α, β *are the proper values of* $\mathscr{U}$ *to which these vectors belong, and* $\alpha\beta \neq 1$, *then* a *and* b *are orthogonal. Similarly, if* $\mathfrak{L}$ *is a Hermitian bilinear-metric space and* $\alpha\bar{\beta} \neq 1$, *then* a *and* b *are orthogonal.*

The proof for ordinary and for Hermitian spaces is the same. Therefore we consider only an ordinary space. By assumption,

$$a(\alpha\mathscr{E} - \mathscr{U})^s = \theta\,, \quad b(\beta\mathscr{E} - \mathscr{U})^t = \theta \qquad (\alpha\beta \neq 1)\,, \tag{11}$$

where s and t are some nonnegative integers. We must show that equality $(a, b) = 0$ follows from relation (11). The proof proceeds by induction on the value of the sum $s + t$. If $s + t = 0$, then $s = t = 0$, (11) gives $a = b = \theta$, and hence $(a, b) = 0$.

Now suppose that some value of the sum $s + t$ is given, and that for all smaller values the assertion has already been proved. Let

$$a(\alpha\mathscr{E} - \mathscr{U}) = a_1\,, \quad b(\beta\mathscr{E} - \mathscr{U}) = b_1\,.$$

Since

$$a_1(\alpha\mathscr{E} - \mathscr{U})^{s-1} = a(\alpha\mathscr{E} - \mathscr{U})^s = \theta\,,$$
$$b_1(\beta\mathscr{E} - \mathscr{U})^{t-1} = b(\beta\mathscr{E} - \mathscr{U})^t = \theta\,,$$

then, by the inductive assumption,

$$(a, b_1) = (a_1, b) = (a_1, b_1) = 0\,.$$

But the equality $(a, b_1) = 0$ gives $(a, b(\beta\mathscr{E} - \mathscr{U})) = 0$, or

$$(a, b\mathscr{U}) = \beta(a, b) . \tag{12}$$

Similarly, it follows from $(a_1, b) = 0$ that

$$(a\mathscr{U}, b) = \alpha(a, b) . \tag{13}$$

Finally, the equality $(a_1, b_1) = 0$ gives

$$0 = (a(\alpha\mathscr{E} - \mathscr{U}), b(\beta\mathscr{E} - \mathscr{U})) = \alpha\beta(a, b) - \alpha(a, b\mathscr{U}) - \beta(a\mathscr{U}, b) + (a\mathscr{U}, b\mathscr{U}),$$

from which, in view of (12) and (13), we obtain

$$0 = -\alpha\beta(a, b) + (a, b) . \tag{14}$$

Since $\alpha\beta \neq 1$, (14) yields the desired equality $(a, b) = 0$.

THEOREM 4. *If $\mathscr{A}$ is an isometric, symmetric, or skew-symmetric transformation of a space $\mathfrak{L}$,* and $\mathfrak{A}$ *is a subspace of $\mathfrak{L}$ which is invariant under $\mathscr{A}$, then the subspaces right and left orthogonal to $\mathfrak{A}$ are also invariant under $\mathscr{A}$.*

Let $\mathscr{A}$ be an isometric transformation of the space $\mathfrak{L}$. The right orthogonal subspace $\mathfrak{A}^\perp$ consists of vectors b which satisfy, for a in $\mathfrak{A}$, the relation $(a, b) = 0$. Since $\mathscr{A}$ is nonsingular, $\mathfrak{A}$ is also invariant under $\mathscr{A}^{-1}$. Consequently, the vector $a\mathscr{A}^{-1}$ belongs to $\mathfrak{A}$, and hence $(a\mathscr{A}^{-1}, b) = 0$. But

$$(a\mathscr{A}^{-1}, b) = (a\mathscr{A}^{-1}\mathscr{A}, b\mathscr{A}) = (a, b\mathscr{A}) ,$$

and thus $(a, b\mathscr{A}) = 0$ for all a in $\mathfrak{A}$. Consequently, $b\mathscr{A}$ belongs to $\mathfrak{A}^\perp$ and $\mathfrak{N}^\perp$ is invariant under $\mathscr{A}$. The remaining assertions are proved analogously.

THEOREM 5. *Let an ordinary or Hermitian bilinear-metric space $\mathfrak{L}$ decompose into the direct sum of two-sided orthogonal subspaces $\mathfrak{L}_1, \cdots, \mathfrak{L}_s$. If all these subspaces are invariant under a linear transformation $\mathscr{A}$ of the space $\mathfrak{L}$, and if $\mathscr{A}$ is isometric or respectively symmetric or skew-symmetric on each of the subspaces $\mathfrak{L}_1, \cdots, \mathfrak{L}_s$, then $\mathscr{A}$ is also isometric or respectively symmetric or skew-symmetric on $\mathfrak{L}$.*

This theorem shows the way in which direct decompositions can be used in the study of the properties of the indicated types of linear transformations. Its proof is obvious and is left to the reader.

101. Symmetric and Skew-symmetric Transformations

We recall that a transformation $\mathscr{A}$ of an ordinary or Hermitian bilinear-metric space $\mathfrak{L}$ is called ***symmetric*** if

$$(x\mathscr{A}, y) = (x, y\mathscr{A})$$

for all x, y in $\mathfrak{L}$.

THEOREM 6. *Root vectors a, b belonging to distinct proper values ρ, σ of* *a symmetric transformation $\mathscr{A}$ of an ordinary or Hermitian bilinear-metric space are orthogonal.*

By assumption,

$$a(\rho\mathscr{E} - \mathscr{A})^s = \theta\,, \quad b(\sigma\mathscr{E} - \mathscr{A})^t = \theta\,, \tag{15}$$

where s and t are some nonnegative integers. We must show that (15) implies the orthogonality of the vectors a and b. The proof proceeds by induction on the sum $s+t$. For $s+t=1$, either s or t is zero; consequently either $a=\theta$ or $b=\theta$, and hence $(a, b)=0$.

Now suppose some value of the sum $s+t$ is given and that the assertion has already been proved for all smaller values of $s+t$. Let

$$a_1 = a(\rho\mathscr{E} - \mathscr{A}), \quad b_1 = b(\sigma\mathscr{E} - \mathscr{A})\,.$$

We have

$$a_1(\rho\mathscr{E} - \mathscr{A})^{s-1} = a(\rho\mathscr{E} - \mathscr{A})^s = \theta\,,$$
$$b_1(\sigma\mathscr{E} - \mathscr{A})^{t-1} = b(\sigma\mathscr{E} - \mathscr{A})^t = \theta\,.$$

Therefore, by the inductive assumption,

$$(a, b_1) = (a_1, b) = 0\,,$$

or

$$\sigma(a, b) = (a, b\mathscr{A})\,, \quad \rho(a, b) = (a\mathscr{A}, b)\,.$$

Since $\mathscr{A}$ is symmetric, the right sides of these equalities are equal; consequently, $(\sigma - \rho)(a, b) = 0$, and hence $(a, b) = 0$, which was to be proved.

A transformation $\mathscr{A}$ of an ordinary bilinear-metric space $\mathfrak{L}$ that satisfies the relation

$$(x\mathscr{A}, y) = -(x, y\mathscr{A})$$

for all x, y in $\mathfrak{L}$ is called ***skew-symmetric*** (compare Section 99).

THEOREM 7. *Let a, b be root vectors of a skew-symmetric transformation of an ordinary bilinear-metric space that belong to the proper values ρ, σ. If $\rho + \sigma \neq 0$, then $(a, b) = 0$.*

The proof is almost exactly the same as the proofs of the analogous Theorems 3 and 6, and is omitted here.

The isometric transformations of an arbitrary nondegenerate bilinear-metric space $\mathfrak{L}$ are very closely connected with the skew-symmetric transformations of $\mathfrak{L}$. We have the following theorem, which coincides in its formulation with Theorem 2 of Section 85 on Cayley's transformation.

THEOREM 8. *Let $\mathfrak{L}$ be an ordinary or Hermitian bilinear-metric space. If $\mathscr{A}$ is a skew-symmetric transformation of $\mathfrak{L}$ which does not have -1 as a proper value, then*

$$\mathscr{U} = (\mathscr{E} - \mathscr{A})(\mathscr{E} + \mathscr{A})^{-1} \tag{16}$$

is an isometric transformation of $\mathfrak{L}$ that also does not have -1 as a proper value. Moreover, $\mathcal{A}$ is expressed in terms of $\mathcal{U}$ by the formula

$$\mathcal{A} = (\mathcal{E} - \mathcal{U})(\mathcal{E} + \mathcal{U})^{-1} . \tag{17}$$

Conversely, if $\mathcal{U}$ is an isometric transformation of the space $\mathfrak{L}$ that does not have -1 as a proper value, then the transformation $\mathcal{A}$ given by formula (17) *is skew-symmetric and does not have -1 as a proper value; $\mathcal{U}$ is expressed in terms of $\mathcal{A}$ by formula* (16).

Formulas (16) and (17), as in the case of unitary spaces, are called Cayley's transformations. The proof is exactly the same as the proof of these formulas given in Section 85 for unitary spaces, and is therefore omitted here. We remark that the analogous formulas

$$\mathcal{U} = -(\mathcal{E} - \mathcal{A})(\mathcal{E} + \mathcal{A})^{-1} , \tag{18}$$

$$\mathcal{A} = (\mathcal{E} + \mathcal{U})(\mathcal{E} - \mathcal{U})^{-1} \tag{19}$$

give a correspondence between skew-symmetric transformations of the space $\mathfrak{L}$ that do not have -1 as a proper value and isometric transformations of $\mathfrak{L}$ that do not have $+1$ as a proper value.

Cayley's transformations would completely reduce the study of isometric transformations to the study of skew-symmetric transformations if it were not for the exceptional proper values ± 1. The existence of these values makes necessary a more detailed independent study of the properties of isometric transformations.

Finally, we prove

THEOREM 9. *If $(\lambda - \alpha)^m$ occurs k times in the system of elementary divisors of a skew-symmetric transformation $\mathcal{A}$ of a nondegenerate ordinary bilinear-metric space $\mathfrak{L}$, then $(\lambda + \alpha)^m$ also appears k times in the system of elementary divisors of the transformation $\mathcal{A}$.*

The matrix B of the conjugate transformation $\mathcal{A}^*$ satisfies the relation (19) of Section 99,

$$B' = G^{-1}AG ,$$

where G is the Gram matrix and A is the matrix of the transformation $\mathcal{A}$. It follows that the elementary divisors of the matrix B coincide with the elementary divisors of the matrix A. However, from the condition of skew-symmetry, $B = -A$; thus, changing the sign of α in each elementary divisor $(\lambda - \alpha)^m$ of the transformation $\mathcal{A}$ results in another elementary divisor of $\mathcal{A}$, which was to be proved.

• EXAMPLES AND PROBLEMS

1. Let $\mathcal{U}$ be a mapping of a nondegenerate bilinear-metric space $\mathfrak{L}$ onto itself, which preserves inner products: $(a\mathcal{U}, b\mathcal{U}) = (a, b)$. Show that $\mathcal{U}$ is linear, and consequently is an isometric transformation of the space $\mathfrak{L}$.

2. The determinant of an isometric transformation of a nondegenerate ordinary bilinear-metric space equals ± 1, and the determinant of an isometric transformation of a nondegenerate Hermitian bilinear-metric space has modulus 1.
3. In each nondegenerate bilinear-metric space $\mathfrak{L}$ there exists a linear transformation $\mathscr{T}$ that satisfies the condition $(x, y) = (y\mathscr{T}, x)$ if $\mathfrak{L}$ is ordinary, and the condition $(x, y) = \overline{(y\mathscr{T}, x)}$ if $\mathfrak{L}$ is Hermitian. Show that the transformation $\mathscr{T}$ is isometric and that its matrix equals $G'G^{-1}$ or $\bar{G}'G^{-1}$, according to whether $\mathfrak{L}$ is ordinary or Hermitian. (G is the Gram matrix of the space $\mathfrak{L}$.)
4. If the right and left conjugate transformations of every linear transformation of a nondegenerate ordinary bilinear-metric space $\mathfrak{L}$ coincide, then the metric of the space $\mathfrak{L}$ is either symmetric or skew-symmetric.

2. *Complex Euclidean Spaces*

In the present and the two succeeding paragraphs we will examine in more detail the simplest forms to which it is possible to reduce the matrices of symmetric, skew-symmetric, and isometric transformations of Euclidean, symplectic, and pseudo-unitary spaces over the field of complex numbers (these spaces are classified at the end of Section 98). We shall always make use of some special coordinate system with a fully determined Gram matrix, since only under such conditions will the transformations be known to within similarity. This problem was solved in Chapter V for unitary and real Euclidean spaces. There an orthonormal coordinate system was chosen, in which the Gram matrix was the identity matrix. In spaces of more complicated types it is more convenient to take as a fundamental or normal coordinate system a coordinate system with a more complicated Gram matrix. We begin with a study of complex Euclidean spaces.

102. Symmetric Transformations

As mentioned above, complex Euclidean spaces are nondegenerate spaces with ordinary symmetric metrics over the field of complex numbers. The Gram matrix of a complex Euclidean space is nonsingular and symmetric. Conversely, each complex bilinear-metric space with a nonsingular symmetric Gram matrix is a complex Euclidean space. But all complex Euclidean spaces of a given dimension n are isomorphic; therefore, in each such space there exists a coordinate system with any previously assigned nonsingular symmetric Gram matrix. In particular, there exists a coordinate system $a_1, \cdots, a_n$ in each complex Euclidean space $\mathfrak{L}$ such that the Gram matrix of $\mathfrak{L}$ has the form

$$G = \begin{bmatrix} 0 & \cdot & \cdot & \cdot & 0 & 1 \\ 0 & \cdot & \cdot & \cdot & 1 & 0 \\ \cdot & \cdot & \cdot & \cdot & \cdot & \cdot \\ 1 & \cdot & \cdot & \cdot & 0 & 0 \end{bmatrix} \qquad (1)$$

in this coordinate system. We call a coordinate system with such a matrix ***normal***. The vectors of a normal coordinate system satisfy the relations

$$(a_j, a_{n+1-j}) = 1, \quad (a_j, a_k) = 0 \tag{2}$$

where $j + k \neq n + 1$, $j, k = 1, \cdots, n$, which are also sufficient for normality.

The usefulness of normal bases is given in the following property: *a linear transformation is symmetric if its matrix relative to a normal basis is a Jordan block.*

Indeed, by Section 99, the transformation $\mathscr{A}$ is symmetric if the matrix AG is symmetric, where G is the Gram matrix of the coordinate basis and A is the matrix of the transformation $\mathscr{A}$ in this basis. But multiplying a Jordan block of order n by the matrix G yields, by an immediate calculation, a symmetric matrix.

This observation permits us to prove at once the following fundamental theorem.

THEOREM 1. *Let an arbitrary system of expressions of the form $(\lambda - \rho_1)^{m_1}, \cdots, (\lambda - \rho_s)^{m_s}$ be given. Then a symmetric transformation $\mathscr{A}$ of a complex Euclidean space of dimension $n = m_1 + \cdots + m_s$ can be found for which these expressions are a complete system of elementary divisors.*

To prove this, set

$$G_j = \begin{bmatrix} 0 & \cdot & \cdot & \cdot & 0 & 1 \\ 0 & \cdot & \cdot & \cdot & 1 & 0 \\ \cdot & \cdot & \cdot & \cdot & \cdot & \cdot \\ 1 & \cdot & \cdot & \cdot & 0 & 0 \end{bmatrix}, \quad A_j = \begin{bmatrix} \rho_j & 1 & \cdot & \cdot & \cdot & \cdot \\ \cdot & \rho_j & 1 & \cdot & \cdot & \cdot \\ \cdot & \cdot & \cdot & \cdot & \rho_j & 1 \\ \cdot & \cdot & \cdot & \cdot & \cdot & \rho_j \end{bmatrix}, \tag{3}$$

where G_j, A_j have order m_j for $A_j = 1, \cdots, s$. Let

$$G = G_1 \dotplus \cdots \dotplus G_s, \qquad A = A_1 \dotplus \cdots \dotplus A_s. \tag{4}$$

In a complex Euclidean space $\mathfrak{L}$ of dimension n find a basis with Gram matrix G. Let $\mathscr{A}$ denote the linear transformation with matrix A in this basis. By the observation above, the matrix AG is symmetric, and hence the transformation $\mathscr{A}$ is symmetric. At the same time, it is evident from (3) and (4) that $\mathscr{A}$ has the required system of elementary divisors.

In view of Theorem 1 of Section 100, this last theorem completely solves the question of the classification to within similarity of all symmetric transformations of a complex Euclidean space. In particular, we have

THEOREM 2. *Let $\mathscr{A}$ be a symmetric transformation of a complex Euclidean space $\mathfrak{L}$. Then $\mathfrak{L}$ may be decomposed into the direct sum of pairwise orthogonal subspaces invariant under $\mathscr{A}$, each of which has a normal basis in which the matrix of the transformation induced by $\mathscr{A}$ is a Jordan block.*

To prove this, we denote the set of elementary divisors of the transformation $\mathscr{A}$ by $(\lambda - \rho_1)^{m_1}, \cdots, (\lambda - \rho_s)^{m_s}$. Choose a basis $a_1, \cdots, a_n$ of $\mathfrak{L}$, whose Gram matrix equals the matrix G in (4), and let $\mathscr{B}$ be the linear transformation with matrix A in (4) in the basis $a_1, \cdots, a_n$. The transformations $\mathscr{A}$, $\mathscr{B}$ are symmetric and similar. It follows from Theorem 1 of Section 100 that there exists an isometric transformation $\mathscr{U}$ for which $\mathscr{A} = \mathscr{U}\mathscr{B}\mathscr{U}^{-1}$. Thus the matrix of the transformation $\mathscr{A}$ in the basis $a_1\mathscr{U}, \cdots, a_n\mathscr{U}$ coincides with the matrix of the transformation $\mathscr{B}$ in the basis $a_1, \cdots, a_n$ that is, with the matrix A. At the same time, the Gram matrix in the basis $a_1\mathscr{U}, \cdots, a_n\mathscr{U}$ is G, and for the transformation $\mathscr{B}$ the assertion of Theorem 2 is obvious.

The matrix of a symmetric transformation in an orthonormal basis is symmetric. Therefore, it follows from Theorem 1 that there exist complex symmetric matrices with arbitrary sets of elementary divisors.

103. Skew-symmetric Transformations

Let $\mathscr{A}$ be a skew-symmetric transformation of a complex Euclidean space $\mathfrak{L}$. Decompose $\mathfrak{L}$ into the direct sum of root subspaces:

$$\mathfrak{L} = \mathfrak{L}_{\rho_1} \dotplus \cdots \dotplus \mathfrak{L}_{\rho_s} .$$

Collecting the summands in pairs corresponding to proper values with opposite sign, we obtain a new decomposition of $\mathfrak{L}$:

$$\mathfrak{L} = \mathfrak{M}_0 \dotplus \mathfrak{M}_1 \dotplus \cdots \dotplus \mathfrak{M}_t ,$$

where $\mathfrak{M}_0$ is the root subspace corresponding to the proper value 0, and $\mathfrak{M}_j$ for $j = 1, \cdots, t$ is a sum of the form $\mathfrak{L}_\rho \dotplus \mathfrak{L}_{-\rho}$. Theorem 7 of Section 101 shows that the subspaces $\mathfrak{M}_0, \cdots, \mathfrak{M}_t$ are pairwise orthogonal; moreover, they are invariant under $\mathscr{A}$. Therefore, the study of the effect of $\mathscr{A}$ on $\mathfrak{L}$ reduces to the study of the effect of this transformation on the separate subspaces $\mathfrak{M}_0, \cdots, \mathfrak{M}_t$. We consider $\mathfrak{M}_0$ in more detail. Suppose that $\mathfrak{M}_0$ is different from zero, and denote by $\mathscr{A}_0$ the transformation induced in $\mathfrak{M}_0$ by $\mathscr{A}$. Since all proper values of the transformation $\mathscr{A}_0$ equal zero, then $\mathscr{A}_0^p = \mathscr{O}$, where p is the dimension of $\mathfrak{M}_0$. Let m denote the smallest power of $\mathscr{A}_0$ which is zero: $\mathscr{A}_0^m = \mathscr{O}$, $\mathscr{A}_0^{m-1} \neq \mathscr{O}$. We consider two cases: m even and m odd. Let m be even; then $m-1$ is odd and the transformation $\mathscr{A}_0^{m-1}$ is skew-symmetric. The bilinear function $(x\mathscr{A}_0^{m-1}, y)$ is also skew-symmetric. Since this function is different from zero, there is a pair of vectors a, b in $\mathfrak{M}_0$ for which

$$(a\mathscr{A}_0^{m-1}, b) = 1 .$$

It follows from the skew-symmetry of the transformation $\mathscr{A}_0$ that

$$(a\mathscr{A}_0^k, b\mathscr{A}_0^l) = -(a\mathscr{A}_0^{k-1}, b\mathscr{A}_0^{l+1}) = \cdots = (-1)^k(a, b\mathscr{A}_0^{l+k}) .$$

In particular, $(a, b\mathscr{A}_0^{m-1}) = (-1)^{m-1}(a\mathscr{A}_0^{m-1}, b) = (-1)^{m-1}$, so $b\mathscr{A}_0^{m-1} \neq \theta$. Set

$$\begin{aligned} a_1 &= a , \quad & a_2 &= a_1\mathscr{A}_0 , \quad \cdots, \quad & a_m &= a_{m-1}\mathscr{A}_0 , \\ b_1 &= b , \quad & b_2 &= b_1\mathscr{A}_0 , \quad \cdots, \quad & b_m &= b_{m-1}\mathscr{A}_0 . \end{aligned}$$

Since $\mathscr{A}_0^m = \mathscr{O}$, the subspace spanned by the vectors $a_1, \cdots, a_m$ and $b_1, \cdots, b_m$

has basis $a_1, \cdots, a_m, b_1, \cdots, b_m$. The relations

$$(a_k, b_{m+1-k}) = (-1)^{m-k}, \quad (a_k, b_j) = 0,$$

where $k + j > m + 1$ and $k, j = 1, \cdots, m$, show that the Gram matrix of this basis has the form

$$\begin{bmatrix} * & \cdot & \cdot & \cdot & \cdot & * & 1 \\ * & \cdot & \cdot & \cdot & \cdot & -1 & 0 \\ \cdot & \cdot & \cdot & \cdot & \cdot & \cdot & \cdot \\ -1 & \cdot & \cdot & \cdot & \cdot & 0 & 0 \end{bmatrix},$$

where all the elements under the diagonal $1, -1, \cdots, 1, -1$ are zero. The determinant of such a matrix is ± 1, and, consequently, the subspace $\mathfrak{N}_1$, spanned by $a_1, \cdots, a_m, b_1, \cdots, b_m$, is nondegenerate. In view of Theorem 2 of Section 98,

$$\mathfrak{M}_0 = \mathfrak{N}_1 \dotplus \mathfrak{N}_1^\perp,$$

and moreover, $\mathfrak{N}_1^\perp$ is also a subspace invariant under $\mathscr{A}_0$.

We now consider the case when m is odd. The transformation $\mathscr{A}_0^{m-1}$ is symmetric, and consequently the bilinear function $(x\mathscr{A}_0^{m-1}, y)$ corresponding to it is also symmetric. Since this function is not identically zero, there is a vector a for which $(a\mathscr{A}_0^{m-1}, a) \neq 0$. Set

$$a_1 = a, \quad a_2 = a_1\mathscr{A}_0, \cdots, \quad a_m = a_{m-1}\mathscr{A}_0.$$

The subspace $\mathfrak{N}_1$, spanned by $a_1, \cdots, a_m$, is invariant under $\mathscr{A}_0$. Its Gram matrix in the coordinate system $a_1, \cdots, a_m$ has the form

$$G = \begin{bmatrix} (a_1, a_1) \cdots (a_1, a_{m-1}) & (a_1, a_m) \\ (a_2, a_1) \cdots (a_2, a_{m-1}) & 0 \\ \cdot \; \cdot \; \cdot \; \cdot \; \cdot \; \cdot \; \cdot \; \cdot & \cdot \\ (a_m, a_1) \cdots \qquad 0 & 0 \end{bmatrix},$$

and $(a_j, a_k) = (a\mathscr{A}_0^{j-1}, a\mathscr{A}_0^{k-1}) = (-1)^{k-1}(a\mathscr{A}_0^{j+k-2}, a) = 0$ for $j + k > m + 1$. Under this,

$$(a_1, a_m) = -(a_2, a_{m-1}) = \cdots = (a_m, a_1) = \alpha \neq 0.$$

It is now evident that the matrix G is nonsingular; this means that the subspace $\mathfrak{N}_1$ is nondegenerate, and we again have

$$\mathfrak{M}_0 = \mathfrak{N}_1 \dotplus \mathfrak{N}_1^\perp,$$

where $\mathfrak{N}_1^\perp$ is invariant under $\mathscr{A}_0$.

Thus, in the first case we split off from $\mathfrak{M}_0$ a subspace $\mathfrak{N}_1$, represented as the sum of two subspaces of even dimension; in the second case $\mathfrak{N}_1$ is a subspace of odd dimension. Applying the same process to the complementary subspace $\mathfrak{N}_1^\perp$, we decompose it into the direct sum of invariant subspaces, and so on. As a result, the subspace $\mathfrak{M}_0$ turns out to be decomposable into the direct sum of invariant subspaces, each of which is either the direct sum of two subspaces of even dimension or is a subspace of odd dimension. In this decomposition an elementary divisor of the transformation $\mathscr{A}_0$ having the form λ^p corresponds to each subspace, where p is the dimension of the subspace. Consequently, *a skew-symmetric transformation of a complex Euclidean space contains each elementary divisor of the form λ^{2s} an even number of times.* This result and Theorem 9 of Section 101 impose known conditions on the system of elementary divisors of a skew-symmetric transformation. We show that these conditions are sufficient for the existence of a skew-symmetric transformation.

THEOREM 3. *Skew-symmetric transformations of complex Euclidean spaces contain elementary divisors corresponding to nonzero proper values in pairs $(\lambda - \alpha)^m$, $(\lambda + \alpha)^m$, elementary divisors of the form λ^p, for p even, also in pairs λ^p, λ^p, and elementary divisors of the form λ^p, for p odd, in arbitrary combinations. Conversely, each set of a finite number of expressions $(\lambda - \alpha_i)^{m_i}$, subject to these conditions, is the system of elementary divisors of some skew-symmetric transformation of a complex Euclidean space of suitable dimension.*

The first part of this theorem has already been shown. Therefore, to complete the proof we must construct a skew-symmetric transformation corresponding to an arbitrary system of expressions subject to the conditions of the theorem. By analogy with the preceding section, this may be done in the following way. To each pair of expressions $(\lambda - \alpha_i)^{m_i}$, $(\lambda + \alpha_i)^{m_i}$, including those pairs with $\alpha_i = 0$, we place in correspondence the matrices

$$G_i = \begin{bmatrix} 0 & D_i \\ D_i & 0 \end{bmatrix}, \qquad A_i = \begin{bmatrix} B_i & 0 \\ 0 & -B_i \end{bmatrix},$$

where D_i is a normal symmetric matrix of the form (1), Section 102, and B_i is a Jordan block of order m_i having proper value α_i. If expressions $\lambda^{2s_j - 1}$, not occurring in pairs, appear among the given expressions, we place in correspondence to them the matrices

$$G_j = \begin{bmatrix} 0 & \cdot & \cdot & \cdot & 0 & 1 \\ 0 & \cdot & \cdot & \cdot & 1 & 0 \\ \cdot & \cdot & \cdot & \cdot & \cdot & \cdot \\ 1 & \cdot & \cdot & \cdot & 0 & 0 \end{bmatrix}, \qquad A_j = \begin{bmatrix} 0 & 1 & 0 & 0 & \cdot & \cdot & \cdot \\ & 0 & -1 & 0 & \cdot & \cdot & \cdot \\ & & 0 & 1 & \cdot & \cdot & \cdot \\ & & & & \cdot & \cdot & \cdot \\ & & & & & 0 & -1 \\ & & & & & & 0 \end{bmatrix}$$

of order $2s_j - 1$. Let

$$G = G_1 \dotplus \cdots \dotplus G_s, \quad A = A_1 \dotplus \cdots \dotplus A_s, \tag{5}$$

and let $\mathfrak{L}$ denote the complex space with Gram matrix G. Since G is symmetric and nonsingular, $\mathfrak{L}$ is a complex Euclidean space. Consider the linear transformation $\mathscr{A}$ of the space $\mathfrak{L}$ which has matrix A. The bilinear function corresponding to the transformation $\mathscr{A}$ has matrix AG; moreover,

$$AG = A_1G_1 \dotplus \cdots \dotplus A_sG_s .$$

An immediate calculation shows that the blocks A_iG_i, and hence the matrix AG, are skew-symmetric. Therefore the bilinear function and the transformation $\mathscr{A}$ are also skew-symmetric. It is apparent from the form of the matrix A that the elementary divisors of the transformation $\mathscr{A}$ have the required values.

According to Theorem 1 of Section 100, all skew-symmetric transformations of a complex Euclidean space that have the same system of elementary divisors are similar. Therefore, it follows from Theorem 3 that for each skew-symmetric transformation $\mathscr{A}$ of a complex Euclidean space $\mathfrak{L}$ there exists a coordinate system of $\mathfrak{L}$ in which the Gram matrix G and the matrix A of the transformation have the form (5).

104. Complex Orthogonal Transformations

Isometric transformations of a complex Euclidean space $\mathfrak{L}$ are usually called ***complex orthogonal*** transformations. If a coordinate system with Gram matrix G is chosen in $\mathfrak{L}$, then the complex orthogonal transformations are exactly those whose matrices U satisfy the relation

$$UGU' = G\,. \tag{6}$$

In particular, if the coordinate system is orthonormal, then $G = E$ and (6) becomes

$$UU' = E\,.$$

In other words, *in an orthonormal coordinate system, the matrices of orthogonal transformations are orthogonal*.

By Theorem 1 of Section 100, orthogonal transformations with identical elementary divisors are similar. Therefore, for the classification of orthogonal transformations it is sufficient to show which systems of expressions of the form $(\lambda - \alpha_i)^{m_i}$ can serve as the systems of elementary divisors of orthogonal transformations. The scheme for solving this problem is the following: the elementary divisors of skew-symmetric transformations are known to us, and orthogonal transformations may be expressed in terms of skew-symmetric transformations by means of Cayley's formula (Section 101); consequently, with the help of the theorem on the elementary divisors of functions of matrices (see Section 65), we can also find the elementary divisors of orthogonal transformations. However, in carrying out this scheme it is necessary to take into account the presence of exceptional values in Cayley's formula, which cause the solution to assume the following somewhat more cumbersome form.

Let $\mathscr{U}$ be an orthogonal transformation of a complex Euclidean space $\mathfrak{L}$. Representing $\mathfrak{L}$ in the form of a direct sum of root subspaces of the transformation $\mathscr{U}$, and grouping together subspaces corresponding to proper values differing only in sign, we obtain the decomposition

$$\mathfrak{L} = \mathfrak{M}_{-1} \dotplus \mathfrak{M}_1 \dotplus \mathfrak{M}_2 \dotplus \cdots \dotplus \mathfrak{M}_t\,,$$

where all the $\mathfrak{M}_j$ are pairwise orthogonal, and $\mathfrak{M}_{-1}$, $\mathfrak{M}_1$ are the root subspace of the transformation $\mathscr{U}$ that correspond to the proper values -1,

$+1$. The transformation $\mathscr{U}$ induces an orthogonal transformation $\mathscr{U}_j$ in each subspace $\mathfrak{M}_j$, and the elementary divisors of the transformation $\mathscr{U}$ are divided into the systems of elementary divisors of these induced transformations. We consider the transformation $\mathscr{U}_1$. All of its proper values equal $+1$. Cayley's formula

$$\mathscr{A}_1 = (\mathscr{E} - \mathscr{U}_1)(\mathscr{E} + \mathscr{U}_1)^{-1}$$

carries $\mathscr{U}_1$ into a skew-symmetric transformation $\mathscr{A}_1$. We represent this formula in the form $\mathscr{A}_1 = f(\mathscr{U}_1)$, where $f(\lambda) = (1 - \lambda)(1 + \lambda)^{-1}$. Since the derivative of $f(\lambda)$ at $\lambda = 1$ is not zero, then (compare Section 65), replacing α in each elementary divisor $(\lambda - \alpha)^m$ of the transformation $\mathscr{U}$ by the number $(1 - \alpha)(1 + \alpha)^{-1}$, we obtain an elementary divisor of the transformation $\mathscr{A}_1$. But the elementary divisors of the transformation $\mathscr{U}_1$ have the form $(\lambda - 1)^s$; consequently, the elementary divisors of the transformation $\mathscr{A}_1$ have the form λ^s. Skew-symmetric transformations contain each elementary divisor λ^s an even number of times when s is even; therefore the transformation $\mathscr{U}_1$ also contains each elementary divisor $(\lambda - 1)^s$ an even number of times when s is even.

Applying Cayley's formula

$$\mathscr{A} = (\mathscr{E} + \mathscr{U})(\mathscr{E} - \mathscr{U})^{-1}$$

to the transformation $\mathscr{U}_{-1}$, we find in a similar fashion that the transformation $\mathscr{U}$ contains each elementary divisor of the form $(\lambda + 1)^s$ an even number of times when s is even.

THEOREM 4. *The elementary divisors of a complex orthogonal transformation corresponding to proper values different from* ± 1 *occur in pairs of the form* $(\lambda - \alpha)^m$, $(\lambda - \alpha^{-1})^m$; *elementary divisors of the form* $(\lambda \pm 1)^{2s}$ *occur an even number of times, and elementary divisors of the form* $(\lambda \pm 1)^{2s+1}$ *occur in arbitrary combinations. Conversely, any system of expressions of the form* $(\lambda - \alpha_i)^{m_i}$, *for* $\alpha_i \neq 0$, *that satisfies these requirements is the system of elementary divisors of some complex orthogonal transformation.*

The first part of the theorem has already been shown. Therefore, suppose that some system of expressions of the form $(\lambda - \alpha_i)^{m_i}$, for $\alpha_i \neq 0$, is given that satisfies the conditions of the theorem. We single out from this system the expressions of the form $(\lambda + 1)^p$; and for each of the remaining expressions $(\lambda - \alpha_i)^{m_i}$ construct the expression $(\lambda - \beta_i)^{m_i}$, where $\beta_i = (1 - \alpha_i)(1 + \alpha_i)^{-1}$. The system of expressions $(\lambda - \beta_i)^{m_i}$ satisfies the requirements of Theorem 3, and consequently is the system of elementary divisors of some skew-symmetric transformation $\mathscr{A}_0$ of a complex Euclidean space $\mathfrak{L}_0$. Since we chose only values of α_i different from -1, all the β_i are also different from -1. Applying Cayley's transformation to $\mathscr{A}_0$, we obtain an orthogonal transformation $\mathscr{U}_0$ with elementary divisors $(\lambda - \alpha_i)^{m_i}$ for $\alpha_i \neq -1$. Similarly, for each expression of the form $(\lambda + 1)^{m_i}$ we take the expression λ^{m_i} and find a skew-symmetric transformation $\mathscr{A}_1$ of some space $\mathfrak{L}_1$ that has the λ^{m_i} as its elementary divisors. Then the transformation

$$\mathscr{U}_1 = -(\mathscr{E} - \mathscr{A}_1)(\mathscr{E} + \mathscr{A}_1)^{-1}$$

is an orthogonal transformation of the space $\mathfrak{L}_1$ having elementary divisors $(\lambda + 1)^{m_i}$. Choose orthonormal coordinate systems in $\mathfrak{L}_0$ and $\mathfrak{L}_1$, and denote by U_0 and U_1 the matrices of the transformations $\mathscr{U}_0$ and $\mathscr{U}_1$. These matrices are orthogonal, and therefore the direct sum $U = U_1 \dotplus U_2$ is also an orthogonal matrix.

By construction, the system of elementary divisors of the matrix U is the given system of expressions $(\lambda - \alpha_i)^{m_i}$, and the theorem is proved.

● EXAMPLES AND PROBLEMS

1. Construct an orthogonal matrix with elementary divisors $(\lambda - 1)^2$, $(\lambda - 1)^2$, $\lambda - 1/2$, $\lambda - 2$.
2. Show that matrices of the form $\lambda A + B$, where A is symmetric and nonsingular, and B is skew-symmetric, contain each elementary divisor of the form λ^{2m} an even number of times.
3. With the help of Theorem 2, reduce the following pair of quadratic forms to the simplest form:

$$2\xi_1^2 + 2\xi_2^2 + 2\xi_1\xi_3 + 2\xi_2\xi_4 - 2\xi_2\xi_3 - 2\xi_3\xi_4\,,$$
$$\xi_1^2 + 3\xi_2^2 + 2\xi_3^2 + 2\xi_1\xi_3 - 4\xi_2\xi_3 + 2\xi_2\xi_4 - 2\xi_3\xi_4\,.$$

Answer: $2(\xi_1\xi_2 + \xi_3\xi_4)\,,\quad \xi_2^2 + 2\xi_3\xi_4 + \xi_4^2$.

4. Construct a complex skew-symmetric matrix with elementary divisors $(\lambda - 3)^2$, $(\lambda + 3)^2$, λ^2, λ^2, λ^3.
5. Construct a complex symmetric matrix with elementary divisors $(\lambda - 2)^3$, λ^2, λ^3.

3. *Symplectic Spaces*

105. Symmetric Transformations

According to Section 98, a symplectic space is a bilinear-metric space with a nondegenerate skew-symmetric metric. The dimension of a symplectic space is an even number. Since all symplectic spaces of a given dimension are isomorphic to each other, each symplectic space of dimension $n = 2m$ has a basis whose Gram matrix equals any previously assigned nonsingular skew-symmetric matrix of order n. In particular, each symplectic space $\mathfrak{L}$ has a coordinate system in which the Gram matrix has the form

$$S = \begin{bmatrix} 0 & 1 \\ -1 & 0 \end{bmatrix} \dotplus \begin{bmatrix} 0 & 1 \\ -1 & 0 \end{bmatrix} \dotplus \cdots \dotplus \begin{bmatrix} 0 & 1 \\ -1 & 0 \end{bmatrix}. \qquad (1)$$

We call these coordinate systems ***symplectic***. Similarly, $\mathfrak{L}$ has a coordinate system in which the Gram matrix has the form

$$J = \begin{bmatrix} 0 & E \\ -E & 0 \end{bmatrix},$$

where E is an identity matrix. Such systems are called ***normal***. In what follows we will consider only *complex* symplectic spaces.

Let $\mathscr{A}$ be some symmetric transformation of $\mathfrak{L}$. We decompose $\mathfrak{L}$ into the direct sum

$$\mathfrak{L} = \mathfrak{L}_{\rho_1} \dot{+} \cdots \dot{+} \mathfrak{L}_{\rho_s},$$

where $\rho_1, \cdots, \rho_s$ are the distinct proper values of the transformation $\mathscr{A}$, and $\mathfrak{L}_{\rho_1}, \cdots, \mathfrak{L}_{\rho_s}$ are the corresponding root subspaces. By Section 101 the subspaces $\mathfrak{L}_{\rho_i}$ are pairwise orthogonal. In view of the nondegeneracy of the space $\mathfrak{L}$, the subspaces $\mathfrak{L}_{\rho_1}, \cdots, \mathfrak{L}_{\rho_s}$ are also nondegenerate and, consequently, are symplectic. Take one of them, say $\mathfrak{L}_{\rho_i}$, and denote it by $\mathfrak{M}$. Let $\mathscr{A}_0$ be the transformation induced in $\mathfrak{M}$ by $\mathscr{A}$. Further, let $\mathscr{A}_0 - \rho_i \mathscr{E} = \mathscr{B}$. Since $\mathscr{A}_0$ and $\mathscr{E}$ are symmetric transformations, $\mathscr{B}$ is also a symmetric transformation. All the proper values of the transformation $\mathscr{A}_0$ equal ρ_i; therefore, denoting the dimension of $\mathfrak{M}$ by p, we obtain

$$(\mathscr{A}_0 - \rho_i \mathscr{E})^p = \mathscr{B}^p = \mathscr{O}.$$

Let m be the smallest exponent for which $\mathscr{B}^m = \mathscr{O}$. The expression $(x\mathscr{B}^{m-1}, y)$ is a skew-symmetric bilinear function corresponding to the transformation $\mathscr{B}^{m-1}$. Since $\mathscr{B}^{m-1} \neq \mathscr{O}$, the function $(x\mathscr{B}^{m-1}, y)$ is not identically 0 and, consequently, there exists a pair of vectors a, b in $\mathfrak{M}$ for which $(a\mathscr{B}^{m-1}, b) = 1$. Let

$$a\mathscr{B}^j = a_{j+1}, \qquad b\mathscr{B}^j = b_{j+1} \qquad (j = 0, 1, \cdots, m-1).$$

As a consequence of the symmetry of $\mathscr{B}$ we have

$$(a_j, a_k) = (a\mathscr{B}^{j-1}, a\mathscr{B}^{k-1}) = (a\mathscr{B}^{j+k-2}, a) = (a, a\mathscr{B}^{j+k-2}).$$

However, the space $\mathfrak{L}$ is skew-symmetric, hence

$$(a\mathscr{B}^{j+k-2}, a) = -(a, a\mathscr{B}^{j+k-2}).$$

Comparing this with the preceding, we see that

$$(a_j, a_k) = 0, \qquad j, k = 1, \cdots, m. \tag{2}$$

Similarly, we obtain the relations

$$(b_j, b_k) = 0, \qquad j, k = 1, \cdots, m. \tag{3}$$

Further, from the conditions $(a\mathscr{B}^{m-1}, b) = 1$, $\mathscr{B}^m = \mathscr{O}$ it follows that

$$(a_{m-s}, b_{s+1}) = (a\mathscr{B}^{m-s-1}, b\mathscr{B}^s) = (a\mathscr{B}^{m-1}, b) = (a_m, b_1) = 1, \tag{4}$$

$$(a_j, b_k) = (a\mathscr{B}^{j-1}, b\mathscr{B}^{k-1}) = (a\mathscr{B}^{j+k-2}, b) = 0 \qquad (j + k > m + 1). \tag{5}$$

Now constructing the Gram matrix for the vectors $a_1, \cdots, a_m, b_1, \cdots, b_m$, we see from (2) through (5) that it has triangular form, with zeros under the secondary diagonal. Since the elements lying on the secondary diagonal are ± 1, the determinant of this matrix is different from zero. Consequently, the subspace $\mathfrak{M}_1$ spanned by the vectors $a_1, \cdots, a_m$ and $b_1, \cdots, b_m$ is nondegenerate. Let $\mathfrak{M}_{11}$ and $\mathfrak{M}_{12}$ denote the subspaces spanned by the vectors $a_1, \cdots, a_m$ and $b_1, \cdots, b_m$ respectively. By relation (5), the subspaces $\mathfrak{M}_{11}$ and $\mathfrak{M}_{12}$ have the same dimensions, and $\mathfrak{M}_1$ is their direct sum. Since $\mathfrak{M}_1$ is nondegenerate, by Section 98 we have

$$\mathfrak{M} = \mathfrak{M}_1 \dotplus \mathfrak{M}_1^{\perp} .$$

The subspace $\mathfrak{M}_1$ is invariant under $\mathscr{B}$, and hence $\mathfrak{M}_1^{\perp}$ is also invariant under $\mathscr{B}$. Now treating $\mathfrak{M}_1^{\perp}$ in the same way as $\mathfrak{M}_1$, we single out from $\mathfrak{M}_1^{\perp}$ a subspace $\mathfrak{M}_2$, which is the direct sum of two subspaces $\mathfrak{M}_{21}, \mathfrak{M}_{22}$, and so on. After a finite number of steps we obtain a direct decomposition,

$$\mathfrak{M} = \mathfrak{M}_1 \dotplus \cdots \dotplus \mathfrak{M}_t ,$$

where each of the subspaces $\mathfrak{M}_1, \cdots, \mathfrak{M}_t$ is, in turn, a direct sum of two subspaces of the same dimension. An elementary divisor $(\lambda - \rho_i)^{m_i}$ of the transformation $\mathscr{A}$ corresponds to each subspace of dimension m_i contained in this decomposition. Thus, we conclude that the elementary divisors of symmetric transformations of a symplectic space must occur in pairs.

Conversely, we show that for each system of pairs of expressions $(\lambda-\rho_i)^{m_i}$, $(\lambda - \rho_i)^{m_i}$ there exists a symmetric transformation of a symplectic space $\mathfrak{L}$ having these expressions as its elementary divisors.

For each pair $(\lambda - \rho_i)^{m_i}$, $(\lambda - \rho_i)^{m_i}$, construct the matrices

$$G_i = \begin{bmatrix} 0 & E_i \\ -E_i & 0 \end{bmatrix}, \quad A_i = \begin{bmatrix} B_i & 0 \\ 0 & B_i \end{bmatrix},$$

where E_i is the identity matrix of order m_i and B_i is a Jordan block of order m_i with proper value ρ_i, and let

$$G = G_1 \dotplus \cdots \dotplus G_s , \quad A = A_1 \dotplus \cdots \dotplus A_s . \tag{6}$$

Consider the complex bilinear-metric space $\mathfrak{L}$ with Gram matrix G. Since G is nonsingular and skew-symmetric, $\mathfrak{L}$ is a symplectic space. An immediate calculation shows that

$$AG = A_1G_1 \dotplus \cdots \dotplus A_sG_s$$

is a skew-symmetric matrix. Therefore the linear transformation $\mathscr{A}$ of $\mathfrak{L}$ which has matrix A is symmetric. At the same time, the elementary divisors of the transformation $\mathscr{A}$ have the required form. This proves

THEOREM 1. *Each elementary divisor of a symmetric transformation of a symplectic space occurs an even number of times. Conversely, every system of expressions* $(\lambda - \rho_i)^{m_i}$ *with this property is the system of elementary divisors of some symmetric transformation of a symplectic space.*

We already know (see Section 100) that symmetric transformations of a symplectic space which have identical elementary divisors are similar. Therefore, Theorem 1 completely solves the problem of the classification of symmetric transformations. In particular, it shows that for each symmetric transformation $\mathscr{A}$ of a symplectic space $\mathfrak{L}$ there exists a basis in which the Gram matrix G and the matrix A of the transformation have the form (6).

106. Skew-symmetric Transformations

A linear transformation $\mathscr{A}$ of a bilinear-metric space $\mathfrak{L}$ is skew-symmetric if $(x\mathscr{A}, y) = -(x, y\mathscr{A})$ for all x, y in $\mathfrak{L}$.

By Theorem 3 of Section 103, the elementary divisors of a skew-symmetric transformation $\mathscr{A}$ of a symplectic space $\mathfrak{L}$ which correspond to nonzero proper values occur in pairs of the form $(\lambda - \rho)^m$, $(\lambda + \rho)^m$. We show that the elementary divisors of $\mathscr{A}$ corresponding to the proper value zero—having the form λ^m—also must occur in pairs λ^m, λ^m if m is odd. The proof is completely analogous to the proof of the corresponding assertion in Section 103, and we give only a sketch of it here.

We start by representing $\mathfrak{L}$ in the form of a direct sum of the root subspaces of the transformation $\mathscr{A}$. Collecting in this representation the subspaces corresponding to proper values differing only in sign, we obtain the decomposition

$$\mathfrak{L} = \mathfrak{M}_0 \dotplus \mathfrak{M}_1 \dotplus \cdots \dotplus \mathfrak{M}_s ,$$

where the subspaces $\mathfrak{M}_0, \cdots, \mathfrak{M}_s$ are invariant and pairwise orthogonal; $\mathfrak{M}_0$ is the root subspace corresponding to the proper value zero. Let $\mathscr{A}_0$ be the transformation induced in the subspace $\mathfrak{M}_0$ by the transformation $\mathscr{A}$. All the proper values of $\mathscr{A}_0$ are equal to zero; hence $\mathscr{A}_0^p = \mathscr{O}$, where p is the dimension of $\mathfrak{M}_0$. Let m denote the smallest exponent for which $\mathscr{A}_0^m = \mathscr{O}$. The transformation $\mathscr{A}$ is skew-symmetric, and hence $\mathscr{A}_0^{m-1}$, as in Section 103, is symmetric for odd m and skew-symmetric for even m. However, the corresponding bilinear function $(x\mathscr{A}_0^{m-1}, y)$ is now symmetric for even m and skew-symmetric for odd m, since the metric of a symplectic space is skew-symmetric. The rest of the argument is as in Section 103, with the difference that now pairs of subspaces are obtained for m odd.

THEOREM 2. *The elementary divisors of skew-symmetric transformations of symplectic spaces which correspond to nonzero proper values occur in pairs $(\lambda - \rho)^m$, $(\lambda + \rho)^m$; elementary divisors of the form λ^m, for m odd, also occur in pairs λ^m, λ^m, and elementary divisors λ^m for m even may occur in arbitrary combinations. Conversely, every system of expressions $(\lambda - \rho_i)^{m_i}$ having these properties is the system of elementary divisors of some skew-symmetric transformation of a symplectic space.*

We need only prove the second part of the theorem. For each pair of expressions $(\lambda - \rho_i)^{m_i}$, $(\lambda + \rho_i)^{m_i}$, including pairs with $\rho_i = 0$, construct the matrices

$$G_i = \begin{bmatrix} 0 & E_i \\ -E_i & 0 \end{bmatrix}, \quad A_i = \begin{bmatrix} B_i & 0 \\ 0 & -B_i \end{bmatrix},$$

where E_i is the identity matrix of order m_i, and B_i is a Jordan block of order m_i with proper value ρ_i. For the remaining expressions of the form λ^{m_j} with even m_j, construct the matrices of order m_j:

$$G_j = \begin{bmatrix} 0 & 0 & \cdot & \cdot & \cdot & 0 & 1 \\ 0 & 0 & \cdot & \cdot & \cdot & -1 & 0 \\ \cdot & \cdot & \cdot & \cdot & \cdot & \cdot & \cdot \\ 0 & 1 & \cdot & \cdot & \cdot & 0 & 0 \\ -1 & 0 & \cdot & \cdot & \cdot & 0 & 0 \end{bmatrix}, \quad A_j = \begin{bmatrix} 0 & 1 & 0 & \cdot & \cdot & \cdot & 0 & 0 \\ & 0 & 1 & \cdot & \cdot & \cdot & 0 & 0 \\ & & & & & \cdot & \cdot & \cdot \\ & & & & & & 0 & 1 \\ & & & & & & & 0 \end{bmatrix}.$$

Let

$$G = G_1 \dotplus \cdots \dotplus G_s, \qquad A = A_1 \dotplus \cdots \dotplus A_s.$$

Consider the complex bilinear-metric space $\mathfrak{L}$ with Gram matrix G. The matrix G is skew-symmetric and nonsingular, and so $\mathfrak{L}$ is symplectic. The linear transformation $\mathscr{A}$ of $\mathfrak{L}$ with matrix A has the given expressions as elementary divisors. At the same time, $\mathscr{A}$ is skew-symmetric, since an immediate calculation shows that the matrix

$$AG = A_1G_1 \dotplus \cdots \dotplus A_sG_s$$

is symmetric. This proves the theorem.

107. Symplectic Transformations

An isometric transformation of a symplectic space $\mathfrak{L}$ is usually called a ***symplectic transformation*** of this space. Thus, if $\mathscr{U}$ is a symplectic transformation of the space $\mathfrak{L}$, then $(x\mathscr{U}, y\mathscr{U}) = (x, y)$ for all x, y in $\mathfrak{L}$. In matrix form this equality becomes

$$[x]UGU'[y]' = [x]G[y]',$$

and hence

$$UGU' = G, \tag{7}$$

where G is the Gram matrix and U is the matrix of the transformation $\mathscr{U}$. Choosing a symplectic coordinate system of $\mathfrak{L}$, (7) becomes

$$USU' = S, \tag{8}$$

where S is a symplectic matrix of the form (1). A matrix U satisfying condition (8) is called a ***symplectic matrix***. Consequently, in order that some linear transformation of a symplectic space be symplectic, it is necessary and sufficient that its matrix in a symplectic coordinate system be symplectic. It also immediately follows from (8) that the direct sum of symplectic matrices is symplectic.

Let $\mathscr{U}$ be an arbitrary symplectic transformation of a symplectic space $\mathfrak{L}$. If we represent $\mathfrak{L}$ in the form of the direct sum of the root subspaces of the transformation $\mathscr{U}$ and then collect the summands corresponding to proper values differing only in sign, we obtain a decomposition

$$\mathfrak{L} = \mathfrak{M}_{-1} \dotplus \mathfrak{M}_1 \dotplus \mathfrak{M}_2 \dotplus \cdots \dotplus \mathfrak{M}_s ,$$

where $\mathfrak{M}_{-1}$, $\mathfrak{M}_1$ are the root subspaces belonging to the proper values -1, $+1$. By Theorem 4 of Section 103, the subspaces $\mathfrak{M}_{-1}, \cdots, \mathfrak{M}_s$ are pairwise orthogonal.

The investigation of the effect of $\mathscr{U}$ on $\mathfrak{L}$ is now reduced to the investigation of the effect of $\mathfrak{L}$ on each subspace $\mathfrak{M}_i$ separately. If we repeat the arguments of Section 104 and use—instead of the theorem on elementary divisors of skew-symmetric transformations of complex Euclidean spaces—the corresponding theorem for symplectic spaces, we obtain

THEOREM 3. *The elementary divisors of a symplectic transformation corresponding to proper values different from* ± 1 *occur in pairs* $(\lambda - \rho)^m$, $(\lambda - \rho^{-1})^m$; *elementary divisors of the form* $(\lambda \pm 1)^{2m+1}$ *also occur in pairs* $(\lambda + 1)^{2m+1}$, $(\lambda + 1)^{2m+1}$ *or* $(\lambda - 1)^{2m+1}$, $(\lambda - 1)^{2m+1}$, *and elementary divisors of the form* $(\lambda \pm 1)^{2m}$ *may occur an arbitrary number of times. Conversely, every system of expressions of the form* $(\lambda - \rho_i)^{m_i}$, *for* $\rho_i \neq 0$, *having these properties is the system of elementary divisors of some symplectic transformation.*

By Theorem 1 of Section 100, symplectic transformations having the same elementary divisors are similar. Therefore, Theorem 3 gives a complete classification up to similarity of symplectic transformations. This theorem, in particular, shows that if -1 is a proper value of a symplectic transformation, then its multiplicity is necessarily an even number. Since all the remaining proper values are either $+1$ or occur with the same multiplicity as their inverses, the product of all the proper values of a symplectic transformation is $+1$.* This product equals the determinant of the matrix of the transformation, and we conclude that *the determinant of the matrix of a symplectic transformation equals* 1.

● EXAMPLES AND PROBLEMS

1. Construct a symplectic matrix with elementary divisors $\lambda + 1$, $\lambda + 1$, $(\lambda - 1)^2$.

2. Show that matrices of the form $\begin{bmatrix} A & B \\ C & A' \end{bmatrix}$, where B, C are square, skew-symmetric, and of the same order, contain each elementary divisor an even number of times.

3. Formulate Theorem 1 as a theorem on pairs of skew-symmetric bilinear forms.

4. *Pseudo-unitary Spaces*

A pseudo-unitary space was defined in Section 98 as a Hermitian bilinear-

* Each proper value is taken as often as indicated by its multiplicity.

metric space over the field of complex numbers whose metric is nondegenerate and symmetric: $(x, y) = \overline{(y, x)}$. It was shown there that all these spaces are determined up to isomorphism by their dimension n and signature s; moreover, for a given n, s may assume any of the values $n, n-2, \cdots, -n$. As before, we are interested in the properties of symmetric, skew-symmetric, and isometric transformations. The classification of these transformations in complex Euclidean and symplectic spaces was based on Theorem 1 of Section 100. In pseudo-unitary spaces such a theorem, generally speaking, does not hold. Consider, for example, the two-dimensional Hermitian bilinear-metric space $\mathfrak{L}$ with basis e_1, e_2 and Gram matrix $\begin{bmatrix} 1 & 0 \\ 0 & -1 \end{bmatrix}$. The linear transformations $\mathscr{U}_1, \mathscr{U}_2$ defined by the equalities

$$e_1\mathscr{U}_1 = 2e_1, \qquad e_1\mathscr{U}_2 = \frac{1}{2}e_1,$$

$$e_2\mathscr{U}_1 = \frac{1}{2}e_2, \qquad e_2\mathscr{U}_2 = 2e_2$$

are evidently isometric transformations of this space. The elementary divisors of these transformations are the same; $\lambda - 2$ and $\lambda - 1/2$. Nevertheless, $\mathscr{U}_1$ and $\mathscr{U}_2$ are not similar. For suppose the contrary; then their root subspaces corresponding to the proper value 2 could be carried into each other by an automorphism of the space $\mathfrak{L}$. The root subspace corresponding to the proper value 2 of the transformation $\mathscr{U}_1$ is the line αe_1, and similarly the root subspace for $\mathscr{U}_2$ is the line αe_2. At the same time, the inner product of any nonzero vector of the first line with itself is positive, while the inner product of any nonzero vector of the second line with itself is negative. Thus, no automorphism of the space $\mathfrak{L}$ can carry the first line into the second, and this means that $\mathscr{U}_1$ and $\mathscr{U}_2$ are not similar.

This example shows that for the study of transformations of pseudo-unitary spaces the purely geometrical approach is in a certain sense necessary.

108. Symmetric Transformations

Let $\mathfrak{L}$ be a pseudo-unitary space of dimension n and signature s. Consider an arbitrary linear subspace $\mathfrak{R}$ of $\mathfrak{L}$. We say that a coordinate system in $\mathfrak{R}$ is ***positive normal*** if its Gram matrix has the form

$$N = \begin{bmatrix} 0 & \cdot & \cdot & \cdot & 0 & 1 \\ 0 & \cdot & \cdot & \cdot & 1 & 0 \\ \cdot & \cdot & \cdot & \cdot & \cdot & \cdot \\ 1 & \cdot & \cdot & \cdot & 0 & 0 \end{bmatrix}, \tag{1}$$

and ***negative normal*** if its Gram matrix has the form

$$N = \begin{bmatrix} 0 & \cdot & \cdot & \cdot & 0 & -1 \\ 0 & \cdot & \cdot & \cdot & -1 & 0 \\ \cdot & \cdot & \cdot & \cdot & \cdot & \cdot \\ -1 & \cdot & \cdot & \cdot & 0 & 0 \end{bmatrix}. \tag{2}$$

Obviously not every subspace admits a normal coordinate system. This depends on the signature and dimension of the subspace. Subspaces of even dimension which admit a positive or negative normal coordinate system have signature zero; subspaces of odd dimension with a positive normal coordinate system have signature $+1$, and those with a negative normal coordinate system have signature -1. The proof follows easily from the definition of signature (see Section 98).

We investigate the elementary divisors of a symmetric transformation $\mathscr{A}$ of a pseudo-unitary space $\mathfrak{L}$. Decompose $\mathfrak{L}$ into the direct sum of the root subspaces of the transformation $\mathscr{A}$ and collect the summands corresponding to complex conjugate proper values. As a result, we obtain a decomposition of $\mathfrak{L}$ into a direct sum of invariant subspaces:

$$\mathfrak{L} = \mathfrak{M}_1 \dotplus \cdots \dotplus \mathfrak{M}_t . \tag{3}$$

By Section 101 these subspaces are pairwise orthogonal; hence the study of the transformation $\mathscr{A}$ is reduced to the study of the effect of $\mathscr{A}$ inside each $\mathfrak{M}_i$. The space $\mathfrak{L}$ is nondegenerate; therefore all the $\mathfrak{M}_i$ are also nondegenerate. We remark now that the subspaces $\mathfrak{M}_i$ may be of two types: 1) $\mathfrak{M}_i$ is the direct sum of two root subspaces corresponding to nonreal proper values*, and 2) $\mathfrak{M}_i$ is a root subspace corresponding to a real proper value. Consider the first case: let

$$\mathfrak{M}_i = \mathfrak{M}_i' \dotplus \mathfrak{M}_i'' ,$$

where $\mathfrak{M}_i'$, $\mathfrak{M}_i''$ are the root subspaces corresponding to the proper values α, $\bar{\alpha}$, where $\alpha \neq \bar{\alpha}$. By Section 100,

$$(a_1', a_2') = 0 , \qquad (a_1'', a_2'') = 0 , \tag{4}$$

where a_1', a_2' are any vectors in $\mathfrak{M}_i'$ and a_1'', a_2'' are any vectors in $\mathfrak{M}_i''$. If some vector a' in $\mathfrak{M}_i'$ should turn out to be orthogonal to all the vectors in $\mathfrak{M}_i''$, then a' would be isotropic in $\mathfrak{M}_i$. In view of the nondegeneracy of the subspace $\mathfrak{M}_i$, this gives $a' = \theta$. Thus, for each nonzero vector of the subspace $\mathfrak{M}_i'$ there is a nonorthogonal vector in the subspace $\mathfrak{M}_i''$.

We have assumed that $\mathfrak{M}_i'$ is the root subspace of the transformation $\mathscr{A}$ belonging to the proper value α. Consequently, for some natural number m we have

$$\mathfrak{M}_i'(\mathscr{A} - \alpha\mathscr{E})^m = \theta , \qquad \mathfrak{M}_i'(\mathscr{A} - \alpha\mathscr{E})^{m-1} \neq \theta . \tag{5}$$

Choose a vector a in $\mathfrak{M}_i'$ for which $a(\mathscr{A} - \alpha\mathscr{E})^{m-1} \neq \theta$. Then there is a vector b in $\mathfrak{M}_i''$ which is not orthogonal to $a(\mathscr{A} - \alpha\mathscr{E})^{m-1}$. We normalize b so that

$$(a(\mathscr{A} - \alpha\mathscr{E})^{m-1}, b) = 1 .$$

Now let

* If α is a proper value but $\bar{\alpha}$ is not a proper value, then we will formally consider that $\mathfrak{L}_{\bar{\alpha}}$ is the zero space. It will be seen, however, that this case is impossible.

$$a(\mathscr{A}-\alpha\mathscr{E})^j = a_{j+1}\,,\quad b(\mathscr{A}-\bar{\alpha}\mathscr{E})^j = b_{j+1}\,,\qquad (j=0,1,\cdots,m-1)\,.$$

The transformation $\mathscr{A}$ is symmetric; therefore

$$(\mathscr{A}-\alpha\mathscr{E})^* = \mathscr{A}-\bar{\alpha}\mathscr{E}\,,$$
$$(\mathscr{A}-\alpha\mathscr{E})^{*t} = (\mathscr{A}-\bar{\alpha}\mathscr{E})^t\,.$$

Consequently, for $j+k=m+1$ we have

$$\begin{aligned}(a_j, b_k) &= (a(\mathscr{A}-\alpha\mathscr{E})^{j-1}, b(\mathscr{A}-\bar{\alpha}\mathscr{E})^{k-1})\\ &= (a(\mathscr{A}-\alpha\mathscr{E})^{j+k-2}, b) = 1\,,\end{aligned} \tag{6}$$

and for $j+k>m+1$,

$$(a_j, b_k) = (a(\mathscr{A}-\alpha\mathscr{E})^{j+k-2}, b) = 0\,. \tag{7}$$

In particular, it follows from (6) that $b(\mathscr{A}-\bar{\alpha}\mathscr{E})^{m-1}\neq\theta$. Further, if a' belongs to $\mathfrak{M}_i'$, then

$$(a', b(\mathscr{A}-\bar{\alpha}\mathscr{E})^m) = (a'(\mathscr{A}-\alpha\mathscr{E})^m, b) = 0\,.$$

In other words, the vector $b(\mathscr{A}-\bar{\alpha}\mathscr{E})^m$ in the subspace $\mathfrak{M}_i''$ is orthogonal to all the vectors in $\mathfrak{M}_i'$. By a previous remark this gives $b(\mathscr{A}-\bar{\alpha}\mathscr{E})^m=\theta$. Let $\mathfrak{N}_1'$, $\mathfrak{N}_1''$ denote the subspaces spanned by the vectors $a_1, \cdots, a_m$ and $b_1, \cdots, b_m$ respectively.

Let

$$c_1 = a_1 + \alpha_2 a_2 + \cdots + \alpha_m a_m\,,$$
$$c_{j+1} = c_j(\mathscr{A}-\alpha\mathscr{E})\,,\qquad j=1,\cdots,m-1\,.$$

It follows from (6) and (7) that $(c_1(\mathscr{A}-\alpha\mathscr{E})^{m-1}, b_1)=1$, for all values of $\alpha_2, \cdots, \alpha_m$, and again

$$(c_j, b_{m+1-j}) = 1\,,\quad (c_j, b_k)=0\qquad (j+k>m+1,\quad j,k=1,\cdots,m)\,. \tag{8}$$

It is easy to see that the coefficients $\alpha_2, \cdots, \alpha_m$ may be chosen so that

$$(c_1, b_{m-1}) = (c_1, b_{m-2}) = \cdots = (c_1, b_1) = 0\,.$$

Then for $j+k<m+1$ we have

$$(c_j, b_k) = (c_1, b_1(\mathscr{A}-\bar{\alpha}\mathscr{E})^{j+k-2}) = (c_1, b_{j+k-1}) = 0\,. \tag{9}$$

Let $\mathfrak{N}_1=\mathfrak{N}_1'+\mathfrak{N}_1''$. Relations (4), (8), and (9) show that the system $c_1, \cdots, c_m$, $b_1, \cdots, b_m$ is a *positive normal* coordinate system of $\mathfrak{N}_1$. At the same time, the matrix of the transformation $\mathscr{A}$ (restricted to $\mathfrak{N}_1$) decomposes in this coordinate system into a pair of Jordan blocks with elementary divisors $(\lambda-\alpha)^m$, $(\lambda-\bar{\alpha})^m$.

The subspace $\mathfrak{N}_1$ is nondegenerate; consequently

$$\mathfrak{M}_i = \mathfrak{N}_1 \dotplus \mathfrak{N}_1^\perp\,,$$

where $\mathfrak{N}_1^\perp$ is again invariant under $\mathscr{A}$. If $\mathfrak{N}_1^\perp\neq\theta$, then, applying the above process to $\mathfrak{N}_1^\perp$, we split off another invariant subspace $\mathfrak{N}_2$, and so on. As a result, we obtain for $\mathfrak{M}_i$ a representation of the form

$$\mathfrak{M}_i = \mathfrak{N}_1 \dotplus \cdots \dotplus \mathfrak{N}_{s_i} ,$$

where $\mathfrak{N}_1, \cdots, \mathfrak{N}_{s_i}$ are invariant pairwise orthogonal subspaces; moreover, each of these subspaces has a positive normal coordinate system in which the matrix of the transformation $\mathscr{A}$ decomposes into two Jordan blocks with elementary divisors of the form $(\lambda - \alpha)^m$, $(\lambda - \bar{\alpha})^m$.

We consider the second case. Let $\mathfrak{M}_i$ be a root subspace corresponding to a real proper value α. Again we find a natural number m such that

$$\mathfrak{M}_i(\mathscr{A} - \alpha\mathscr{E})^m = \theta , \qquad \mathfrak{M}_i(\mathscr{A} - \alpha\mathscr{E})^{m-1} \neq \theta .$$

Since $(\mathscr{A} - \alpha\mathscr{E})^* = \mathscr{A} - \bar{\alpha}\mathscr{E} = \mathscr{A} - \alpha\mathscr{E}$, the transformation $\mathscr{A} - \alpha\mathscr{E}$ and together with it the transformation $(\mathscr{A} - \alpha\mathscr{E})^{m-1}$ are symmetric. The corresponding Hermitian bilinear function $(x(\mathscr{A} - \alpha\mathscr{E})^{m-1}, y)$ is also symmetric and is not identically zero on $\mathfrak{M}_i$. Therefore, there is a vector a in $\mathfrak{M}_i$ for which

$$(a(\mathscr{A} - \alpha\mathscr{E})^{m-1}, a) = \beta \neq 0 . \tag{10}$$

It follows from the symmetry of the function that β is real. Setting $a_1 = \sqrt{|\beta|^{-1}}\, a$, we obtain in place of (10) the relation

$$(a_1(\mathscr{A} - \alpha\mathscr{E})^{m-1}, a_1) = \varepsilon , \qquad \varepsilon = \pm 1 . \tag{11}$$

The sign in this relation depends on the properties of the transformation $\mathscr{A}$ itself and, in any case, we cannot change it by a normalization. Let

$$a_{j+1} = a_j(\mathscr{A} - \alpha\mathscr{E}) ,$$

for $j = 1, \cdots, m-1$. It follows from (11) that

$$(a_j , a_{m+1-j}) = (a_1(\mathscr{A} - \alpha\mathscr{E})^{m-1}, a_1) = \varepsilon . \tag{12}$$

Similarly, from the condition $\mathfrak{M}_i(\mathscr{A} - \alpha\mathscr{E})^m = \theta$, we obtain

$$(a_j , a_k) = (a_1(\mathscr{A} - \alpha\mathscr{E})^{j+k-2}, a_1) = 0 \qquad (j + k > m + 1) . \tag{13}$$

Let

$$b_1 = a_1 + \alpha_2 a_2 + \cdots + \alpha_m a_m ,$$

where $\alpha_2, \cdots, \alpha_m$ for the time being are arbitrary, and let

$$b_{j+1} = b_j(\mathscr{A} - \alpha\mathscr{E}) \qquad (j = 1, \cdots, m-1) . \tag{14}$$

Equalities (12), (13) give

$$(b_j , b_{m+1-j}) = \varepsilon , \quad (b_j , b_k) = 0 \qquad (j + k > m + 1;\, j, k = 1, \cdots, m) . \tag{15}$$

It is easy to see that the numbers $\alpha_2, \cdots, \alpha_m$ may be chosen so that

$$(b_1 , b_{m-1}) = (b_1 , b_{m-2}) = \cdots = (b_1 , b_1) = 0 .$$

Then for $j + k < m + 1$ we have

$$(b_j , b_k) = (b_1 , b_1(\mathscr{A} - \alpha\mathscr{E})^{j+k-2}) = (b_1 , b_{j+k-1}) = 0 . \tag{16}$$

Consider the space $\mathfrak{N}_1$ spanned by $b_1, \cdots, b_m$. It follows from (14) that $\mathfrak{N}_1$

is invariant under $\mathscr{A}$, and the matrix of the transformation $\mathscr{A}$ (restricted to $\mathfrak{N}_1$) in this coordinate system is a Jordan block with elementary divisor $(\lambda - \alpha)^m$. On the other hand, from (15), (16) it is evident that the system $b_1, \cdots, b_m$ is a *normal* coordinate system in $\mathfrak{N}_1$, *positive* if $\varepsilon = 1$ and *negative* if $\varepsilon = -1$. The space $\mathfrak{N}_1$ is nondegenerate, and hence, if $\mathfrak{N}_1 \neq 0$,

$$\mathfrak{M}_i = \mathfrak{N}_1 \dotplus \mathfrak{N}_1^{\perp},$$

where $\mathfrak{N}_1^{\perp}$ is an invariant subspace of lower dimension. Applying the same process to $\mathfrak{N}_1^{\perp}$, we split off an invariant subspace $\mathfrak{N}_2$, and so on, until we obtain a decomposition of $\mathfrak{M}_i$ into a direct sum of pairwise orthogonal subspaces.

Now applying these results to each subspace $\mathfrak{M}_i$, we represent the space $\mathfrak{L}$ in the form

$$\mathfrak{L} = \mathfrak{B}_1 \dotplus \cdots \dotplus \mathfrak{B}_l, \qquad (17)$$

where $\mathfrak{B}_1, \cdots, \mathfrak{B}_l$ are pairwise orthogonal subspaces, each of which either corresponds to a real elementary divisor $(\lambda - \alpha)^m$ of the transformation $\mathscr{A}$, or is a direct sum of two subspaces corresponding to complex conjugate elementary divisors $(\lambda - \alpha)^m$, $(\lambda - \bar{\alpha})^m$; each subspace of the first kind has a normal *positive* or *negative* coordinate system, in which the matrix of the transformation $\mathscr{A}$ is a Jordan block, and each subspace of the second kind has a normal positive coordinate system, in which the matrix of the transformation $\mathscr{A}$ is the direct sum of two complex conjugate Jordan blocks.

An elementary divisor $(\lambda - \alpha)^m$ of the transformation $\mathscr{A}$ corresponds to each subspace $\mathfrak{B}_j$ which belongs to a real proper value α. Let us agree to associate with the subspace $\mathfrak{B}_j$ the elementary divisor $+(\lambda - \alpha)^m$ if $\mathfrak{B}_j$ has a positive normal coordinate system in which the matrix of the transformation $\mathscr{A}$ is a Jordan block, and to associate the elementary divisor $-(\lambda - \alpha)^m$ if $\mathfrak{B}_j$ has a negative normal coordinate system possessing this property. Starting from the decomposition (17) and using this rule, we obtain a system of elementary divisors of the transformation $\mathscr{A}$ in which each real elementary divisor is provided with a definite sign. We will call such a system of elementary divisors ***sign-determinate***. Repeating the arguments used at the end of Section 102, we find that symmetric transformations of the space $\mathfrak{L}$ having identical sign-determinate systems of elementary divisors are similar.

Suppose now that an arbitrary system of expressions of the form $\pm(\lambda - \alpha_i)^{m_i}$ is given, in which all nonreal expressions occur in complex conjugate pairs and carry the plus sign. Does there exist a pseudo-unitary space $\mathfrak{L}$ and a symmetric transformation $\mathscr{A}$ of $\mathfrak{L}$ such that the given system $\pm(\lambda - \alpha_i)^{m_i}$ is the sign-determinate system of elementary divisors of the transformation $\mathscr{A}$? The answer is evidently in the affirmative. The construction of the space $\mathfrak{L}$ and of the transformation $\mathscr{A}$ may be carried out in the same way as in Section 102. Since nothing new is required in this construction, we leave it to the reader.

There remains for us to prove a somewhat more subtle fact—that the sign-determinate system of elementary divisors of the transformation $\mathscr{A}$ does not depend on the choice of the decomposition (17) and is entirely determined by the transformation itself.

The decomposition (17) was obtained as the result of decomposing the subspaces $\mathfrak{M}_1, \cdots, \mathfrak{M}_t$ into cyclic subspaces $\mathfrak{B}_i$. Since each subspace $\mathfrak{M}_i$ is either a root subspace or a sum of root subspaces, each $\mathfrak{M}_i$ is uniquely determined, and nonuniqueness of (17) can arise only in the decomposition of the $\mathfrak{M}_i$. We need not be concerned with the subspaces $\mathfrak{M}_i$ which are the sums of two root subspaces, since their decomposition leads to pairs of cyclic subspaces with pairs of complex conjugate elementary divisors $(\lambda - \alpha)^m$, $(\lambda - \bar{\alpha})^m$. Consequently, there is left only to show that, no matter what method we use to decompose a root subspace $\mathfrak{M}_j$ with real proper value α into the sum of pairwise orthogonal nondecomposable subspaces, the sign-determinate system of elementary divisors of the form $\pm(\lambda - \alpha)^m$ will be the same. Let

$$\mathfrak{M}_j = \mathfrak{N}_1 \dotplus \cdots \dotplus \mathfrak{N}_t , \tag{18}$$

$$\mathfrak{M}_j = \mathfrak{B}_1 \dotplus \cdots \dotplus \mathfrak{B}_t \tag{19}$$

be two decompositions of $\mathfrak{M}_j$ into orthogonal sums of nondecomposable subspaces. Denote the sign-determinate elementary divisors corresponding to the subspaces $\mathfrak{N}_i$ and $\mathfrak{B}_i$ by $\delta_i(\lambda - \alpha)^{m_i}$ and $\varepsilon_i(\lambda - \alpha)^{m_i}$, for $i = 1, \cdots, t$ and $\delta_i, \varepsilon_i = \pm 1$. We order the summands in the sums (18), (19) so that $m_1 \geqq m_2 \geqq \cdots \geqq m_t$. Suppose that there are several summands of the highest dimension: $m_1 = \cdots = m_k > m_{k+1}$. We show that the systems of elementary divisors of the highest orders, $\varepsilon_1(\lambda - \alpha)^{m_1}, \cdots, \varepsilon_k(\lambda - \alpha)^{m_k}$ and $\delta_1(\lambda - \alpha)^{m_1}, \cdots, \delta_k(\lambda - \alpha)^{m_k}$, are identical. Consider the bilinear function $f_1(x, y) = (x(\mathscr{A} - \alpha\mathscr{E})^{m_1 - 1}, y)$. The transformation $\mathscr{A} - \alpha\mathscr{E}$ is symmetric, and therefore the function $f_1(x, y)$ is also symmetric. We compute its signature with the help of decomposition (18) and with the help of decomposition (19). All the subspaces in decomposition (18) are orthogonal under the function $f_1(x, y)$. Therefore, the signature of the function $f_1(x, y)$ on $\mathfrak{M}_j$ equals the sum of its signatures computed on each summand separately. However, for $p > k$ we have

$$\mathfrak{N}_p(\mathscr{A} - \alpha\mathscr{E})^{m_1 - 1} = \theta ,$$

and consequently $f_1(x, y)$ is zero on $\mathfrak{N}_p$. Now consider the subspaces $\mathfrak{N}_1, \cdots, \mathfrak{N}_k$. Let $a_1, \cdots, a_m$ be a basis of $\mathfrak{N}_1$ for which

$$a_{j+1} = a_j(\mathscr{A} - \alpha\mathscr{E}) \qquad (j = 1, \cdots, m_1 - 1) .$$

Since $a_1(\mathscr{A} - \alpha\mathscr{E})^{m_1} = \theta$, for $j + k > 2$ we have

$$f_1(a_j, a_k) = (a_j(\mathscr{A} - \alpha\mathscr{E})^{m_1 - 1}, a_k) = 0 .$$

On the other hand, by definition the sign of the elementary divisor corresponding to $\mathfrak{N}_1$ is

$$f_1(a_1, a_1) = (a_1(\mathscr{A} - \alpha\mathscr{E})^{m_1-1}, a_1) = \delta_1 .$$

Consequently, the matrix of the function $f_1(x, y)$ in the basis $a_1, \cdots, a_m$ contains a single nonzero element δ_1, which stands in the upper left corner. It is now evident that the signature of the function $f_1(x, y)$ on $\mathfrak{N}_1$ is also δ_1. A similar argument applies to the subspaces $\mathfrak{N}_2, \cdots, \mathfrak{N}_k$. As a result, we find that the signature of the function $f_1(x, y)$ on $\mathfrak{M}_j$ equals $\delta_1 + \delta_2 + \cdots + \delta_k$. Using the decomposition (19) instead of (18), we conclude that the signature of the function $f_1(x, y)$ on $\mathfrak{M}_j$ also equals $\varepsilon_1 + \cdots + \varepsilon_k$. Thus,

$$\delta_1 + \cdots + \delta_k = \varepsilon_1 + \cdots + \varepsilon_k . \tag{20}$$

Since $\delta_i, \varepsilon_i = \pm 1$, it follows from (20) that the systems of numbers $\delta_1, \cdots, \delta_k$ and $\varepsilon_1, \cdots, \varepsilon_k$ can differ only in the ordering of these numbers, and this means that the two systems of elementary divisors of the highest order, $\delta_1(\lambda - \alpha)^{m_1}, \cdots, \delta_k(\lambda - \alpha)^{m_k}$ and $\varepsilon_1(\lambda - \alpha)^{m_1}, \cdots, \varepsilon_k(\lambda - \alpha)^{m_k}$, coincide.

Now consider the bilinear function

$$f_2(x, y) = (x(\mathscr{A} - \alpha\mathscr{E})^{m_{k+1}-1}, y) .$$

This function is zero on all the subspaces of dimension less than m_{k+1}. Therefore, for the signature of $f_2(x, y)$ on $\mathfrak{M}_j$ we also have the expressions:

$$\begin{aligned} \operatorname{sig}\mathfrak{M}_j &= \operatorname{sig}\mathfrak{N}_1 + \cdots + \operatorname{sig}\mathfrak{N}_k + \operatorname{sig}\mathfrak{N}_{k+1} + \cdots + \operatorname{sig}\mathfrak{N}_p , \\ \operatorname{sig}\mathfrak{M}_j &= \operatorname{sig}\mathfrak{B}_1 + \cdots + \operatorname{sig}\mathfrak{B}_k + \operatorname{sig}\mathfrak{B}_{k+1} + \cdots + \operatorname{sig}\mathfrak{B}_p , \end{aligned} \tag{21}$$

where it is understood that $m_{k+1} = \cdots = m_p > m_{p+1}$. Since the signatures of the function f_2 on the corresponding subspaces of highest dimension coincide, by what has been proved above, it follows from (21) that

$$\operatorname{sig}\mathfrak{N}_{k+1} + \cdots + \operatorname{sig}\mathfrak{N}_p = \operatorname{sig}\mathfrak{B}_{k+1} + \cdots + \operatorname{sig}\mathfrak{B}_p ,$$

or

$$\delta_{k+1} + \cdots + \delta_p = \varepsilon_{k+1} + \cdots + \varepsilon_p . \tag{22}$$

It is evident from (22) that the (signed) elementary divisors of the transformation $\mathscr{A}$ of degree m_{k+1} also coincide. Continuing this process further, we conclude that the sign-determinate systems of elementary divisors of the transformation $\mathscr{A}$, computed from the decompositions (18) and (19), coincide.

We now consider what it is possible to say about the signature of the fundamental space $\mathfrak{L}$, if the sign-determinate system of elementary divisors of some symmetric transformation $\mathscr{A}$ of this space is known. The decomposition (17) shows that the signature of the space $\mathfrak{L}$ equals the sum of the signatures of the subspaces $\mathfrak{B}_1, \cdots, \mathfrak{B}_l$. There exist positive normal coordinate systems in those subspaces $\mathfrak{B}_j$ that correspond to complex conjugate pairs of proper values. However, these subpaces have even dimension, and hence have signature zero.

The signature of a subspace of even dimension corresponding to a real elementary divisor is also zero. Therefore, we need only consider the subspaces of odd dimension that correspond to real elementary divisors. Their signatures are ± 1, depending on the positivity or negativity of the corresponding elementary divisors. Consequently,

$$s = s_1 - s_2 \, , \tag{23}$$

where s is the signature of the space $\mathfrak{L}$, s_1 is the number of positive, and s_2 is the number of negative, real elementary divisors of odd degree of the transformation.

It follows in particular from formula (23) that *each symmetric transformation of a pseudo-unitary space of signature s has at least* $|s|$ *real elementary divisors of odd degree.*

The study of skew-symmetric transformations of pseudo-unitary spaces reduces immediately to the study of symmetric transformations, since if $\mathscr{A}$ is symmetric, then $i\mathscr{A}$ is skew-symmetric, and conversely.

109. Pseudo-unitary Transformations

Isometric transformations of pseudo-unitary spaces are called ***pseudo-unitary*** transformations. Let $\mathscr{U}$ be a pseudo-unitary transformation of a space $\mathfrak{L}$. Representing $\mathfrak{L}$ as the direct sum of the root subspaces of the transformation $\mathscr{U}$, and collecting summands that correspond to proper values α, β for which $\alpha\bar{\beta} = 1$, we obtain a decomposition of $\mathfrak{L}$,

$$\mathfrak{L} = \mathfrak{M}_{-1} \dotplus \mathfrak{M}_1 \dotplus \mathfrak{M}_2 \dotplus \cdots \dotplus \mathfrak{M}_s \, ,$$

where the subspaces $\mathfrak{M}_j$ are invariant under $\mathscr{U}$ and, by Theorem 3 of Section 100, are pairwise orthogonal. To each of these subspaces we may apply one of the formulas of Cayley (compare Section 101),

$$\mathscr{A} = i(\mathscr{E} - \mathscr{U})(\mathscr{E} + \mathscr{U})^{-1}. \tag{24}$$

or

$$\mathscr{A} = i(\mathscr{E} + \mathscr{U})(\mathscr{E} - \mathscr{U})^{-1}. \tag{25}$$

We obtain, as a result, symmetric transformations of the subspaces $\mathfrak{M}_j$. From (24), (25) we have, conversely,

$$\mathscr{U} = (\mathscr{E} + i\mathscr{A})(\mathscr{E} - i\mathscr{A})^{-1}$$

or respectively

$$\mathscr{U} = -(\mathscr{E} + i\mathscr{A})(\mathscr{E} - i\mathscr{A})^{-1}.$$

In the first case, each elementary divisor of the transformation $\mathscr{A}$ of the form $(\lambda - \alpha)^m$ is carried into an elementary divisor $(\lambda - \gamma)^m$, where $\gamma = (1 + i\alpha)(1 - i\alpha)^{-1}$, and in the second case into $(\lambda - \gamma)^m$, where $\gamma = -(1 + i\alpha)(1 - i\alpha)^{-1}$. Since $\mathscr{A}$ is a symmetric transformation, its nonreal elementary divisors of the form $(\lambda - \alpha)^m$ occur in pairs $(\lambda - \alpha)^m$, $(\lambda - \bar{\alpha})^m$. However, $(1 + i\bar{\alpha})(1 - i\bar{\alpha})^{-1} = \overline{(1 - i\alpha)(1 + i\alpha)^{-1}}$, therefore, the corresponding elementary divisors of the transformation $\mathscr{U}$ also occur in pairs $(\lambda - \gamma)^m$, $(\lambda - \bar{\gamma}^{-1})^m$. If α is real, then for $\gamma = (1 + i\alpha)(1 - i\alpha)^{-1}$ we obtain the relation $\gamma\bar{\gamma} = 1$. Conversely, it follows from $\gamma\bar{\gamma} = 1$ that α is real. Thus, formulas (24) and (25) establish a correspondence between the elementary divisors of the pseudo-unitary transformation $\mathscr{U}$ and the elementary divisors of the symmetric transformation $\mathscr{A}$. We have seen that symmetric transformations are given, up to similarity, by their sign-determinate systems of elementary divisors. Therefore, pseudo-unitary transformations are determined, up to similarity, by their sign-determinate systems of elementary divisors. However, in these systems the signs ± 1 must now be attached to elementary divisors corresponding to proper values with modulus 1.

● EXAMPLES AND PROBLEMS

1. Give complete proofs of all the assertions in Sections 108 and 109.
2. Let $\mathfrak{L}$ be a four-dimensional pseudo-unitary space with signature 2 (the complex space of Lorentz). Choose as a principal coordinate system of $\mathfrak{L}$ the system e_1, e_2, e_3, e_4, in which the inner product of a vector $x = \xi_1 e_1 + \xi_2 e_2 + \xi_3 e_3 + \xi_4 e_4$ with itself has the form $(x, x) = \xi_1^2 + \xi_2^2 + \xi_3^2 - \xi_4^2$. Show that the matrix of any symmetric transformation of the space $\mathfrak{L}$ may be reduced in a suitable ***principal*** coordinate system to one of the following forms:

$$\begin{bmatrix} \alpha & & & \\ & \beta & & \\ & & \gamma & \\ & & & \delta \end{bmatrix}, \quad \begin{bmatrix} \alpha & & & \\ & \beta & & \\ & & \gamma & \delta \\ & & -\delta & \gamma \end{bmatrix}, \quad \begin{bmatrix} \alpha & & & \\ & \beta & 0 & 1 \\ & 0 & \beta & 1 \\ & -1 & -1 & \beta \end{bmatrix},$$

where $\alpha, \beta, \gamma, \delta$ are real numbers. Solve the analogous problem for the matrices of pseudo-unitary transformations of the space $\mathfrak{L}$.
3. If n is the dimension of a space and s the signature of a Hermitian bilinear function f over the space, then the expression $\chi = (n - |s|)/2$ is called the ***characteristic*** of f. Show that the characteristics of a pseudo-unitary space $\mathfrak{L}$, in which there exists a symmetric transformation $\mathscr{A}$, satisfy the inequality

$$\chi \geqq h + \Sigma \left[\frac{k}{2}\right],$$

where h equals half the sum of the exponents of the complex elementary divisors of the transformation $\mathscr{A}$ and k runs over all the exponents of the real elementary divisors. The symbol $[k/2]$ denotes the largest integer not exceeding $k/2$.
4. Under the conditions of the preceding problem, let $f(x, y) = (x\mathscr{A}, y)$. Show that the characteristic of the function f satisfies the inequality

$$\chi \geq h + \Sigma \left[\frac{k'}{2}\right] + \Sigma \left[\frac{k'' - 1}{2}\right],$$

where h is as before, k' runs over the exponents of the elementary divisors of $\mathscr{A}$ corresponding to nonzero real proper values, and k'' runs over the exponents of elementary divisors of the form λ^m.

8 MULTILINEAR FUNCTIONS. TENSORS

1. *General Definitions*

The study of bilinear forms, carried out in detail in the preceding paragraphs, is only a special case of the general theory of multilinear forms, usually called the theory of invariants. A detailed exposition of the theory of invariants is beyond the framework of the present book. For this reason this chapter is devoted to an exposition of only the most primitive notions of the theory.

In the theory of bilinear forms two kinds of transformations of forms were considered: 1) the case where both systems of indeterminates are subjected to distinct, independent linear transformations, and 2) the case where both systems are subjected to the same transformation. It is clear that in the general theory of multilinear forms we have similar cases. However, it is now necessary to consider a most important case which we do not meet in the theory of bilinear forms—the case when some of the systems of indeterminates of the form are subjected to a linear transformation with matrix T, and the other systems are subjected to the so-called contragredient transformation with the transpose-inverse matrix T'^{-1}. It will be shown later that the theory of bilinear forms in which one system of indeterminates is subjected to a transformation with matrix T and the other to a transformation with matrix T'^{-1} is completely equivalent to the theory of linear transformations, which is why this case is usually not considered in the theory of bilinear forms.

We turn now to an exposition of the theory of conjugate, or dual, spaces, from the point of view of which the origin of contragredient transformations becomes clearer.

110. Conjugate Space

According to Section, 74, the set of all linear functions defined on a linear space $\mathfrak{L}$ with base field K is itself a linear space over K with respect to the usual operations of addition of functions and multiplication of a function by a scalar. This new linear space, the vectors of which are linear functions, is called the ***conjugate,*** or ***dual, space*** of $\mathfrak{L}$ and is denoted by $\mathfrak{L}'$. Since in what follows it will often be necessary to consider vectors of both spaces at the same time, the vectors of the fundamental space $\mathfrak{L}$ will be called ***contravariant,*** and the vectors of the conjugate space $\mathfrak{L}'$ will be called ***covariant.***

Let $x \in \mathfrak{L}$, $f \in \mathfrak{L}'$. We agree to call the number $f(x)$ the ***inner product*** of f and x, and denote it by (x, f). It is clear that this inner product possesses the usual properties;

1) $(x, \alpha f + \beta g) = \alpha(x, f) + \beta(x, g)$,
2) $(\alpha x + \beta y, f) = \alpha(x, f) + \beta(y, f)$.

The first of these is merely another form of the notions of sum of functions and product of functions by scalars, and the second expresses the linearity of the function $f(x)$. Both properties together mean that the inner product introduced is a bilinear function, except that it is not defined on a single space $\mathfrak{L}$, as in the preceding chapters, but on a pair of spaces $\mathfrak{L}$ and $\mathfrak{L}'$.

A covariant vector f and a contravariant vector x are called ***orthogonal*** if $(x, f) = 0$. Since the inner product is defined only for vectors of different type, the notion of orthogonality has meaning only for such vectors.

Choose a coordinate basis $e_1, \cdots, e_n$ in $\mathfrak{L}$ and denote by $f_1, \cdots, f_n$ the functions defined by the equalities

$$f_i(x) = \xi_i \tag{1}$$

for $i = 1, \cdots, n$, where $x = \xi_1 e_1 + \cdots + \xi_n e_n$. The functions $f_i(x)$ are linear and therefore are vectors of the conjugate space $\mathfrak{L}'$. They constitute a basis of $\mathfrak{L}'$, since if $f \in \mathfrak{L}'$ and $f(e_i) = \alpha_i$, then

$$f(x) = \alpha_1 f_1(x) + \cdots + \alpha_n f_n(x) .$$

If we define the symbols δ_i^j by

$$\delta_i^j = \begin{cases} 1 & \text{if } i = j, \\ 0 & \text{if } i \neq j, \end{cases} \qquad (i, j = 0, 1, 2, \cdots)$$

the equalities (1) yield

$$(e_i, f_j) = \delta_i^j \tag{2}$$

for $i, j = 1, \cdots, n$.

Arbitrary systems of vectors $a_1, \cdots, a_m$ in $\mathfrak{L}$ and $g_1, \cdots, g_m$ in $\mathfrak{L}'$ are called ***biorthogonal*** if

$$(a_i, g_j) = \delta_i^j \qquad (i, j = 1, \cdots, m) .$$

Relation (2) shows that *for each basis of the space $\mathfrak{L}$ there exists a biorthogonal basis of $\mathfrak{L}'$*. It is clear that for *each basis of $\mathfrak{L}$ there can be only one biorthogonal basis* of $\mathfrak{L}'$ since the condition of biorthogonality gives the values of the functions of the biorthogonal basis at all the basis vectors e_i, and the values of linear functions at the basis vectors determine the values at all vectors (see Section 74).

Fixing the element f in the expression (x, f) and considering it as a function of x, we obtain a linear function on $\mathfrak{L}$. But it is also possible to fix x and consider (x, f) as a function of f. This is a linear function defined on $\mathfrak{L}'$. Therefore, each element $x \in \mathfrak{L}$ determines a linear function on $\mathfrak{L}'$. It is evident from equalities (1) that not only do the elements $f_1, \cdots, f_n$ from a basis of $\mathfrak{L}'$, but the elements $e_1, \cdots, e_n$, considered as linear functions on $\mathfrak{L}'$, form a basis of the space of all linear functions on $\mathfrak{L}'$. This shows that the connection between $\mathfrak{L}$ and $\mathfrak{L}'$ goes both ways.

We now introduce the following important condition concerning further notation: the coordinates of contravariant vectors will be denoted by letters with superscripts, and the coordinates of covariant vectors by letters with subscripts. For the vectors themselves the opposite convention will be used. Thus, for example, if $e_1, \cdots, e_n$ is a basis of the space $\mathfrak{L}$, then the corresponding biorthogonal basis of $\mathfrak{L}'$ is denoted by $e^1, \cdots, e^n$. Let $\xi^1, \cdots, \xi^n$ be the coordinates of some vector x in $\mathfrak{L}$ and $\varphi_1, \cdots, \varphi_n$ be the coordinates of an arbitrary vector f in $\mathfrak{L}'$ in the biorthogonal basis. Then

$$(x, f) = (\sum \xi^i e_i, \sum \varphi_j e^j) = \sum \xi^i \varphi_j (e_i, e^j) = \sum \xi^i \varphi_i ,$$

that is, in biorthogonal bases the inner product has the form

$$(x, f) = \xi^1 \varphi_1 + \cdots + \xi^n \varphi_n = [x][f]' ,$$

where $[x]$, $[f]$ are the coordinate rows of x and f.

Now if a coordinate basis $e_1, \cdots, e_n$ of the space $\mathfrak{L}$ is transformed into a new basis $e'_1, \cdots, e'_n$, it is necessary in the conjugate space $\mathfrak{L}'$ to change the biorthogonal basis $e^1, \cdots, e^n$ to some basis $e'^1, \cdots, e'^n$ which is biorthogonal to the new basis of $\mathfrak{L}$. Let

$$e'_i = \sum \tau_{i\lambda} e_\lambda , \quad e'^i = \sum \sigma_{i\lambda} e^\lambda \qquad (i = 1, \cdots, n) .$$

We consider the connection between the matrices of the transformations of coordinates $T = ||\tau_{ij}||$ and $S = ||\sigma_{ij}||$. Since the new bases are biorthogonal, $(x, f) = [x]_1 [f]'_1$, and this means (compare Section 97) that

$$(x, f) = [x][f]' = [x]_1 T([f]_1 S)' = [x]_1 T S' [f]'_1 = [x]_1 [f]'_1 ,$$

and hence

$$TS' = E, \quad S = T'^{-1} . \tag{3}$$

The matrix T'^{-1}, the inverse of the transpose of T, is called the ***contragredient*** of T. Thus the meaning of (3) is that *if a transformation of bases with matrix T is performed in a space $\mathfrak{L}$, then the corresponding transformation of biorthogonal bases of the conjugate space has the contragredient matrix T'^{-1}*

The existence of biorthogonal bases permits the construction of a unique linear transformation $\mathscr{A}'$ of the space $\mathfrak{L}'$ corresponding to each linear transformation $\mathscr{A}$ of the space $\mathfrak{L}$. To this end we consider the expression

$$g(x) = (x\mathscr{A}, f) . \tag{4}$$

It is clear that for fixed $f \in \mathfrak{L}'$ and variable $x \in \mathfrak{L}$, $g(x)$ is a linear function on $\mathfrak{L}$. Therefore the correspondence $f \rightarrow g$ is some transformation of the space $\mathfrak{L}'$, which is usually denoted $\mathscr{A}'$ and is called the ***conjugate***, or ***dual***, of $\mathscr{A}$. It is easy to convince oneself (see Section 75) that $\mathscr{A}'$ is a linear transformation of the space $\mathfrak{L}'$.

Relation (4) may be written in the new notation in the form

$$(x\mathscr{A}, f) = (x, f\mathscr{A}') , \tag{5}$$

which uniquely characterizes the transformation $\mathscr{A}'$.

Let the matrix of the transformation $\mathscr{A}$ be $||\alpha_{ij}||$ in some basis $e_1, \cdots, e_n$, and let the matrix of the transformation $\mathscr{A}'$ be $||\alpha'_{ij}||$ in the biorthogonal basis $e^1, \cdots, e^n$. Then

$$(e_i, e^j\mathscr{A}') = (e_i, \sum \alpha'_{j\lambda}e^\lambda) = \alpha'_{ji} ,$$
$$(e_i, e^j\mathscr{A}') = (e_i\mathscr{A}, e^j) = (\sum \alpha_{i\lambda}e_\lambda, e^j) = \alpha_{ij} ,$$

and hence $\alpha'_{ji} = \alpha_{ij}$; that is, *transposing the matrix of the transformation* $\mathscr{A}$, *we obtain the matrix of the conjugate transformation* $\mathscr{A}'$ *in the biorthogonal basis.*

We now see immediately that for conjugate transformations we have the usual relations

$$(\alpha\mathscr{A} + \beta\mathscr{B})' = \alpha\mathscr{A}' + \beta\mathscr{B}', \quad (\mathscr{A}\mathscr{B})' = \mathscr{B}'\mathscr{A}' .$$

These relations are also easily derived as immediate consequences of equality (5), which defines the conjugate transformations.

111. Multilinear Functions

Suppose that to each sequence $x, y, \cdots, z, f, g, \cdots, h$, consisting of p vectors $x, \cdots, z$ of the space $\mathfrak{L}$ and q vectors $f, \cdots, h$ of the conjugate space $\mathfrak{L}'$, is placed in correspondence a definite number $F(x, \cdots, z, f, \cdots, h)$ of the base field K. We then say that F is a function on $\mathfrak{L}$ of type (p, q) in the variable vectors. The function F is called ***multilinear*** if it is linear in each argument separately. For example, the linearity of F in the second argument means that

$$F(x, \alpha y_1 + \beta y_1, \cdots, z, f, \cdots, h) = \alpha F(x, y_1, \cdots, z, f, \cdots, h)$$
$$+ \beta F(x, y_2, \cdots, z, f, \cdots, h) .$$

The total number of arguments of a multilinear function F is called its ***valence***. In particular, a multilinear function of valence 1 is one of two types: (1, 0) or (0, 1). Those of type (1, 0) are linear functions on $\mathfrak{L}$—that is, elements of the conjugate space. Those of type (0, 1) are linear functions on the conjugate space, which we have identified with the corresponding elements of the space $\mathfrak{L}$.

Multilinear functions of valence 2 are of three possible types: (2, 0), (1, 1), or (0, 2). Functions of type (2, 0) are bilinear functions on the space $\mathfrak{L}$, and functions of type (0, 2) are bilinear functions on the space $\mathfrak{L}'$; these functions we have already studied in detail. We will now consider functions of type (1, 1).

Let $F(x, f)$ be a bilinear function of type (1, 1), or a ***mixed*** bilinear function. For each fixed $x \in \mathfrak{L}$, $F(x, f)$ is a linear function in f, defined on $\mathfrak{L}'$. But each linear function on $\mathfrak{L}'$ uniquely corresponds to a vector in $\mathfrak{L}$. We denote this vector in $\mathfrak{L}$ by $x\mathscr{A}$. Thus, for arbitrary x, f we have

$$F(x, f) = (x\mathscr{A}, f) .$$

It is easy to see that the transformation $\mathscr{A}$ of the space $\mathfrak{L}$ is linear. Thus, each mixed bilinear function turns out to be connected with a linear transformation of the space $\mathfrak{L}$. This connection is one to one, does not depend on the choice of a coordinate basis of $\mathfrak{L}$, and is linear. The latter means that if bilinear functions $F(x, f)$ and $G(x, f)$ correspond to linear transformations $\mathscr{A}$ and $\mathscr{B}$, then the bilinear function $\alpha F(x, f) + \beta G(x, f)$ corresponds to the transformation $\alpha\mathscr{A} + \beta\mathscr{B}$.

Returning to the consideration of arbitrary multilinear functions $F(x, \cdots, z, f, \cdots, h)$ of type (p, q) on $\mathfrak{L}$, we choose some coordinate basis $e_1, \cdots, e_n$ of $\mathfrak{L}$ and introduce the following notation:

$$F(e_\alpha, \cdots, e_\gamma, e^\lambda, \cdots, e^\mu) = F_{\alpha\cdots\gamma\cdots}^{\cdots\lambda\cdots\mu} . \tag{6}$$

The dots above and below are inserted in order not to disarrange the order of the indices. If no confusion arises, the shorter form

$$F(e_\alpha, \cdots, e_\gamma, e^\lambda, \cdots, e^\mu) = F_{\alpha\cdots\gamma}^{\lambda\cdots\mu}$$

may be used.

Knowing the numbers $F_{\alpha\cdots\gamma}^{\lambda\cdots\mu}$, we know the multilinear function F, since for arbitrary vectors

$$x = \xi^1 e_1 + \cdots + \xi^n e_n , \cdots, \quad z = \zeta^1 e_1 + \cdots + \zeta^n e_n ,$$
$$f = \varphi_1 e^1 + \cdots + \varphi_n e^n , \cdots, \quad h = \chi_1 e^1 + \cdots + \chi_n e^n ,$$

it follows from the linearity of F in each argument that

$$\begin{aligned} F(x, \cdots, z, f, \cdots, h) &= F(\sum \xi^\alpha e_\alpha, \cdots, \sum \zeta^\gamma e_\gamma, \sum \varphi_\lambda e^\lambda, \cdots, \sum \chi_\mu e^\mu) \\ &= \sum F(e_\alpha, \cdots, e_\gamma, e^\lambda, \cdots, e^\mu)\xi^\alpha \cdots \zeta^\gamma \varphi_\lambda \cdots \chi_\mu \\ &= \sum F_{\alpha\cdots\gamma}^{\lambda\cdots\mu} \xi^\alpha \cdots \zeta^\gamma \varphi_\lambda \cdots \chi_\mu . \end{aligned} \tag{7}$$

Therefore, the numbers $F_{\alpha\cdots\gamma}^{\lambda\cdots\mu}$ are called the ***coordinates of the multilinear function in the basis*** $e_1, \cdots, e_n$. Each coordinate $F_{\alpha\cdots\gamma}^{\lambda\cdots\mu}$ may be identified by its set of indices. If there is one index, the coordinates may be arranged in a row, and we speak of the coordinate row. If there are two indices, the coordinates fall naturally into a square table in the plane—the matrix of coordinates. We take the first index as the row number and the second index as the column number, on the intersection of which must be placed the given coordinate. In particular, we have taken for $F_{i\cdots}^{\cdots j}$ the abbreviated form F_i^j, and in writing the coordinates F_i^j in a matrix we will consider the lower index as denoting the row, the upper index as denoting the column.

Following the same idea further, we place the coordinates of a multilinear function in three arguments in the form of a three-dimensional cube, the coordinates of a multilinear function in four arguments in the form of a four-dimensional cube, and so on. Although, even in three dimensions, the manufacture of cubic tables is difficult, we nevertheless use the indicated terminology, and speak of the ***r*-dimensional table** of the coordinates of a multilinear function of valence r; that is, the coordinates are not considered simply as a set of n^r numbers, but as a system of n^r numbers which are enumerated in a definite way by using the sequences $(\alpha_1, \cdots, \alpha_r)$, $\alpha_1, \cdots, \alpha_r = 1, \cdots, n$.

By analogy with matrices we call the dimension of the space $\mathfrak{L}$ the ***order*** of the table, and r the ***valence*** of the table. Two tables of identical order and valence are ***equal*** if the elements standing in corresponding positions are equal. To multiply a table by a scalar α means to multiply all the elements of the table by α. Finally, to add tables of the same type means to add the elements standing in corresponding positions and construct a new table from the sums obtained.

It is clear that the sum of two multilinear functions of the same type is again a multilinear function of the same type. The table of coordinates of the sum equals the sum of the tables of coordinates of the summands. The same observation holds for the product of a multilinear function by a scalar.

The notion of the product of two multilinear functions requires somewhat more attention. Let $F(x_1, \cdots, x_p, f_1, \cdots, f_q)$ and $G(x_1, \cdots, x_s, f_1, \cdots, f_t)$ be multilinear functions of types (p, q) and (s, t). Then the product

$$H(x_1, \cdots, x_{p+s}, f_1, \cdots, f_{q+t})$$
$$= F(x_1, \cdots, x_p, f_1, \cdots, f_q)G(x_{p+1}, \cdots, x_{p+s}, f_{q+1}, \cdots, f_{q+t}) \qquad (8)$$

is evidently again a multilinear function, but of type $(p+s, q+t)$. It is called the ***product*** of F and G. We remark that for the multiplication of multilinear functions the arguments of the factors are considered independent, whereas for addition corresponding arguments are identified. We also remark that: 1) it is possible to multiply multilinear functions of arbitrary types; 2) the product depends on the order of the factors; 3) the valence of the product equals the sum of the valences of the factors.

We now calculate how the coordinates of a multilinear function change under a change of coordinate bases. Let the new basis be connected to the old by the usual formulas [compare (3) of Section 110]:

$$e'_i = \tau_{i1}e_1 + \tau_{i2}e_2 + \cdots + \tau_{in}e_n\,,$$
$$e'^i = \sigma_{i1}e^1 + \sigma_{i2}e^2 + \cdots + \sigma_{in}e^n\,. \qquad (i = 1, \cdots, n)$$

Then for the new coordinates we have the following expression:

$$F'^{\lambda\cdots\mu}_{\alpha\cdots\gamma} = F(e'_\alpha, \cdots, e'_\gamma, e'^\lambda, \cdots, e'^\mu)$$
$$= \sum F(e_i, \cdots, e_k, e^r, \cdots, e^t)\tau_{\alpha i}\cdots\tau_{\gamma k}\sigma_{\lambda r}\cdots\sigma_{\mu t})$$

or

$$F'^{\lambda\cdots\mu}_{\alpha\cdots\gamma} = \sum \tau_{\alpha i}\cdots\tau_{\gamma k}\sigma_{\lambda r}\cdots\sigma_{\mu t}F^{r\cdots t}_{i\cdots k}, \tag{9}$$

where the summation extends over all indices which occur twice on the right side. Formula (9) plays a fundamental role in what follows. It is easily remembered if one observes that the matrix T "operates" on the lower indices, and the matrix S on the upper.

112. Tensors

In the preceding paragraph we met a series of objects which are connected with linear spaces, and which may be given by a set of numbers, provided that some coordinate basis is chosen. First of all we may count among these objects the vectors of the space themselves, then the linear transformations and multilinear functions of various types. These objects are characteristically described by *tables* of numbers, which are transformed according to a definite *law* if the selected basis of the space is replaced by another basis. Conversely, each of the indicated objects determines a law, according to which, for each basis of $\mathfrak{L}$, it is possible to find a definite many-dimensional table of numbers possessing the transformation property (9). From this arises naturally the following

Definition. *A tensor of type (p, q) of a space $\mathfrak{L}$ is a correspondence which associates a definite $(p+q)$-dimensional table of numbers $F^{j_1\cdots j_q}_{i_1\cdots i_p}$ with each basis of $\mathfrak{L}$; tables $F^{j_1\cdots j_q}_{i_1\cdots i_p}$ and $F'^{j_1\cdots j_q}_{i_1\cdots i_p}$ associated with different bases $e_1, \cdots, e_n$ and $e'_1, \cdots, e'_n$ are connected by the relation*

$$F'^{j_1\cdots j_q}_{i_1\cdots i_p} = \sum_{\lambda_1,\cdots,\mu_q} \tau_{i_1\lambda_1}\cdots\tau_{i_p\lambda_p}\sigma_{j_1\mu_1}\cdots\sigma_{j_q\mu_q}F^{\mu_1\cdots\mu_q}_{\lambda_1\cdots\lambda_p}, \tag{10}$$

where $T = \|\tau_{ij}\|$ is the matrix of the transformation from the first basis to the second—that is, $e'_i = \sum \tau_{i\lambda}e_\lambda$ — *and* $\|\sigma_{ij}\| = S = T'^{-1}$.

A tensor of the indicated type is called ***p* times covariant** and ***q* times contravariant.** The sum $p+q$ is the ***valence*** of the tensor, and the number $F^{j_1\cdots j_q}_{i_1\cdots i_p}$ is the ***component*** or ***coordinate*** of the number $\binom{j_1\cdots j_q}{i_1\cdots i_p}$ of the given tensor in the coordinate basis $e_1, \cdots, e_n$.

We consider several examples.

1) *Vectors of a space $\mathfrak{L}$.* In each basis a vector x has a coordinate row $[x]=[\xi', \cdots, \xi^n]$. Under a transformation to a new basis the coordinates of the vector x are changed according to the law (compare Section 110)

$$[x] = [x]_1T, \quad [x]_1 = [x]T^{-1} = [x]S'. \tag{11}$$

or

$$\xi'^i = \sum \xi^\lambda\sigma_{i\lambda}.$$

Comparing with formula (10), we see that *the coordinate row of a vector in* $\mathfrak{L}$ *is a contravariant tensor of valence* 1.

2) *Vectors of the space* $\mathfrak{L}'$. Choose a basis $e_1, \cdots, e_n$ of $\mathfrak{L}$ and a biorthogonal basis $e^1, \cdots, e^n$ of $\mathfrak{L}'$. The coordinate row of a vector $f \in \mathfrak{L}'$ in the basis $e^1, \cdots, e^n$ will also be called ***the coordinate row of*** f ***in the basis*** $e_1, \cdots, e_n$. A transformation to a new basis of $\mathfrak{L}$ implies a transformation to a new basis of $\mathfrak{L}'$ with matrix $S = T'^{-1}$. Therefore, the new coordinate row $[f]_1$ of the vector f in the basis $e'_1, \cdots, e'_n$ is connected to the old by the relation

$$[f] = [f]_1 S, \quad [f]_1 = [f]S^{-1} = [f]T' ,$$

or

$$\varphi'_i = \sum \varphi_\lambda \tau_{i\lambda} .$$

Consequently, the coordinate row of a vector in the conjugate space is a covariant tensor of valence 1.

3) *Linear transformations of* $\mathfrak{L}$. Let the matrix of a linear transformation $\mathscr{A}$ in the basis $e_1, \cdots, e_n$ be $A = \| \alpha_{ij} \|$. Then the matrix of the transformation $\mathscr{A}$ in a new basis is (see Section 36)

$$A_1 = \| \alpha'_{ij} \| = TAT^{-1} = TAS' ,$$

that is,

$$\alpha'_{ij} = \sum \tau_{i\lambda} \alpha_{\lambda\mu} \sigma_{j\mu} .$$

Comparing with (10), we see that the matrix of a linear transformation is a mixed tensor of valence 2, covariant in the first index and contravariant in the second. Therefore, the elements of the matrix of a linear transformation may be conveniently enumerated by setting $\alpha_{\lambda\mu} = \alpha_\lambda^\mu$.

4) *Bilinear functions.* Let a bilinear function $F(x, y)$ be given on $\mathfrak{L}$. Place in correspondence to each basis the matrix $A = \| \alpha_{ij} \|$ of this function, where $\alpha_{ij} = F(e_i, e_j)$. The matrix of $F(x, y)$ in a new basis is

$$\| \alpha'_{ij} \| = TAT' ,$$

and hence

$$\alpha'_{ij} = \sum \tau_{i\lambda} \alpha_{\lambda\mu} \tau_{j\mu} .$$

Consequently, the matrix of a bilinear function on $\mathfrak{L}$ is a twice covariant tensor of valence 2. Similarly, the matrix of a bilinear function on $\mathfrak{L}'$ is a twice contravariant tensor of valence 2.

The last example need not have been considered separately, since, comparing formulas (10) and (9), we immediately convince ourselves that *the coordinates of a multilinear function of type* (p, q) *on a space* $\mathfrak{L}$ *form a* p *times covariant and* q *times* contravariant tensor. This connection between tensors and multilinear functions is invariant and one to one.

The invariance — that is, independence of the choice of coordinate basis — is obvious, and the one to oneness follows immediately from

THEOREM 1. *If the coordinates of two tensors of the same type are respectively equal relative to one basis, then they are equal relative to all bases, and therefore the tensors are equal.*

Indeed, knowing the table of coordinates of a tensor in some initial basis, and knowing which indices are covariant and which are contravariant, one may, by formula (10), compute uniquely the table of coordinates in any other basis.

THEOREM 2. *Let an arbitrary* $(p+q)$*-valence table of numbers* $F_{i_1\cdots i_{p+q}}$ *be given in a linear space* $\mathfrak{L}$ *with basis* $e_1, \cdots, e_n$*, and let the indices of the numbers be divided in an arbitrary way into two categories* $\alpha_1, \cdots, \alpha_p$ *and* $\alpha_{p+1}, \cdots, \alpha_{p+q}$. *Then there exists one and only one tensor of the space* $\mathfrak{L}$ *whose coordinates in the basis* $e_1, \cdots, e_n$ *form the given table, with, moreover, the indices of the first category covariant and those of the second category contravariant.*

The uniqueness follows from the preceding theorem, and the existence of the required tensor may be established in the following way. Consider the function $F(x_1, \cdots, x_{p+q})$ of the vectors $x_{\alpha_1}, \cdots, x_{\alpha_p}$ in the space $\mathfrak{L}$ and the vectors $x_{\alpha_{p+1}}, \cdots, x_{\alpha_{p+q}}$ in the space $\mathfrak{L}'$, whose values are computed from the formula

$$F(x_1, \cdots, x_{p+q}) = \sum F_{i_1\cdots i_{p+q}} \xi_1^{i_1} \cdots \xi_{p+q}^{i_{p+q}} ,$$

where $\xi_\alpha^1, \cdots, \xi_\alpha^n$ are the coordinates of the vector x_α in the basis $e_1, \cdots, e_n$. It is clear that $F(x_1, \cdots, x_{p+q})$ is a multilinear function whose coordinates in the given basis are the numbers $F_{i_1\cdots i_{p+q}}$. However, it has already been observed that the coordinates of a multilinear function constitute a tensor. Therefore the table of the coordinates of the function F is the desired tensor.

We remark in conclusion that formula (10) expresses the *new* coordinates of the tensors in terms of the old. Sometimes it is necessary to have an expression for the *old* coordinates in terms of the new. For this the same formula (10) may be used, calling the old coordinate basis the new, and the new the old. The formulas for the transformation of coordinates of a vector have the form (11). Thus the matrices T_1, S_1 of the inverse transformation have the form

$$T_1 = S', \quad S_1 = T_1'^{-1} = S^{-1} = T' .$$

Therefore, changing formula (10) to the inverse transformation, we obtain

$$F_{i_1\cdots i_p}^{j_1\cdots j_q} = \sum \sigma_{\lambda_1 i_1} \cdots \sigma_{\lambda_p i_p} \tau_{\mu_1 j_1} \cdots \tau_{\mu_q j_q} F'^{\mu_1\cdots\mu_q}_{\lambda_1\cdots\lambda_p} . \tag{12}$$

Rule (12) may be briefly formulated as follows: *to find the old coordinates of a tensor, operate on the lower indices of its new coordinates with the matrix S and on the upper indices with the matrix T.* Here one must also stipulate which indices, the first or second, of the matrices S and T are to participate in the summation; this is made superfluous if we use the tensor notation for the elements of the matrices: instead of τ_{ij}, σ_{ij} we write respectively τ_i^j and σ_i^j. Then formulas (10) and (12) acquire the following final form:

$$F'^{j_1\cdots j_q}_{i_1\cdots i_p} = \sum \tau_{i_1}^{\lambda_1}\cdots\tau_{i_p}^{\lambda_p}\sigma_{\mu_1}^{j_1}\cdots\sigma_{\mu_q}^{j_q}F^{\mu_1\cdots\mu_q}_{\lambda_1\cdots\lambda_p},$$

$$F^{j_1\cdots j_q}_{i_1\cdots i_p} = \sum \sigma_{i_1}^{\lambda_1}\cdots\sigma_{i_p}^{\lambda_p}\tau_{\mu_1}^{j_1}\cdots\tau_{\mu_q}^{j_q}F'^{\mu_1\cdots\mu_q}_{\lambda_1\cdots\lambda_p}.$$

The summation is now taken over the indices which appear twice: once as a lower, and once as an upper, index.

This summation over indices standing in both positions is met so often in tensor formulas that in most texts such a tensor notation is understood: if an arbitrary index occurs twice, then it is an index of summation. We will not use this convention, and will always use the summation sign when summation is necessary.

● EXAMPLES AND PROBLEMS

1. Fix some vector x in a space $\mathfrak{L}$ and place in correspondence with each basis $e_1, \cdots, e_n$ of the space $\mathfrak{L}$ the table of numbers $\alpha^{ij} = \xi^i\xi^j$, where the ξ^i, are the coordinates of x in the indicated basis. Show that this correspondence is a twice contravariant tensor.
2. Place in correspondence to each basis of $\mathfrak{L}$ the table α_{ij}^{kl} for $i, j, k, l = 1, \cdots, n$, defined in the following way:

$$\alpha_{ij}^{kl} = \begin{cases} 1 & \text{if } i = k,\ j = l, \\ 0 & \text{otherwise}. \end{cases}$$

   Show that this is a tensor of type (2, 2). A simpler example of the same kind is obtained by using the table of numbers $\alpha_i^j = \delta_i^j$, to obtain a mixed tensor with fixed coordinates.
3. Show that every tensor of valence 2 whose coordinates are identical in all bases is a tensor of the form $\alpha\delta_i^j$, where α is a fixed number and the δ_i^j are as defined in Section 110.

2. *Tensor Algebra*

113. Addition and Multiplication of Tensors

As we have seen, there exists a one-to-one correspondence between tensors and multilinear functions. At the same time, addition, multiplication, and multiplication by a scalar are defined in a natural way for multilinear functions. This correspondence is used to define these three operations for tensors; to do this it is sufficient to consider the operations with tensors as corresponding to the operations with multilinear functions. Attention to the results of Section 111 leads us to the following:

1) *The product of a scalar α and a tensor F is the tensor αF, whose coordinates in each basis are α times the corresponding coordinates of the tensor F.*

2) *The sum of two tensors of the same type with coordiantes* $F_{i\cdots j}^{k\cdots l}$ *and* $G_{i\cdots j}^{k\cdots l}$ *is the tensor* $H_{i\cdots j}^{k\cdots l}$, *whose coordinates equal the sums of the corresponding coordinates of the tensors F and G.*

Since the operations with tensors correspond to the operations with multilinear functions, they are subject to the same laws as are the operations with functions. In particular, it is evident that the set of all tensors of a given type form a linear space with respect to the operations of addition and multiplication by a scalar. It is clear that the dimension of this space is n^r, where r is the valence of the tensors considered.

3) *The product FG of tensors F and G having coordinates* $F_{i\cdots j}^{k\cdots l}$ and $G_{\alpha\cdots\beta}^{\lambda\cdots\mu}$ *in an arbitrary basis is the tensor whose coordinates in the same basis are computed from the formula*

$$H_{i\cdots j\alpha\cdots\beta}^{k\cdots l\lambda\cdots\mu} = F_{i\cdots j}^{k\cdots l} G_{\alpha\cdots\beta}^{\lambda\cdots\mu} .$$

It is clear that the multilinear function corresponding to the product of tensors equals the product of the multilinear functions corresponding to the factors. Therefore the coordinate definition of the product of tensors is indeed independent of the coordinate basis.

It is obvious from the definition that multiplication of tensors of different types is also possible. If the types of the factors are (p_1, q_1) and (p_2, q_2), then the product of the tensors has type $(p_1 + p_2, q_1 + q_2)$. In particular, the valence of the product of tensors equals the sum of the valences of the factors.

Multiplication and addition of tensors are connected by the usual distributive laws

$$F(G+H) = FG + FH, \quad (G+H)F = GF + HF ,$$

where the tensors G and H are assumed to be of the same type.

The three operations considered permit the construction, starting from some supply of tensors, of new tensors, among which are tensors of higher valence. As previously mentioned, the vectors of the space $\mathfrak{L}$ and of the conjugate space $\mathfrak{L}'$ may be regarded as tensors of valence 1. Products of the form x_1x_2, f_1f_2, x_1f_2, where $x_1, x_2 \in \mathfrak{L}, f_1, f_2 \in \mathfrak{L}'$, are tensors of valence 2 of type (2, 0), (0, 2) and (1, 1) respectively; the products $x_1x_2x_1$, $x_1x_2f_1$ are tensors of valence three, and so on. Naturally, not every tensor is the product of tensors of valence 1; however, *every tensor may be represented as a sum of such products.*

Indeed, let the given tensor have coordinates $F_{i_1\cdots i_p}^{j_1\cdots j_q}$ in some basis $e_1, \cdots, e_n$. It is easy to see that the product $e_{j_1}e_{j_2}\cdots e_{j_q}e^{i_1}e^{i_2}\cdots e^{i_p}$ is a tensor of the same type as F, and that all the coordinates of this product in the basis $e_1, \cdots, e_n$ are zero except for the coordinate indexed by $\binom{j_1\cdots j_q}{i_1\cdots i_p}$, which is 1. It follows from this that the coordinate indexed by $\binom{j_1\cdots j_q}{i_1\cdots i_p}$ of the tensor

$$\sum F_{i_1\cdots i_p}^{j_1\cdots j_q} e_{j_1}\cdots e_{j_q} e^{i_1}\cdots e^{i_p}$$

equals $F^{j_1\cdots j_q}_{i_1\cdots i_p}$; that is, this tensor coincides with F. Thus, we obtain the formula

$$F = \sum F^{j_1\cdots j_q}_{i_1\cdots i_p} e_{j_1} \cdots e_{j_q} e^{i_1} \cdots e^{i_p} ,$$

expressing an arbitrary tensor F in terms of ***elementary tensors***—that is, products of vectors.

114. Contraction of a Tensor

Besides the three indicated operations, there is also the operation of the contraction of tensors. In order to give the definitions sufficient generality, we will agree to call numbers not depending on the choice of a basis ***tensors of valence zero,*** or ***scalars.***

Consider first a mixed bilinear function $F(x,f)$. By Section 111 there exists one and only one linear transformation $\mathscr{A}$ of the space $\mathfrak{L}$ which satisfies the condition

$$F(x,f) = f(x\mathscr{A}) .$$

The trace of the matrix of the transformation $\mathscr{A}$ does not depend on the basis of $\mathfrak{L}$, and is called (see Section 45) the trace of the transformation $\mathscr{A}$. We will also call it the ***trace of the bilinear function*** $F(x,f)$ itself, and denote it by $\underset{(x,f)}{S} F(x, f)$. Thus,

$$\underset{(x,f)}{S} F(x,f) = \sum_{i=1}^{n} F^{i}_{i} , \tag{1}$$

where F_i^j are the coordinates of the function F.

In view of the fact that the trace is a linear function of matrices, we have

$$\underset{(x,f)}{S} [\alpha F(x,f) + \beta G(x,f)] = \alpha \underset{(x,f)}{S} F(x,f) + \beta \underset{(x,f)}{S} G(x,f) , \tag{2}$$

where G, F are any bilinear functions of mixed type.

Now let $F(x_1, \cdots, x_p, f_1, \cdots, f_q)$ be a multilinear function of mixed type in any number of arguments. Fixing the values of all the arguments except one contravariant x_i and one covariant f_j, we turn F into a bilinear function of mixed type in x_i and f_j. Denote by $\underset{(i,j)}{S} F$ the trace of this bilinear function. Relations (1), (2) show that $\underset{(i,j)}{S} F$ is a multilinear function in the remaining arguments of F.

We consider what the operation of taking the trace means in the language of the tensor calculus. For simplicity assume that the function F has the form $F(x, y, f, g)$, and denote its coordinates in the basis $e_1, \cdots, e_n$ by F^{kl}_{ij}. Then the coordinates of the bilinear function $H(y,f) = F(x,y,f,g)$ for fixed x and g are

$$H^{j}_{i} = \sum F^{j\beta}_{\alpha i} \xi^{\alpha} \psi_{\beta} ,$$

where $\xi^{\alpha}, \psi_{\beta}$ are the coordinates of the vectors x and g. For the trace of

H, considered as a function G of x, g we have:

$$G(x, g) = \underset{(y,f)}{S} F(x, y, f, g) = \sum_{i,\alpha,\beta} F_{\alpha i}^{i\beta} \xi^{\alpha} \psi_{\beta} ,$$

and consequently, the coordinates of the new tensor have the expression

$$G_{\alpha}^{\beta} = \sum_{i} F_{\alpha i}^{i\beta} . \tag{3}$$

In the tensor calculus the operation of taking the trace is called the operation of ***contraction***. It is evident from (3) that contraction always operates on two indices, one upper and one lower (contravariant and covariant), according to the formula

$$G_{i\cdots jk\cdots m}^{\alpha\cdots\beta\gamma\cdots\delta} = \sum_{\lambda=1}^{n} F_{i\cdots j\lambda k\cdots m}^{\alpha\cdots\beta\lambda\gamma\cdots\delta} ,$$

where the coordinates of the *contracted* tensor F stand on the left.

As a result of a contraction, the number of contravariant and of covariant coordinates of the tensor are reduced by 1, and the valence of the tensor is decreased by 2. If the contracted tensor is still mixed, then the operation of contraction may be applied again, and so on. The result of a *complete* contraction is either a purely covariant or purely contravariant tensor, or a scalar.

Often the operation of contraction is combined with a preliminary multiplication of tensors, according to the scheme

$$H_{i\cdots jk\cdots m}^{\alpha\cdots\beta\gamma\cdots\delta} = \sum_{\lambda} F_{i\cdots\lambda\cdots j}^{\alpha\cdots\beta} G_{k\cdots m}^{\gamma\cdots\lambda\cdots\delta} .$$

In this case we say that the tensor H is obtained by *a contraction of the tensor F with the tensor G.* This combined operation has a particularly simple geometric meaning. Let the first tensor correspond to the multilinear function $F(x_1, \cdots, x_p, f_1, \cdots, f_q)$, and the second to the function $G(y_1, \cdots, y_s, g_1, \cdots, g_t)$. Fixing all the arguments of the first function except x_i and all the arguments of the second except g_j, we obtain in the first case a linear function on $\mathfrak{L}$ — that is, a covariant vector — and in the second case a linear function on $\mathfrak{L}'$ — that is, a contravariant vector. The inner product of these vectors in the sense of Section 110 is also the contraction of the product FG in the arguments x_i and g_j.

115. Raising and Lowering Indices

In the case of a tensor of valence 2, either purely covariant or purely contravariant, with a nonsingular matrix, the above-mentioned operations may be supplemented by the peculiar operation of raising or lowering indices, thanks to which the study of tensors of arbitrary type may be reduced to the study of tensors of a fixed type. A particular case of this law has already been considered in Section 99, where it was remarked that the study of pairs of bilinear forms could be replaced by the study of pairs consisting of a bilinear form and a linear transformation.

Thus, suppose a twice covariant tensor g_{ij} is given in a space $\mathfrak{L}$, or (what is the same thing) suppose given a bilinear function $g(x, y)$, with nonsingular matrix $\| g_{ij} \|$. The formula

$$g(x, a) = f_a(x) \tag{4}$$

places in correspondence with each vector a in $\mathfrak{L}$ a linear function f_a—that is, an element of $\mathfrak{L}'$. By Section 110 the correspondence $a \to f_a$ is an isomorphism between $\mathfrak{L}$ and $\mathfrak{L}'$. If h_1, h_2 are two elements of $\mathfrak{L}'$, then there are unique vectors a, b in $\mathfrak{L}$ such that $h_1 = f_a$, $h_2 = f_b$. Setting

$$g(h_1, h_2) = g(f_a, f_b) = g(a, b) ,$$

we define a function of two arguments on $\mathfrak{L}'$. This function is bilinear, and therefore its coordinates G^{ij} constitute a twice contravariant tensor on $\mathfrak{L}$. Thus, being given a twice covariant tensor g_{ij}, we have constructed a twice contravariant tensor G^{ij}. In an analogous way, given a twice contravariant tensor with nonsingular matrix, we may "lower" its indices by constructing the corresponding twice covariant tensor.

We find the connection between the coordinates g_{ij} of the given covariant tensor and the coordinates G^{ij} of the corresponding contravariant tensor in an arbitrary coordinate basis $e_1, \cdots, e_n$. Denote by g^{ij} the elements of the matrix G'^{-1}, the contragredient of the matrix $G = \| g_{ij} \|$. From $G'G'^{-1} = G'^{-1}G' = E$, we obtain

$$\Sigma\, g_{i\lambda} g^{j\lambda} = \Sigma\, g_{\lambda i} g^{\lambda j} = \delta_i^j \qquad (i, j = 1, \cdots, n) . \tag{5}$$

By definition we have

$$G^{ij} = g(e^i, e^j) ,$$

where $e^1, \cdots, e^n$ is a biorthogonal basis of $\mathfrak{L}'$. To find G^{ij}, we observe first of all that

$$(e_j, f_{e_i}) = f_{e_i}(e_j) = g(e_j, e_i) = g_{ji} .$$

Multiplying the left and right sides of these equalities by $g^{\alpha i}$, summing over i, and using (5), we obtain

$$(e_j, \Sigma\, g^{\alpha i} Fe_i) = \delta_j^\alpha ,$$

and hence

$$e^\alpha = \Sigma\, g^{\alpha i} f_{e_i} = f_{a_\alpha} \qquad (a_\alpha = \Sigma\, g^{\alpha i} e_i) ,$$

But then

$$\begin{aligned} G^{\alpha\beta} &= g(e^\alpha, e^\beta) = g(a_\alpha, a_\beta) = \Sigma\, g^{\alpha i} g(e_i, e_j) g^{\beta j} \\ &= \Sigma\, g^{\alpha i} g_{ij} g^{\beta j} = \Sigma\, g^{\alpha i} \delta_i^\beta = g^{\alpha\beta} . \end{aligned}$$

Consequently, *if the coodrinates of the given twice covariant tensor g_{ij} form a nonsingular matrix $G = \| g_{ij} \|$, then the elements of the contragredient matrix $G'^{-1} = \| g^{ij} \|$ form the corresponding twice contravariant tensor.*

Now suppose that we are considering jointly tensors $g(x, y)$, $F(x_1, \cdots,$

$x_p, f_1, \cdots, f_q$), of which the first is twice covariant with nonsingular matrix, or is a nondegenerate bilinear function. Calling the value of this function $g(x, y) = (x, y)$ the inner product of the vectors x and y, we turn the space $\mathfrak{L}$ into a *bilinear-metric* space, and the joint study of the given system of tensors reduces to the study of the tensors F on a bilinear-metric space. As we have seen, in the case of a bilinear-metric space there exists a natural isomorphic mapping σ of the space $\mathfrak{L}$ onto $\mathfrak{L}'$. Let $F(x, y, k, h)$, with $k, h \in \mathfrak{L}'$, be a given multilinear function on $\mathfrak{L}$. Then the functions

$$F(x, y, z, h) = F(x, y, z\sigma, h),$$
$$F(x, f, k, h) = F(x, f\sigma^{-1}, k, h),$$

and so on, are also multilinear, but are of different types. Thus, it is possible to replace at will a covariant argument by a contravariant one, and conversely, a contravariant argument by a covariant one. Even though such changes give rise to different multilinear functions, from the uniqueness of the correspondence and the possibility of returning to the old function from the new by the same process, it is understood that all the functions arising from one another in this way represent one and the same function F, in different forms.

Let $F_{ij\cdot\cdot}^{\cdot\cdot kl}$ be the coordinates of a multilinear function $F(x, y, k, h)$ in some basis $e_1, \cdots, e_n$. We find the coordinates of $F(x, f, k, h)$. The natural isomorphism σ, mentioned above, is a mapping $a \to f_a$, where $f_a(x) = (x, a)$ $= g(x, a)$. Let $\xi^i, \eta^i, \varphi_i, \psi_i, \chi_i$ be the coordinates of the vectors $x, f\sigma^{-1}, f, k, h$, respectively. Then

$$\sum \varphi_\alpha \xi^\alpha = (x, f) = f_y(x) = g(x, y) = \sum g_{\alpha i} \eta^i \xi^\alpha \qquad (y = f\sigma^{-1}),$$

from which, since the $\xi^1, \cdots, \xi^n$ are arbitrary, it follows that

$$\varphi_\alpha = \sum g_{\alpha i} \eta^i, \quad \sum g^{\alpha j} \varphi_\alpha = \eta^j .$$

We now have

$$F(x, f, k, h) = F(x, y, k, h) = \sum F_{ij\cdot\cdot}^{\cdot\cdot kl} \xi^i \eta^j \psi_k \chi_l = \sum F_{ij\cdot\cdot}^{\cdot\cdot kl} g^{\alpha j} \xi^i \varphi_\alpha \psi_k \chi_l ,$$

or

$$F_{i\cdot\cdot\cdot}^{\cdot jkl} = \sum g^{j\lambda} F_{i\lambda\cdot\cdot}^{\cdot\cdot kl}, \quad F_{ij\cdot\cdot}^{\cdot\cdot kl} = \sum g_{\lambda j} F_{i\cdot\cdot\cdot}^{\cdot\lambda kl} .$$

We obtain similarly, in an obvious notation,

$$F_{ijk\cdot}^{\cdot\cdot\cdot l} = \sum g_{\lambda k} F_{ij\cdot\cdot}^{\cdot\cdot\lambda l}, \quad F_{i\cdot k\cdot}^{\cdot j\cdot l} = \sum g^{j\lambda} F_{i\lambda k}^{\cdot\cdot\cdot l} .$$

Consequently, *if multilinear functions arise from each other by replacing covariant arguments by contravariant ones, or conversely, then the corresponding tensors arise from each other by raising or lowering indices and by contracting the tensor F with the tensor $g_{\lambda i}$* or $g^{i\lambda}$.

The possibility of raising or lowering indices is a characteristic peculiar to tensors of bilinear-metric spaces. In Euclidean spaces this possibility is especially evident. Indeed, in this case we may generally confine ourselves to the consideration only of orthonormal bases. The matrices of transformations of coordinates are then also orthogonal. Orthogonal matrices concide with their contragredient matrices, and therefore the coordinates of covariant and contravariant vectors are transformed identically under an orthogonal transformation of coordinates; as a consequence of this the difference between the covariant and contravariant indices of a tensor vanishes.

● EXAMPLES AND PROBLEMS

1. Show that the tensor z^{ij} is the product of two vectors if and only if its coordinates satisfy the relations

$$z^{\alpha i}z^{\beta j} - z^{\alpha j}z^{\beta i} = 0 \qquad (i, j, \alpha, \beta = 1, \cdots, n)\,.$$

2. Show that in a Euclidean space the magnitude of the sum $\sum_j (\sum_i F_{iij})^2$, where $F(x, y, z)$ is any trilinear function, is the same in all orthonormal bases.
3. A linear space $\mathfrak{L}$ over K is called an ***algebra*** over K if, besides the usual operations of addition and multiplication by a scalar, the operation of multiplying vectors a and b is defined, such that the product ab is bilinear—that is, $(\alpha a + \beta b)c = \alpha\cdot ac + \beta\cdot bc$, $a(\alpha b + \beta c) = \alpha\cdot ab + \beta\cdot ac$. In some basis $e_1, \cdots, e_n$, suppose that $e_i e_j = \sum \gamma_{ij}^{\lambda} e_\lambda$. Show that the numbers γ_{ij}^{λ} are the coordinates of a tensor (the structure tensor of the algebra). For fixed a and variable x in $\mathfrak{L}$ the transformations $\mathscr{A}_a$, $\mathscr{B}_a$ are defined by the formulas $ax = x\mathscr{A}_a$, $xa = x\mathscr{B}_a$; these are linear transformations of $\mathfrak{L}$, and the expressions trace $(\mathscr{A}_a\mathscr{A}_b)$, trace $(\mathscr{B}_a\mathscr{B}_b)$ are symmetric bilinear functions of a, b in $\mathfrak{L}$. Demonstrate the formula

$$\operatorname{tr}(\mathscr{A}_a\mathscr{A}_b) = \sum \gamma_{i\mu}^{\lambda}\gamma_{j\lambda}^{\mu}\alpha^i\beta^j \qquad (a = \sum \alpha^i e_i\,,\ b = \sum \beta^j e_j)\,.$$

3. Exterior Algebra

116. Symmetric Tensors

Let $F(x_1, \cdots, x_p, f^1, \cdots, f^q)$ be a multilinear function of type (p, q) defined on a linear space $\mathfrak{L}$. It is evident that the function G, defined by the formula

$$G(x_1, \cdots, x_p, f^1, \cdots, f^q) = F(x_{i_1}, \cdots, x_{i_p}, \cdots, f^1, \cdots, f^q)\,,$$

where $i_1, \cdots, i_p$ is some permutation of the indices $1, \cdots, p$, is also a multilinear function. This function G is called (compare Section 33) the result of operating on the function F with the permutation

$$\sigma = \binom{1 \cdots p}{i_1 \cdots i_p}\,, \tag{1}$$

and is denoted by σF. If the coordinates of F in some basis are $F_{\lambda_1\cdots\lambda_p}^{\mu_1\cdots\mu_q}$, then the coordinates of G have the form

$$G_{\lambda_1\cdots\lambda_p}^{\mu_1\cdots\mu_q} = F_{\lambda_{i_1}\cdots\lambda_{i_p}}^{\mu_1\cdots\mu_q} = F_{\lambda_{1\sigma}\cdots\lambda_{p\sigma}}^{\mu_1\cdots\mu_q}\,,$$

that is, they are obtained from the coordinates of F by a simple permutation of indices. Consequently, from a p times covariant tensor F, we may obtain, by means of the operation of permuting indices, $p!$ tensors, which are in general all different.

It is clear that the operation of permuting indices may also be applied to the contravariant indices. The permutation of covariant indices with contravariant indices does not have an invariant character, and does not give a tensor.

A multilinear function F is called ***symmetric*** in the variables x_λ, x_μ if

$$F(\cdots, x_\lambda, \cdots, x_\mu, \cdots) = F(\cdots, x_\mu, \cdots, x_\lambda, \cdots) . \tag{2}$$

A function F is called symmetric in a set of variables if it is symmetric in each pair of these variables. The tensor $F^{j_1\cdots j_q}_{i_1\cdots i_p}$ is called symmetric in the covariant indices $i_\alpha, \cdots, i_\gamma$ if the corresponding multilinear function is symmetric in the corresponding variables.

THEOREM 1. *A tensor $F^{j_1\cdots j_q}_{i_1\cdots i_p}$ is symmetric in the indices $i_1, \cdots, i_s$ $(s \leqq p)$ if and only if*

$$F^{j_1\cdots\quad\cdots j_q}_{i_1\cdots i_s\cdots i_p} = F^{j_1\cdots\quad\cdots j_q}_{k_1\cdots k_s\cdots i_p} , \tag{3}$$

for every permutation $k_1, \cdots, k_s$ of the indices $i_1, \cdots, i_s$.

Indeed, if the tensor F is symmetric in the indicated indices, then the corresponding multilinear function $F(x_1, \cdots, x_p, f^1, \cdots, f^q)$ is symmetric in each pair of variables x_λ, x_μ for $\lambda, \mu \leqq s$. Since every permutation may be obtained by means of permutations of pairs of indices, $\sigma F = F$ for every permutation σ of $1, \cdots, s$. In coordinate form this coincides with (3). Conversely, if (3) holds, then (2) also holds—the tensor F is symmetric.

It is clear that Theorem 1 also holds for all other sets of either covariant or contravariant indices.

Given a tensor F, by setting

$$G = \frac{1}{s!} \sum_\sigma \sigma F , \tag{4}$$

where the summation extends over all possible permutations of the numbers $1, \cdots, s$, we obtain a tensor symmetric in the first s lower indices. The process of obtaining G from F is the ***symmetrization*** of the tensor F with respect to the indicated indices. The coefficient $1/s!$ in formula (4) is used by tradition so that the symmetrization of a symmetric tensor does not change the latter.

Clearly the process of symmetrization may be carried out for any system of covariant and any system of contravariant indices. To symmetrize a tensor with respect to a mixed system, consisting of covariant and contravariant indices, is, generally speaking, impossible, since the permutations of indices, which lie at the basis of the operations of symmetrization, has an invariant character only for indices of one kind.

The operation of symmetrization is denoted symbolically by enclosing the indices involved in parentheses. For example,

$$F_{(ij)k} = \frac{1}{2}(F_{ijk} + F_{jik}) ,$$

$$F_{i(jkl)} = \frac{1}{6}(F_{ijkl} + F_{ijlk} + F_{ilkj} + F_{iklj} + F_{ikjl} + F_{iljk}) .$$

If the multilinear function $F(x_1, \cdots, x_p, f^1, \cdots, f^q)$ corresponds to the tensor $F^{j_1 \cdots j_q}_{i_1 \cdots i_p}$, then from formula (4) it is apparent that the symmetrized tensor $F^{j_1 \cdots j_q}_{(i_1 \cdots i_s) \cdots i_p}$ corresponds to the function

$$G(x_1, \cdots, x_p, f^1, \cdots, f^q) = \frac{1}{s!} \sum_{\sigma} F(x_{1\sigma}, \cdots, x_{s\sigma}, \cdots, x_p, f^1, \cdots, f^q) ,$$

where the summation, as in (4), is taken over all permutations σ of the numbers $1, \cdots, s$.

It was shown in Chapter VI that the theory of symmetric bilinear forms is equivalent to the theory of quadratic forms. An analogous connection also exists in the general case of multilinear forms. A function $F(x)$ of one variable vector x is called **homogeneous of degree p** if

$$F(x) = G(x, x, \cdots, x) ,$$

where $G(x_1, \cdots, x_p)$ is some multilinear function of the vectors $x_1, \cdots, x_p$ in the space $\mathfrak{L}$. Denoting by $H(x_1, \cdots, x_p)$ the result of symmetrizing $G(x_1, \cdots, x_p)$ in all variables, we have

$$F(x) = H(x, \cdots, x) ,$$

that is, *each homogeneous function of degree p arises from a symmetric multilinear function of p vectors by identifying the variables.* This symmetric multilinear function is called the ***polar*** of the homogeneous function.

The uniqueness of the polar function is easily perceived from its coordinate expression. In fact, if

$$H(x, \cdots, z) = \sum H_{i_1 \cdots i_p} \xi^{i_1} \cdots \zeta^{i_p} ,$$

then

$$F(x) = \sum H_{i_1 \cdots i_p} \xi^{i_1} \cdots \xi^{i_p} . \tag{5}$$

The polynomial $F_0(\xi^1, \cdots, \xi^n)$, expressing the value of the function F, may be written in a unique way in the form

$$F_0(\xi^1, \cdots, \xi^n) = \sum_{i_1 \leq \cdots \leq i_p} a_{i_1 \cdots i_p} \xi^{i_1} \cdots \xi^{i_p} .$$

Comparing this equality with (5), we see that

$$a_{i_1 \cdots i_p} = m H_{i_1 \cdots i_p} ,$$

where m is the number of distinct permutations of the numbers $i_1, \cdots, i_p$. For example, the coefficients of the fourth degree form $\sum_{i \leq j \leq k \leq l} a_{ijkl} \xi^i \xi^j \xi^k \xi^l$ and the coefficients of the corresponding polar multilinear form $\sum H_{ijkl} \xi^i \eta^j \zeta^k \chi^l$

are connected by the relations

$$H_{ijkl} = \frac{1}{24} a_{ijkl}, \quad H_{iikl} = \frac{1}{12} a_{iikl},$$

$$H_{ijjk} = \frac{1}{12} a_{ijjk}, \quad H_{iiij} = \frac{1}{4} a_{iiij}, \quad H_{iijj} = \frac{1}{6} a_{iijj},$$

and so on. Thus, the theory of symmetric tensors turns out to be equivalent to the theory of homogeneous polynomials.

117. Anti-symmetric Tensors

A multilinear function $F(x_1, \cdots, x_p, f^1, \cdots, f^q)$ is called ***anti-symmetric*** in x_1, x_2 if

$$F(x, x, x_3, \cdots, x_p, f^1, \cdots, f^q) = 0 \tag{6}$$

for arbitrary x in $\mathfrak{L}$. Replacing x by the sum $x_1 + x_2$, we obtain

$$F(x_1, x_2, \cdots, x_p, f^1, \cdots, f^q) = -F(x_2, x_1, \cdots, x_p, f^1, \cdots, f^q) . \tag{7}$$

In coordinate form, conditions (6) and (7) are equivalent to the equalities

$$F^{j_1 \cdots j_q}_{i i i_3 \cdots i_p} = 0, \quad F^{j_1 \cdots j_q}_{i_1 i_2 \cdots i_p} = -F^{j_1 \cdots j_q}_{i_2 i_1 \cdots i_p}, \tag{8}$$

where the $F^{j_1 \cdots j_q}_{i_1 \cdots i_p}$ are the coordinates of the function F.

Corresponding to this, an arbitrary tensor $F^{j_1 \cdots j_q}_{i_1 \cdots i_p}$ is called anti-symmetric in the first and second covariant indices if its coordinates satisfy condition (8) — that is, if under the transposition of these two indices all the coordinates of the tensor change their sign. Antisymmetry with respect to any other pair of covariant or of contravariant indices is similarly defined. A tensor is called antisymmetric in some *set* of indices if it is antisymmetric in each pair of indices belonging to the set.

Let σ denote an arbitrary permutation of the numbers $1, \cdots, s$. We introduce the notation (compare Section 33)

$$\varepsilon_\sigma = \begin{cases} 1 & \text{for even } \sigma , \\ -1 & \text{for odd } \sigma . \end{cases}$$

Then it is easy to see that, for an arbitrary multilinear function $F(x_1 \cdots, x_p, f^1 \cdots, f^q)$, where $s \leqq p$, the multilinear function

$$G(x_1, \cdots, x_p, f^1 \cdots, f^q) = \frac{1}{s!} \sum_\sigma \varepsilon_\sigma F(x_{1\sigma}, \cdots, x_{s\sigma}, \cdots, x_p, f^1, \cdots, f^q) \tag{9}$$

is antisymmetric in the arguments $x_1, \cdots, x_s$. The operation (9), by means of which an antisymmetric function is obtained from an arbitrary multilinear function, is called the operation of ***alternatization*** of the function F with respect to the arguments $x_1, \cdots, x_s$. Similarly, the operation of alternatization may also be applied to any other system of contravariant or of covariant arguments.

If we denote the tensor of the function F in some coordinate basis by

$F_{i_1\cdots i_p}^{j_1\cdots j_q}$, then, as a consequence of (9), we have

$$G_{i_1\cdots i_s\cdots i_p}^{j_1\cdots\cdots\cdots j_q} = \frac{1}{s!}\sum_\sigma \varepsilon_\sigma F_{i_{1\sigma}\cdots i_{s\sigma}\cdots i_p}^{j_1\cdots\cdots\cdots j_q},$$

where $G_{i_1\cdots i_p}^{j_1\cdots j_q}$ is the tensor of the alternatized function G.

The alternatization of a tensor with respect to some set of indices is denoted by enclosing these indices in square brackets. For example,

$$F_{[ij]} = \frac{1}{2}(F_{ij} - F_{ji}),$$

$$F_{i[jkl]} = \frac{1}{6}(F_{ijkl} - F_{ikjl} + F_{iklj} - F_{ilkj} + F_{iljk} - F_{ijlk})$$

It was shown in Section 112 that, relative to a fixed basis of the space $\mathfrak{L}$ an arbitrary choice of n^{p+q} numbers, $F_{i_1\cdots i_p}^{j_1\cdots j_q}$ determines a tensor of type (p, q). If the tensor F is antisymmetric in the first s indices, its coordinates are subject to relations of the type (8), and therefore cannot be given arbitrarily. To fully define a tensor F in this case it is sufficient to know only those coordinates $F_{i_1\cdots i_p}^{j_1\cdots j_q}$ for which $i_1 < i_2 < \cdots < i_s$. The number of such coordinate evidently equals $n^{p+q-s}C_s^n = \dfrac{n!}{s!\,(n-s)!}n^{p+q-s}$. In particular, a purely covariant tensor $F_{i_1}\cdots_{i_p}$, antisymmetric in all indices, is fully determined by the coordinates $F_{i_1}\cdots_{i_p}$ with $i_1 < \cdots < i_p$, which may be given arbitrarily. The number of these coordinates equals $\dfrac{1}{p!}n(n-1)\cdots(n-p+1)$.

A purely covariant tensor $F_{i_1\cdots i_p}$ which is *symmetric* in all indices is fully determined by the coordinates $F_{i_1\cdots i_p}$ for which $i_1 \leqq i_2 \leqq \cdots \leqq i_p$. It is easy to show by induction that the number of these coordinates equals $\dfrac{1}{p!}n(n+1)\cdots(n+p-1)$.

We show, finally, the following useful proposition concerning the operation of alternatization.

THEOREM 2. *Let $\boldsymbol{a}_I$ denote the operation of alternatization with respect to the set of indices I. Then for any admissible tensors F, G we have:*

$$\boldsymbol{a}_I(\alpha F + \beta G) = \alpha\cdot\boldsymbol{a}_I F + \beta\cdot\boldsymbol{a}_I G.$$

Further, if $I \subset J$, then

$$\boldsymbol{a}_J(\boldsymbol{a}_I G) = \boldsymbol{a}_J G,$$

or $\boldsymbol{a}_J\boldsymbol{a}_I = \boldsymbol{a}_J$.

The first assertion is obvious. To prove the second it is sufficient to consider the case where I is the set of the first p covariant indices and J is the set of all the covariant indices of some tensor $G_{i_1\cdots i_p\cdots i_q}$. It is required to prove the formula

$$G_{[[i_1\cdots i_p]i_{p+1}\cdots i_q]} = G_{[i_1\cdots i_q]}.$$

By definition we have

$$G_{[[i_1\cdots i_p]i_{p+1}\cdots i_q]} = \frac{1}{p!}\sum_{\sigma} \varepsilon_\sigma G_{[i_{1\sigma}\cdots i_{p\sigma}i_{p+1}\cdots i_q]}$$
$$= \frac{1}{p!}\sum_{\sigma} \varepsilon_\sigma\varepsilon_\sigma G_{[i_1\cdots i_p\, i_{p+1}\cdots i_q]} = G_{[i_1\cdots i_p\, i_{p+1}\cdots i_q]}\,,$$

where σ is an arbitrary permutation of the first p indices.

118. Polyvectors

A purely contravariant tensor $H^{i_1\cdots i_p}$, antisymmetric in all indices, is called a ***contravariant p-vector***. If $p=0$ or $p=1$, the p-vector is respectively a constant or an ordinary vector. Covariant p-vectors are similarly defined. Their properties are the same as those of contravariant p-vectors. Therefore, in what follows only contravariant p-vectors will be considered; moreover, the word *contravariant* will be omitted. Covariant p-vectors are also called p-forms.

THEOREM 3. *In an n-dimensional space, $\mathfrak{L}$, all p-vectors for $p>n$ are zero.*

If the number of indices of a coordinate $z^{i_1\cdots i_p}$ of a p-vector z is larger than n, then at least two indices have the same value, and as a consequence of the antisymmetry of z it follows by (8) that $z^{i_1\cdots i_p}=0$.

THEOREM 4. *In an n-dimensional space, each n-vector z has essentially only one coordinate $z^{12\cdots n}$, which under a change of basis in $\mathfrak{L}$ changes according to the law*

$$z'^{12\cdots n} = \Delta^{-1} z^{12\cdots n}\,,$$

where Δ is the determinant of the matrix $T=\|\tau_{ij}\|$ of the transformation of coordinates. In particular, all n-vectors are proportional to one another.

The first assertion is obvious, since, knowing $z^{12\cdots n}$, all the other coordinates of z are obtained by the formula

$$z^{\lambda_1\cdots\lambda_n} = \varepsilon_\lambda z^{12\cdots n}\,,$$

where λ is the permutation carrying $1,\cdots,n$ into $\lambda_1,\cdots,\lambda_n$, and ε_λ is the sign of λ. Computing the new coordinate $z'^{12\cdots n}$, we obtain

$$z'^{12\cdots n} = \sum \sigma_{1\lambda_1}\cdots\sigma_{n\lambda_n} z^{\lambda_1\cdots\lambda_n}$$
$$= z^{12\cdots n}\sum \varepsilon_\lambda \sigma_{1\lambda_1}\cdots\sigma_{n\lambda_n} = z^{12\cdots n}|S| = \Delta^{-1} z^{12\cdots n}\,.$$

The simplest form of a p-vector for $1\leqq p\leqq n$ is the alternatized product $[x_1x_2\cdots x_p]$ of some p ordinary vectors of the space $\mathfrak{L}$. It is easy to obtain from formula (9) the following expression for the coordinates of the alternatized product:

$$[x_1x_2\cdots x_p]^{i_1\cdots i_p} = \frac{1}{p!}\begin{vmatrix} \xi^{i_1}\xi^{i_2}\cdots\xi^{i_p} \\ \eta^{i_1}\eta^{i_2}\cdots\eta^{i_p} \\ \cdots\cdots\cdots \\ \zeta^{i_1}\zeta^{i_2}\cdots\zeta^{i_p} \end{vmatrix}.$$

In other words, the coordinates of the tensor $p![x_1x_2\cdots x_p]$ are the minors obtained from the matrix of the coordinates of the vectors $x_1, x_2 \cdots x_p$,

$$X = \begin{bmatrix} \xi^1 \xi^2 \cdots \xi^n \\ \eta^1 \eta^2 \cdots \eta^n \\ \cdots\cdots\cdots \\ \zeta^1 \zeta^2 \cdots \zeta^n \end{bmatrix}, \tag{10}$$

having p rows and n columns, by means of striking out all columns except the i_1st, i_2nd, $\cdots$, i_pth.

Since a necessary and sufficient condition for the linear dependence of the rows of the matrix X is the vanishing of all of the pth order minors, *the p-vector $[x_1 x_2 \cdots x_p]$ is zero if and only if the vectors $x_1, x_2, \cdots, x_p$ are linearly dependent.*

Let $e_1, \cdots, e_n$ be a coordinate basis of $\mathfrak{L}$. By Section 113, the following decomposition holds for any p-vector z:

$$z = \sum z^{i_1\cdots i_p} e_{i_1}\cdots e_{i_p} = p! \sum_{i_1<\cdots<i_p} z^{i_1\cdots i_p}[e_{i_1}\cdots e_{i_p}] \,. \tag{11}$$

This shows that *the alternatized products of the form $[e_{i_1}\cdots e_{i_p}]$, for $i_1 < \cdots < i_p$ constitute a basis of the linear space of all p-vectors over $\mathfrak{L}$.*

The operation of multiplying two given purely contravariant (covariant) tensors and then alternatizing the product with respect to all indices is called the ***outer product*** of the tensors, and is denoted by the symbol $\wedge$.

It is now apparent that the outer product of a p-vector and a q-vector is a $(p+q)$-vector. Further, it follows from Theorem 2 that *outer multiplication is associative*:

$$\begin{aligned} F_{[[i_1\cdots i_p} G_{j_1\cdots j_q]} H_{k_1\cdots k_r]} &= F_{[i_1\cdots i_p} G_{[j_1\cdots j_q} H_{k_1\cdots k_r]]} \\ &= F_{[i_1\cdots i_p} G_{j_1\cdots j_q} H_{k_1\cdots k_r]} \,. \end{aligned}$$

In particular, for any vectors $x_1, \cdots, x_p$ in $\mathfrak{L}$ we have

$$[x_1 x_2 \cdots x_p] = x_1 \wedge x_2 \wedge \cdots \wedge x_p \,.$$

For $p = 2$ this formula is trivial. The general case is proved by induction on p, using a simple application of Theorem 2.

From the first assertion of Theorem 2 it also follows that *the outer product is linear with respect to each factor*:

$$F \wedge (\alpha G + \beta H) = \alpha(F \wedge G) + \beta(F \wedge H) \,.$$

119. Linear Subspaces and p-vectors

There exists a close connection between p-vectors and linear subspaces of the space $\mathfrak{L}$, which we now consider in more detail.

THEOREM 5. *Let z be a nonzero p-vector of a linear space $\mathfrak{L}$. Then the vectors x for which $z \wedge x = 0$ constitute a linear subspace $\mathfrak{L}_z$ of the space $\mathfrak{L}$. If the system $e_1, \cdots, e_q$ is a basis of $\mathfrak{L}_z$, then $q \leqq p$, and there exists a $(p-q)$-vector v for which $z = v \wedge e_1 \wedge e_2 \wedge \cdots \wedge e_q$.*

By (11) we have

$$z = p! \sum_{i_1 < \cdots < i_p} z^{i_1,\ldots,i_p} e_{i_1} \wedge \cdots \wedge e_{i_p} , \tag{12}$$

and hence

$$\sum z^{i_1,\ldots,i_p} e_{i_1} \wedge \cdots \wedge e_{i_p} \wedge e_\alpha = z \wedge e_\alpha = 0 \tag{13}$$

for $\alpha = 1, \cdots, q$.

If α is contained among the numbers $i_1, \cdots, i_p$, then $e_{i_1} \wedge \cdots \wedge e_{i_p} \wedge e_\alpha = 0$. Therefore, there remain on the left side of equality (13) only those terms for which the system $i_1, \cdots, i_p$ does not contain the number α. In view of the linear independence of the $(p+1)$-vectors $e_{i_1} \wedge \cdots \wedge e_{i_p} \wedge e_\alpha$ for different sets of indices $i_1, \cdots, i_p$, it follows from (13) that $z^{i_1 \cdots i_p} = 0$ for all choices of $i_1, \cdots, i_p$ which do not contain at least one number of the segment $1, \cdots, q$. Since $z \neq 0$, then $q \leqq p$, and the decomposition (12) may be written in the form

$$z = q! \sum z^{1 \cdots q i_{q+1} \cdots i_p} e_1 \wedge \cdots \wedge e_q \wedge e_{i_{q+1}} \wedge \cdots \wedge e_{i_p} ,$$

or

$$z = e_1 \wedge \cdots \wedge e_q \wedge (q! \sum z^{1 \cdots q\, i_{q+1} \cdots i_p} e_{i_{q+1}} \wedge \cdots \wedge e_{i_p}) , \tag{14}$$

which was to be proved.

For brevity, if a p-vector z of a space $\mathfrak{L}$ can be written $z = x_1 \wedge x_2 \wedge \cdots \wedge x_p$ for suitable vectors $x_1, \cdots, x_p$ in $\mathfrak{L}$, then z is called ***fully decomposable.*** The following assertion now follows immediately from Theorem 4.

COROLLARY. *For every nonzero p-vector z of a space $\mathfrak{L}$ we have* $\dim \mathfrak{L}_z \leqq p$; *$z$ is fully decomposable if and only if* $\dim \mathfrak{L}_z = p$.

By Theorem 5 the number of basis vectors q of the subspace $\mathfrak{L}_z$ is not larger than p. If $q = p$, then formula (14) gives

$$z = \alpha e_1 \wedge e_2 \wedge \cdots \wedge e_p , \tag{15}$$

that is, z is fully decomposable. Conversely, if z is fully decomposable,

$$z = x_1 \wedge x_2 \wedge \cdots \wedge x_p ,$$

where $x_1, \cdots, x_p$ are linearly independent vectors of $\mathfrak{L}$, then $\mathfrak{L}_z$ must contain $x_1, \cdots, x_p$, and this means that the dimension of $\mathfrak{L}_z$ is not less than p. Since it is also not larger than p, $\dim \mathfrak{L}_z = p$.

THEOREM 6. *The linear subspaces of a space $\mathfrak{L}$ spanned respectively by systems of linearly independent vectors $x_1, \cdots, x_p$ and $y_1, \cdots, y_p$ are identical if and only if the p-vectors $x_1 \wedge \cdots \wedge x_p$ and $y_1 \wedge \cdots \wedge y_p$ are proportional.*

Let $z = x_1 \wedge \cdots \wedge x_p$. Then the subspace $\mathfrak{L}_z$ coincides with the subspace spanned by the vectors x_i. If $y_1, \cdots, y_p$ are contained in $\mathfrak{L}_z$, then by (15) we have

$$z = \alpha y_1 \wedge \cdots \wedge y_p .$$

Conversely, if $v = y_1 \wedge \cdots \wedge y_p = \alpha z$, then $\mathfrak{L}_z = \mathfrak{L}_v$, which completes the proof.

Theorems 5 and 6 show that to each fully decomposable nonzero p-vector $z = x_1 \wedge \cdots \wedge x_p$ corresponds the linear subspace of dimension p spanned by the vectors $x_1, \cdots, x_p$. This subspace is called the ***subspace determined by the p-vector*** z. Each subspace of dimension p determines a corresponding p-vector up to a factor of proportionality.

THEOREM 7. *Let the subspaces* $\mathfrak{L}_z$ *and* $\mathfrak{L}_v$ *be determined respectively by the fully decomposable* p*-vector* z *and* q*-vector* v. *Then* $\mathfrak{L}_z \supset \mathfrak{L}_v$ *if and only if there exists a* $(p-q)$*-vector* w *such that* $z = v \wedge w$. *Also* $\mathfrak{L}_z \cap \mathfrak{L}_v = \theta$ *if and only if* $z \wedge v \neq 0$. *In the latter case the subspace* $\mathfrak{L}_z \dotplus \mathfrak{L}_v$ *is determined by the* $(p+q)$*-vector* $z \wedge v$.

The first assertion follows immediately from Theorem 5. The second is also evident, since if $z = x_1 \wedge \cdots \wedge x_p$, $v = y_1 \wedge \cdots \wedge y_q$, and $z \wedge v \neq 0$, then the system $x_1, \cdots, x_p, y_1, \cdots, y_q$ is linearly independent and is a basis of the space $\mathfrak{L}_z \dotplus \mathfrak{L}_v$. If $z \wedge v = 0$, then this system is linearly dependent, and therefore at least one nonzero vector of the space $\mathfrak{L}_z$ is contained in $\mathfrak{L}_v$.

The coordinates of a fully decomposable p-vector z are also called the ***Plücker coordinates*** of the corresponding subspace $\mathfrak{L}_z$ in the given coordinate basis of $\mathfrak{L}$. To find the Plücker coordinates of some subspace $\mathfrak{A}$ it is sufficient to choose some basis $x_1, x_2, \cdots, x_p$ of this subspace and construct the matrix (10) from the coordinate rows of the vectors $x_1, x_2, \cdots, x_p$. The numbers

$$\alpha^{i_1 \cdots i_p} = \begin{vmatrix} \xi^{i_1} \xi^{i_2} \cdots \xi^{i_p} \\ \eta^{i_1} \eta^{i_2} \cdots \eta^{i_p} \\ \cdots\cdots\cdots \\ \zeta^{i_1} \zeta^{i_2} \cdots \zeta^{i_p} \end{vmatrix} \qquad (16)$$

are then the Plücker coordinates of the subspace $\mathfrak{A}$. By Theorem 6, under a transformation to another basis in $\mathfrak{A}$ these numbers acquire only a common factor of proportionality, and therefore the Plücker coordinates are *homogeneous* coordinates.

The vector $c = \gamma^1 e_1 + \cdots + \gamma^n e_n$ belongs to the subspace $\mathfrak{A}$ if and only if $x_1 \wedge x_2 \wedge \cdots \wedge x_p \wedge c = 0$—that is, if and only if

$$\begin{vmatrix} \gamma^{i_1} \cdots \gamma^{i_p} \gamma^{i_{p+1}} \\ \xi^{i_1} \cdots \xi^{i_p} \xi^{i_{p+1}} \\ \cdots\cdots\cdots \\ \zeta^{i_1} \cdots \zeta^{i_p} \zeta^{i_{p+1}} \end{vmatrix} = 0,$$

or

$$\alpha^{i_1 \cdots i_p} \gamma^{i_{p+1}} - \alpha^{i_1 \cdots i_{p-1} i_{p+1}} \gamma^{i_p} + \cdots + (-1)^p \alpha^{i_{p+1} i_2 \cdots i_p} \gamma^{i_1} = 0. \qquad (17)$$

In view of the condition of antisymmetry, the number of essential coordinates among the Plücker coordinates of a p-dimensional subspace equals $C_p^n = \dfrac{n!}{p!\,(n-p)!}$. However, even these coordinates $\alpha^{i_1 \cdots i_p}$ with $i_1 < \cdots < i_p$

are not independent. To obtain the necessary relations, consider the vectors

$$\alpha_{i_1\cdots i_{p-1}} = \sum_{\lambda} \alpha^{i_1\cdots i_{p-1}\lambda} e_\lambda .$$

Multiplying (16) be e_{i_p} and summing over i_p, we obtain an equality of the form

$$\alpha_{i_1\cdots i_{p-1}} = \mu_1 x_1 + \cdots + \mu_p x_p ,$$

which shows that the vectors $a_{i_1\cdots i_{p-1}}$ belong to $\mathfrak{A}$. But in this case their coordinates $\alpha^{i_1\cdots i_{p-1}\lambda}$ must satisfy relation (17), or

$$\alpha^{i_1\cdots i_p}\alpha^{j_1\cdots j_{p-1}\lambda} - \alpha^{i_1\cdots i_{p-1}\lambda}\alpha^{j_1\cdots j_{p-1}i_p} + \cdots$$
$$+ (-1)^p \alpha^{\lambda i_2\cdots i_p i_{p+1}} a^{j_1\cdots j_{p-1}i_1} = 0 . \qquad (18)$$

Now let $\alpha^{i_1\cdots i_p}$ be an arbitrary nonzero system of numbers that satisfy (18) and the condition of antisymmetry. We wish to show that there is a p-dimensional subspace $\mathfrak{A}$ having the numbers $\alpha^{i_1\cdots i_p}$ as its Plücker coordinates. For brevity we restrict ourselves to the case $p = 3$. By assumption at least one of the numbers α^{ijk} is different from zero. Suppose for definiteness that $\alpha^{123} \neq 0$. Dividing all the numbers α^{ijk} by α^{123}, we obtain a new system of numbers possessing all the properties mentioned and for which $\alpha^{123} = 1$. We will consider this system, since it differs from the given system only by a factor of proportionality, and the Plücker coordinates are in general determined only to within such a factor. Take the vectors

$$x_{\beta\gamma} = \alpha^{\beta\gamma 1} e_1 + \alpha^{\beta\gamma 2} e_2 + \cdots + \alpha^{\beta\gamma n} e_n \qquad (\beta, \gamma = 1, 2, 3) .$$

Since

$$\begin{vmatrix} \alpha^{121} & \alpha^{122} & \alpha^{123} \\ \alpha^{131} & \alpha^{132} & \alpha^{133} \\ \alpha^{231} & \alpha^{232} & \alpha^{233} \end{vmatrix} = \begin{vmatrix} 0 & 0 & 1 \\ 0 & -1 & 0 \\ 1 & 0 & 0 \end{vmatrix} \neq 0 ,$$

x_{12}, x_{13}, x_{23} are linearly independent. Denote the subspace spanned by these vectors by $\mathfrak{A}$, and let its Plücker coordinates be β^{ijk}. We have:

$$\beta^{12i} = \begin{vmatrix} \alpha^{121} & \alpha^{122} & \alpha^{12i} \\ \alpha^{131} & \alpha^{132} & \alpha^{13i} \\ \alpha^{231} & \alpha^{232} & \alpha^{23i} \end{vmatrix} = \alpha^{12i} ,$$

and similarly $\beta^{13i} = \alpha^{13i}$, $\beta^{23i} = \alpha^{23i}$, for $i = 1, \cdots, n$. Consequently, all the coordinates β^{ijk} in which two indices have the values 1, 2, 3 coincide with the corresponding numbers α^{ijk}. The numbers α^{ijk} by assumption satisfy the relations (18). The analogous relations

$$\beta^{sti}\beta^{jkl} - \beta^{stj}\beta^{ikl} + \beta^{stk}\beta^{ijl} - \beta^{sti}\beta^{ijk} = 0$$

are satisfied by the numbers β^{ijk} as the Plücker coordinates of $\mathfrak{A}$. Setting $j = 1$, $k = 2$, $l = 3$ in these relations, and using $\alpha^{123} = \beta^{123} = 1$, we obtain:

$$\alpha^{sti} = \alpha^{st1}\alpha^{i23} - \alpha^{st2}\alpha^{i13} + \alpha^{st3}\alpha^{i12} ,$$
$$\beta^{sti} = \beta^{st1}\beta^{i23} - \beta^{st2}\beta^{i13} + \beta^{st3}\beta^{i12} .$$

If s is replaced in these equalities by one of the numbers 1, 2, 3, then the right sides will be equal, by the above remarks. From this it is evident that each coordinate β^{ijk} in which one index has one of the values 1, 2, 3 is equal to the corresponding number α^{ijk}. But in this case the right sides of the equalities are equal for all s, t, i, and hence $\alpha^{ijk} = \beta^{ijk}$; this completes the proof.

120. Duality. *p*-Forms

Let a bilinear function be given on a pair of spaces $\mathfrak{L}$, $\mathfrak{L}^*: F(x,f) = (x,f) \in K$, $x \in \mathfrak{L}$, $f \in \mathfrak{L}^*$. As in Section 110, the vectors $x \in \mathfrak{L}$ and $f \in \mathfrak{L}^*$ are called ***orthogonal*** if $(x,f) = 0$. The function (x,f) is called ***nondegenerate*** if there is no nonzero vector in $\mathfrak{L}^*$ orthogonal to the whole space $\mathfrak{L}$, and no nonzero vector in $\mathfrak{L}$ orthogonal to $\mathfrak{L}^*$. In a pair of spaces $\mathfrak{L}$, $\mathfrak{L}^*$ with a nondegenerate bilinear function (x,f), a linear function $f(x) = (x,f)$ corresponds to each vector $f \in \mathfrak{L}^*$. This correspondence is an isomorphism between $\mathfrak{L}^*$ and the conjugate space of $\mathfrak{L}$; therefore $\mathfrak{L}^*$ may be identified with $\mathfrak{L}'$. Similarly, we may identify $\mathfrak{L}$ with $(\mathfrak{L}^*)'$, and consider each space of the pair $\mathfrak{L}$, $\mathfrak{L}^*$ as the conjugate of the other.

The set of all vectors in $\mathfrak{L}^*$ which are orthogonal to some linear subspace $\mathfrak{A}$ of the space $\mathfrak{L}$ constitute a linear subspace, which we denote by by $\mathfrak{A}^\perp$. If the dimension of $\mathfrak{A}$ equals p, then it is easy to see (compare Section 110) that the dimension of $\mathfrak{A}^\perp$ is $n - p$, where n is the dimension of $\mathfrak{L}$. From the obvious relation $(\mathfrak{A}^\perp)^\perp \supset \mathfrak{A}$ and the equality $\dim \mathfrak{A}^{\perp\perp} = p$, it follows that $\mathfrak{A}^{\perp\perp} = \mathfrak{A}$. Thus, the correspondence $\mathfrak{A} \to \mathfrak{A}^\perp$ is a one-to-one correspondence between the system of all subspaces of the space $\mathfrak{L}$ and the system of all subspaces of the space $\mathfrak{L}^*$. This correspondence is a *duality* in the sense that if the relation $\mathfrak{A} \subset \mathfrak{B}$ holds between subspaces of $\mathfrak{L}$, then the dual relation $\mathfrak{A}^\perp \supset \mathfrak{B}^\perp$ holds between the corresponding subspaces of $\mathfrak{L}^*$.

The duality between the spaces $\mathfrak{L}$, $\mathfrak{L}^*$ finds its expression in terms of tensors in the form of an exchange of contravariant and covariant indices: indices covariant in $\mathfrak{L}$ are contravariant in $\mathfrak{L}^*$, and conversely. In particular, contravariant p-vectors of the space $\mathfrak{L}$ are covariant p-vectors of the space $\mathfrak{L}^*$. In the present section this duality between tensors, and particularly between p-vectors, will be examined in more detail.

Denote by $\mathfrak{M}^p$ the set of all purely contravariant, and by $\mathfrak{M}_p$ the set of all purely covariant, tensors of valence p of the linear space $\mathfrak{L}$. Under the operations of addition and multiplication by a scalar, $\mathfrak{M}^p$ and $\mathfrak{M}_p$ are themselves linear spaces, of dimension n^p. For bases one may choose, for example, the sets of tensors of the form $e_{i_1} \cdots e_{i_p}$ and $e'^{i_1} \cdots e'^{i_p}$ respectively, where $e_1, \cdots, e_n$ is a basis of $\mathfrak{L}$ and $e'^1, \cdots, e'^n$ is a *biorthogonal* basis of $\mathfrak{L}^*$. Any tensor $x \in \mathfrak{M}^p$ may be contracted with any tensor $u \in \mathfrak{M}_p$ by the formula

$$(x, u) = \sum x^{i_1 \cdots i_p} u_{i_1 \cdots i_p}.$$

The result is a scalar (x, u), which does not depend on the choice of a basis of $\mathfrak{L}$. This defines a bilinear function on the pair of spaces $\mathfrak{M}^p$ and $\mathfrak{M}_p$, which we will take as an inner product.

From formula (19) follows immediately the relation

$$(xy, uv) = (x, u)(y, v) , \tag{20}$$

where x, y are purely contravariant, and u, v are purely covariant, tensors of correspondingly equal valences.

In particular, for arbitrary sequences of indices $i_1, \cdots, i_p$ and $j_1, \cdots, j_p$, we have

$$(e_{i_1} \cdots e_{i_p}, e'^{j_1} \cdots e'^{j_p}) = (e_{i_1}, e'^{j_1}) \cdots (e_{i_p}, e'^{j_p}) ,$$

and hence

$$(e_{i_1} \cdots e_{i_p}, e'^{j_1} \cdots e'^{j_p}) = \begin{cases} 0 & \text{for } (i_1, \cdots, i_p) \neq (j_1, \cdots, j_p) , \\ 1 & \text{for } (i_1, \cdots, i_p) = (j_1, \cdots, j_p) . \end{cases}$$

This means that the bases $e_{i_1} \cdots e_{i_p}$ and $e'^{j_1} \cdots e'^{j_p}$ are *biorthogonal*. But then *the bilinear function (x, u) on the pair of spaces $\mathfrak{M}^p, \mathfrak{M}_p$ is nondegenerate, and the spaces $\mathfrak{M}^p, \mathfrak{M}_p$ are duals of one another.*

The set of all p-vectors constitutes a linear subspace of $\mathfrak{M}^p$, which we denote by $\mathfrak{N}^p$. Similarly, we denote by $\mathfrak{N}_p$ the subspace of all p-vectors of $\mathfrak{M}_p$; the elements of $\mathfrak{N}_p$ are also called ***p-forms.*** By formula (20), for arbitrary vectors $x_1, \cdots, x_p$ in $\mathfrak{L}$ and arbitrary $u_1, \cdots, u_p$ in $\mathfrak{L}^*$ we have

$$(x_1 \cdots x_p, u_1 \cdots u_p) = (x_1, u_1) \cdots (x_p, u_p) .$$

Hence

$$(x_1 \wedge \cdots \wedge x_p, u_1 \cdots u_p) = \frac{1}{p!} \sum_{\sigma} \varepsilon_\sigma (x_{1\sigma}, u_1) \cdots (x_{p\sigma}, u_p) = \frac{1}{p!} \det \| (x_i, u_j) \|$$

and, consequently,

$$(x_1 \wedge \cdots \wedge x_p, u_1 \wedge \cdots \wedge u_p) = \frac{1}{p!} \det \| (x_i, u_j) \| , \tag{21}$$

where $\det \| \alpha_{ij} \|$ is the determinant of the matrix $\| \alpha_{ij} \|$.

Now let M be a set of p numbers from the segment $1, \cdots, n$. We arrange the elements of this set in increasing order: $i_1 < \cdots < i_p$, and introduce the notation

$$e_M = e_{i_1} \wedge \cdots \wedge e_{i_p}, \quad e'_M = e'^{i_1} \wedge \cdots \wedge e'^{i_p} .$$

By Section 119 the p-vectors e_M and p-forms e'_M constitute bases of the spaces $\mathfrak{N}^p$ and $\mathfrak{N}_p$. It is evident from formula (20) that *the bases e_M and e'_M are biorthogonal.* Thus, *the inner product (x, u) establishes a duality between p-vectors and p-forms, according to which each p-form may be regarded as a linear function defined on the space of all p-vectors and each p-vector as a linear function on the space of all p-forms.*

Another remarkable form of the duality between p-vectors and $(n-p)$-

forms is most naturally obtained by considering the so-called ***Grassmann algebra.*** The elements of the Grassmann algebra $\mathfrak{G}_m = \mathfrak{G}$ over a space $\mathfrak{L}$ are formal sums of the form

$$g = g_0 + g_1 + g_2 + \cdots + g_n , \tag{22}$$

where $g_0, g_1, \cdots, g_n$ are respectively a 0-vector, a 1-vector, $\cdots$, an n-vector. The element with decomposition (22) and the element

$$h = h_0 + h_1 + h_2 + \cdots + h_n$$

are regarded as equal if $h_i = g_i$ for $i = 0, 1, \cdots, n$. By definition,

$$\lambda g = \lambda g_0 + \lambda g_1 + \cdots + \lambda g_n \qquad (\lambda \in K) ,$$

$$g + h = (g_0 + h_0) + (g_1 + h_1) + \cdots + (g_n + h_n) ,$$

$$g \wedge h = \sum_{i, j} g_i \wedge h_j .$$

As a result, $\mathfrak{G}$ becomes a linear space over K, in which is defined the additional associative operation of outer multiplication $\wedge$, linear in each factor; that is, $\mathfrak{G}$ becomes an ordinary associative algebra over K. As stated before, the elements of the form $e_M = e_{i_1} \wedge \cdots \wedge e_{i_p}$, for $p = 0, \cdots, n$, where M is an arbitrary subset of the set of numbers $1, \cdots, n$ consisting of elements $i_1 < \cdots < i_p$, constitute a basis of the algebra $\mathfrak{G}$. These basis elements are multiplied according to the formula

$$e_M \wedge e_N = \begin{cases} 0 & (M \cap N \neq \phi) \\ \rho_{M,N} e_{M \cup N} & (M \cap N = \phi, \ \rho_{M,N} = (-1)^{\mu}) , \end{cases} \tag{23}$$

where $M \cup N$ denotes the union of M and N, and $\mu = 1$ or 0, depending on whether the number of pairs of the form (i, j), for $i \in M$, $j \in N$, and with $i > j$, is odd or even.

The Grassmann algebra $\mathfrak{G}^*$ over the conjugate space $\mathfrak{L}^*$ is defined similarly, except that instead of p-vectors it is necessary to consider p-forms.

Now let

$$g = g_0 + g_1 + \cdots + g_n ,$$

$$u = u_0 + u_1 + \cdots + u_n ,$$

be arbitrary elements in the algebras $\mathfrak{G}$ and $\mathfrak{G}^*$. By definition, we set

$$(g, u) = (g_0, u_0) + (g_1, u_1) + \cdots + (g_n, u_n) . \tag{24}$$

The expression (g, u) is a bilinear function defined on the pair of spaces $\mathfrak{G}$, $\mathfrak{G}^*$. Its value is called the ***inner product*** of the elements in $\mathfrak{G}$ and $\mathfrak{G}^*$. It follows from (21) and (24) that the elements of the form e_M in the algebra $\mathfrak{G}$ constitute a basis of $\mathfrak{G}$ which is biorthogonal to the basis e'_M of the algebra $\mathfrak{G}^*$. Thus, the duality between p-vectors and p-forms is extended to a duality between the spaces $\mathfrak{G}$ and $\mathfrak{G}^*$.

To each vector g in the space $\mathfrak{G}$ there corresponds a linear transformation $\mathscr{A}_g$, defined by the formula

$$x\mathscr{A}_g = x \wedge g \qquad (x \in \mathfrak{G}) .$$

Observing that the conjugate transformation $(\mathscr{A}_g)'$ operates in the space $\mathfrak{G}^*$, we introduce the new operation of ***inner multiplication*** $\lrcorner$ of elements of $\mathfrak{G}^*$ on the left by elements of $\mathfrak{G}$; the result of which is again an element of $\mathfrak{G}^*$, according to the formula

$$g \lrcorner u = u\mathscr{A}_g' .$$

By Section 110 the conjugate transformation $\mathscr{A}_g'$ is fully characterized by the identity

$$(x\mathscr{A}_g, u) = (x, u\mathscr{A}_g') .$$

Thus, the element $g \lrcorner u$ is uniquely determined by the condition

$$(x, g \lrcorner u) = (x \wedge g, u) .$$

Since

$$x\mathscr{A}_{g\wedge h} = x \wedge (g \wedge h) = (x \wedge g) \wedge h = x\mathscr{A}_g\mathscr{A}_h ,$$

then $\mathscr{A}_{g\wedge h} = \mathscr{A}_g\mathscr{A}_h$ and, consequently,

$$(g \wedge h) \lrcorner u = u\mathscr{A}_g'{}_{\wedge h} = u\mathscr{A}_h'\mathscr{A}_g' = g \lrcorner (h \lrcorner u) ,$$

or

$$(g \wedge h) \lrcorner u = g \lrcorner (h \lrcorner u) . \qquad (25)$$

Equality (25), together with the obvious bilinearity of the product $g \lrcorner u$, shows that $\mathfrak{G}^*$ becomes, with respect to the operation $\lrcorner$, a space over the algebra $\mathfrak{G}$, which is understood as a ***domain of left operators.***

We now wish to compute the value of the product $h \lrcorner u$ for basis elements $h = e_H$ and $u = e_L'$ of the spaces $\mathfrak{G}$, $\mathfrak{G}^*$. Since the bases e_M and e_L' are biorthogonal, the matrix of the transformation $\mathscr{A}_h'$ in the basis e_L' may be obtained as the transpose of the matrix of the transformation $\mathscr{A}_h$ in the basis e_M'.

By (23) we have

$$e_M\mathscr{A}_h = e_M \wedge e_H = \sum_N \alpha_{M,N} e_N ,$$

where $\alpha_{M,N} = \rho_{M,N}$ in case $M \cap H = \phi$, $N = M \cup H$, and $\alpha_{M,N} = 0$ otherwise. By transposition, we obtain

$$e_L'\mathscr{A}_h' = \sum \alpha_{M,L} e_M' ,$$

or

$$e_H \lrcorner e_L' = \begin{cases} 0 & (H \not\subset L) , \\ \rho_{L-H,\,L} e_{L-H}' & (H \subset L) . \end{cases} \qquad (26)$$

In particular, if x is a p-vector, and u is a q-form, then the inner product $x \lrcorner u$ equals zero for $p > q$, equals some $(q-p)$-form for $p < q$, and coincides, as is easily seen, with the inner product (x, u) in case $p = q$.

In Section 118 it was observed that all n-forms over a space $\mathfrak{L}$ differ only by a scalar factor. Denote one of these by $e' \neq 0$, and consider the mapping $x \to x \lrcorner e'$, which determines for each p-vector x a unique $(n-p)$-form $x^\theta = x \lrcorner e'$. This correspondence θ is the second duality that was mentioned above.

We consider the image under the mapping θ of a fully decomposable p-vector $x = x_1 \wedge \cdots \wedge x_p$. If the vectors $x_1, \cdots, x_p$ are linearly dependent, then $x = 0$, and by the linearity of the mapping θ we have $x^\theta = 0$. Therefore, suppose that $x_1, \cdots, x_p$ are linearly independent. Supplement them by vectors $x_{p+1}, \cdots, x_n$ to form a basis of $\mathfrak{L}$, and denote by $x^1, \cdots, x^n$ the biorthogonal basis of $\mathfrak{L}^*$. Since all n-forms over $\mathfrak{L}$ are proportional, for some scalar λ we have

$$e' = \lambda x^1 \wedge \cdots \wedge x^n . \tag{27}$$

Applying (26), we obtain

$$x \lrcorner e' = (-1)^{p(n-p)} \lambda x^{p+1} \wedge \cdots \wedge x^n .$$

Thus, if x is a fully decomposable p-vector, then $x \lrcorner e'$ is a fully decomposable $(n-p)$-form.

In Section 119, the subspace $\mathfrak{L}_x$ of those vectors $z \in \mathfrak{L}$ for which $x \wedge z = 0$ was placed in correspondence to the fully decomposable p-vector x. It was shown there that the subspace $\mathfrak{L}_x$ for $x = x_1 \wedge \cdots \wedge x_p$ has basis $x_1, \cdots, x_p$. Similarly, the subspace $\mathfrak{L}^*_{x'}$ of the space $\mathfrak{L}^*$ which corresponds to the $(n-p)$-form $x' = x^{p+1} \wedge \cdots \wedge x^n$ is spanned by the vectors $x^{p+1}, \cdots, x^n$. But the vectors $x^{p+1}, \cdots, x^n$, by the biorthogonality of the bases, are orthogonal to $x_1, \cdots, x_p$ and, consequently, to $\mathfrak{L}$ — that is, $\mathfrak{L}^*_{x'} \subset \mathfrak{L}^\perp_x$. Since $\dim \mathfrak{L}^*_{x'} = n - p = \dim \mathfrak{L}^\perp_x$, then

$$\mathfrak{L}^*_{x'} = \mathfrak{L}^\perp_x .$$

Thus, *if the fully decomposable p-vector x determines the subspace $\mathfrak{L}_x$, then the corresponding $(n-p)$—form $x \lrcorner e'$ is fully decomposable and determines the subspace $\mathfrak{L}^\perp_x$.*

Interchanging the roles of the spaces $\mathfrak{L}$ and $\mathfrak{L}^*$ in all of the preceding, instead of a left inner multiplication $\lrcorner$ we arrive at a right inner multiplication $\llcorner$, defined by the formula

$$(x \llcorner u, v) = (x, u \wedge v) .$$

Let e be the n-vector connected with the n-form e', defined in (27), by the relation $(e, e') = 1$, or

$$e = \frac{1}{\lambda} x_1 \wedge \cdots \wedge x_n .$$

Then from the formula

$$e_H \llcorner e'_L = \begin{cases} 0 & (L \not\subset H) , \\ \rho_{L,\, H-L} e_{H-L} & (L \subset H) , \end{cases}$$

dual to (26), we obtain the relation

$$(x_1 \wedge \cdots \wedge x_p) \llcorner x^{p+1} \wedge \cdots \wedge x^n) = (-1)^{p(n-p)} \lambda^{-1} x_1 \wedge \cdots \wedge x_p \, ,$$

which shows that the mapping $u \to e \llcorner u$ of the space $\mathfrak{N}_{n-p}$ onto $\mathfrak{N}^p$ is the inverse of the mapping $x \to x \lrcorner e'$ of the space $\mathfrak{N}^p$ onto $\mathfrak{N}_{n-p}$.

The exposition shows that for the analytical study of the p-dimensional subspaces of a linear space $\mathfrak{L}$ it is possible to define these subspaces either by means of the p-vectors belonging to them or by means of the $(n-p)$-forms belonging to the orthogonal subspaces. In particular, $(n-1)$-dimensional subspaces of a space $\mathfrak{L}$ may be given in terms of 1-forms—that is, by simple vectors in $\mathfrak{L}$.

● EXAMPLES AND PROBLEMS

1. Show that for an arbitrary p-vector x and q-vector y, $x \wedge y = (-1)^{pq} y \wedge x$.
2. Prove the formula

$$F_{[i_1 \cdots i_p]} = \frac{1}{p}(F_{i_1 [i_2 \cdots i_p]} - F_{[i_1 | i_2 | i_3 \cdots i_p]} + \cdots + (-1)^{p-1} F_{[i_1 \cdots i_{p-1}] i_p}) \, ,$$

where the vertical strokes indicate the index not participating in the operation of alternatization.

3. The Plücker coordinates of a two-dimensional subspace of a four-dimensional space are subject to only one essential relation:

$$\alpha^{12}\alpha^{34} - \alpha^{13}\alpha^{24} + \alpha^{14}\alpha^{23} = 0 \, .$$

4. A trivector w^{ijk} may be represented in the form $w = v \wedge x$, where x is a vector and v is a bivecter, if and only if

$$w^{[ijk} w^{lm][p} w^{rst]} = 0 \, .$$

5. The outer product of vectors $a = a_1 \wedge \cdots \wedge a_{n-1}$ in an n-dimensional space has only n essential coordinates:

$$\alpha^{(i)} = \alpha^{1 \ldots i-1 \; i+1 \ldots n} \qquad (i = 1, \cdots, n) \, .$$

Let $[a] = [\alpha^{(1)}, \cdots, \alpha^{(n)}]$. Show that $[a]_1 = |T|^{-1}[a]T'$, where $[a]_1$ is the row of essential coordinates of a in a new basis, and T is the matrix of the transformation of coordinates.

4. *Invariants*

121. Comitants

The tensor operations introduced in the preceding sections—addition, multiplication, contraction, and the permutation of indices—permit new tensors to be constructed from one or more given tensors. These tensors are called derived tensors or ***polynomial comitants*** of the given tensors. It immediately follows from the results of the preceding sections that the coordinates of polynomial comitants are expressed in the forms of polynomials in the coordinates of the given tensors; moreover, the coefficients of these polynomials are not dependent upon the choice of a coordinate basis of the fundamental space $\mathfrak{L}$.

A comitant which is a purely covariant tensor is called a ***covariant comitant*** of the given tensors, and a comitant which is a scalar is called an ***invariant*** of the given tensors. If the tensors are considered in a bilinear-metric space, then by Section 115 the difference between covariant and contravariant indices becomes non-essential; therefore, instead of arbitrary comitants, in these spaces it is sufficient to consider only covariant ones.

As an example we consider first a linear transformation $\mathscr{A}$ of a space $\mathfrak{L}$. The elements of the matrix $\|\alpha_i^j\|$ of this transformation define a tensor of type (1, 1), which is usually called in ***affinor***. The contractions

$$b_i^j = \sum \alpha_i^\lambda \alpha_\lambda^j, \cdots, c_i^j = \sum \alpha_i^{\lambda_1} \alpha_{\lambda_1}^{\lambda_2} \cdots \alpha_{\lambda_{n-2}}^j$$

are affinors corresponding to the transformations $\mathscr{A}^2, \cdots, \mathscr{A}^{n-1}$. These are comitants of the affinor of $\mathscr{A}$. Deriving the full contractions

$$a = \sum \alpha_\mu^\mu, \ b = \sum b_\mu^\mu = \sum \alpha_\mu^\lambda \alpha_\lambda^\mu, \cdots, c = \sum c_\mu^\mu = \sum \alpha_\mu^{\lambda_1} \alpha_{\lambda_1}^{\lambda_2} \cdots \alpha_{\lambda_{n-2}}^\mu,$$

we obtain invariants $a, b, \cdots, c$ of the tensor α_i^j. It is clear that these are the traces of the transformations $\mathscr{A}, \mathscr{A}^2, \cdots, \mathscr{A}^{n-1}$.

Suppose there are given on a linear space $\mathfrak{L}$ and its conjugate $\mathfrak{L}'$ two sequences of functions, $F_i(x_1, \cdots, x_{p_i}, u_1, \cdots, u_{q_i})$ and $G_i(x_1, \cdots, x_{p_i}, u_1, \cdots, u_{q_i})$, for $i = 1, \cdots, s$, of respectively, identical types. These two sequences are called ***congruent*** if there exists an automorphism of the space $\mathfrak{L}$—that is, a nonsingular linear transformation $\mathscr{A}$ of this space, for which

$$G_i(x_1, \cdots, x_{p_i}, u_1, \cdots, u_{q_i}) = F_i(x_1\mathscr{A}, \cdots, x_{p_i}\mathscr{A}, u_1\mathscr{A}', \cdots, u_{q_i}\mathscr{A}'),$$

where $\mathscr{A}'$ is the dual transformation of $\mathscr{A}$, $i = 1, \cdots, s$, $x_1 \cdots, x_{p_i}$ are arbitrary vectors in $\mathfrak{L}$, and $u_1, \cdots, u_{q_i}$ are arbitrary vectors in the conjugate space $\mathfrak{L}'$.

Two sequences of tensors, $F_1, \cdots, F_s$ and $G_1, \cdots, G_s$, of a space $\mathfrak{L}$ are called congruent if the sequences of corresponding multilinear functions are congruent. It immediately follows from this definition that the sequence of tensors $F_1, \cdots, F_s$ is congruent to the sequence $G_1, \cdots, G_s$ if and only if the coordinates of the tensors in the first sequence in some basis $e_1, \cdots, e_n$ turn out to be equal to the corresponding coordinates of the corresponding tensors in the second sequence in some second basis $e_1', \cdots, e_n'$ of the space $\mathfrak{L}$.

The problem of finding necessary and sufficient criteria for the congruence of individual tensors or of sequences of tensors must, theoretically speaking, be regarded as the fundamental problem of the theory of tensors. This problem was solved in Chapter IV for tensors of type (1, 1)—affinors or linear transformations. This same problem was fully solved in Chapter VI for symmetric and antisymmetric tensors of valence 2 (symmetric and antisymmetric bilinear forms) and was solved in essence for nonsymmetric tensors of valence 2. Actually, these cases exhaust the general cases for which the fundamental problem may be regarded as solved at the present time. For example, this problem has not been solved to date for pairs of affinors or for the simplest tensors of valence 3—trivectors. It must be stated here that what is being discussed is not a search for a regular algorithm which permits one to recognize the congruence of tensors by their coordinates—the existence of such an algorithm follows from the general theory—but rather the establishing of some kind of closed criteria, similar to those found for linear transformations.

In order to answer the question concerning the congruence of two sequences of tensors, the following theorem is often useful.

THEOREM 1. *If two given sequences of tensors $a, b, \cdots, c$ and $\tilde{a}, \tilde{b}, \cdots, \tilde{c}$ are congruent, then any two sequences of corresponding comitants of the given systems are also congruent. The comitant $F(a, b, \cdots, c)$ of the tensors of the first system is said to correspond to the comitant $G(\tilde{a}, \tilde{b}, \cdots, \tilde{c})$ of the second system if F and G are obtained by means of the same sequence of fundamental tensor operations acting on corresponding tensors of the systems $a, b, \cdots, c$ and $\tilde{a}, \tilde{b}, \cdots, \tilde{c}$.*

In particular, if the given sequences of tensors are congruent, then each invariant of the first sequence maintains the same value for both sequences in all bases.

The proof of the theorem follows immediately from the definitions, and may be omitted here.

It is clear that when studying the congruence of tensors it is very convenient to use invariants. However, the equality of the values, even of all the polynomial invariants of given tensors, usually does not imply the congruence of the tensors. An indication of this is given in the following two examples.

Consider two sequences of vectors $a_1, \cdots, a_s$ and $b_1, \cdots, b_s$ in a space $\mathfrak{L}$. Let $i_1 < \cdots < i_k$ be the subscripts of those vectors of the first system which are not linearly dependent on the preceding ones, and let $j_1 < \cdots < j_l$ be the corresponding subscripts for the second system. Then all the vectors of the first and second systems may be represented in the form

$$a_\lambda = \alpha_{\lambda_1} a_{i_1} + \cdots + \alpha_{\lambda_k} a_{i_k}, \quad b_\lambda = \beta_{\lambda_1} b_{j_1} + \cdots + \beta_{\lambda_l} b_{j_l}.$$

Evidently, for the congruence of the given sequences it is necessary and sufficient that $k = l$, $i_\mu = j_\mu$, $\alpha_{\lambda_\mu} = \beta_{\lambda_\mu}$ for $\mu = 1, \cdots, k$ and $\lambda = 1, \cdots, s$. At the same time, sequences of vectors in general do not have polynomial invariants, since for the construction of these invariants it is necessary to apply the operation of contraction, which in turn is possible only when covariant and contravariant indices are present.

As a second example we find all the polynomial invariants of the affinor $A = \| A_i^j \|$. By definition these invariants are fully contracted linear combinations of tensors derived from some number of copies of the affinor A, or full contractions of expressions of the form

$$\sum \alpha A_{i_1}^{j_1} A_{i_2}^{j_2} \cdots A_{i_s}^{j_s},$$

and, consequently, each invariant of A has the form

$$I = \sum \alpha \operatorname{tr} A^k \operatorname{tr} A^l \cdots \operatorname{tr} A^m .$$

In this expression for I the traces of $A^n, A^{n+1}, \cdots$ may be replaced by linear combinations of the traces of lower powers of A by means of the formula

$$\operatorname{tr} A^{n+s} = -\alpha_1 \operatorname{tr} A^{n+s-1} - \cdots - \alpha_{n-1} \operatorname{tr} A^{s+1} - \alpha_n \operatorname{tr} A^s \qquad (s = 0, 1, \cdots) ,$$

which is obtained from the equality (the Cayley-Hamilton theorem)

$$A^n = -\alpha_1 A^{n-1} - \cdots - \alpha_{n-1} A - \alpha_n E ,$$

where $\lambda^n + \alpha_1 \lambda^{n-1} + \cdots + \alpha_n$ is the characteristic polynomial of A, by multiplying both sides by A^s and taking the traces. As a result, we may represent I in the form of a polynomial in

$$I_0 = n, \quad I_1 = \operatorname{tr} A, \cdots, I_{n-1} = \operatorname{tr} A^{n-1} .$$

Thus, the values of all the polynomial invariants of an affinor are fully determined by the values of the invariants $I_1 \cdots, I_{n-1}$, which in turn are easily expressed in terms of the coefficients of the characteristic polynomial. Consequently, *if two affinors have identical characteristic polynomials, then the value of any polynomial invariant is identical for these affinors.* As we have seen in Chapter IV, this is still a long way from a sufficient condition for the congruence (similarity) of the affinors.

122. General Definition of Comitants

The notion of polynomial comitants, introduced above, is not always adequate for practical matters. Therefore, another notion of comitant is usually used, which we now present. The equivalence of the new and the old definitions in the basic cases is shown in the next section.

Let a sequence of pairs of natural numbers $(p_1, q_1), \cdots, (p_s, q_s)$ be given. Consider the set of variables $x^{j_1 \cdots j_{q_1}}_{i_1 \cdots i_{p_1}}, \cdots, z^{j_1 \cdots j_{q_s}}_{i_1 \cdots i_{p_s}}$, enumerated in the indicated way, and suppose that for all values of these variables from the base field there is a function $F^{j_1 \cdots j_q}_{i_1 \cdots i_p}$ of all of these variables. We take some sequence of tensors $a, b, \cdots, c$ of types $(p_1, q_1), \cdots, (p_s, q_s)$. By choosing an arbitrary basis $e_1, \cdots, e_n$ of $\mathfrak{L}$ and replacing in $F^{j_1 \cdots j_q}_{i_1 \cdots i_p}$ the variables $x, \cdots, z$ by the corresponding coordinates of the tensors $a, \cdots, c$, we associate with each basis a set of numbers $F^{j_1 \cdots j_q}_{i_1 \cdots i_p}(a, \cdots, c)$. If this correspondence is a tensor, then we say, that the function $F^{j_1 \cdots j_q}_{i_1 \cdots i_p}(x, \cdots, z)$ defines an *individual comitant* $F(a, \cdots, c)$ of the sequence of tensors $a, \cdots, c$. It may happen that the system $F^{j_1 \cdots j_q}_{i_1 \cdots i_p}(a, \cdots, c)$ is a tensor for *any* tensors $a, \cdots, c$ of the given type. In this case we say that the function $F^{j_1 \cdots j_q}_{i_1 \cdots i_p}(x, \cdots, z)$ defines a *comitant of general tensors* $a, \cdots, c$ of the indicated types. It is often necessary to consider the case where $F^{j_1 \cdots j_q}_{i_1 \cdots i_p}(x, \cdots, z)$ is a tensor for arbitrary tensors $a, \cdots, c$ that are symmetric or antisymmetric in some given pairs of indices. In this case $F(x, \cdots, z)$ is called a *comitant of general tensors* $a, \cdots, c$ *with given conditions of symmetry*. Finally, there is the case where $F(x, \cdots, z)$ is a tensor for arbitrary tensors $a, \cdots, c$, certain polynomial comitants of which vanish. Here $F(x, \cdots, z)$ is called a *comitant of sequences of tensors with given comitant characteristic* (see Section 126).

It is evident from these definitions that what is being discussed is a peculiar function which associates with each sequence of concrete tensors $a, \cdots, c$ of definite types some new tensor $F^{j_1 \cdots j_q}_{i_1 \cdots i_p}(a, \cdots, c)$. The word *general* in these definitions indicates the functional character of the definitions, and the words following it simply indicate the domain of definition of the comitant function.

In the algebraic theory of tensors one usually takes the function $F^{j_1 \cdots j_q}_{i_1 \cdots i_p}$ $(x, \cdots, z)$ to be a polynomial or a rational function, and one speaks respectively of an ***integral*** or ***rational*** comitant.

Just as in the particular case of polynomial comitants also in the more general case of scalars, that is, tensors without indices, the magnitudes of these scalars are called ***invariants.*** In other words, a function $I(x, \cdots, z)$ in the variables $x^{j_1 \cdots j_{q_1}}_{i_1 \cdots i_{p_1}}, \cdots, z^{j_1 \cdots j_{q_s}}_{i_1 \cdots i_{p_s}}$ is called an invariant of the sequence of tensors $a, \cdots, c$ if I has the same value, for values of the variables $x, \cdots, z$ equal to the coordinates of the tensors $a, \cdots, c$, in all coordinate bases of $\mathfrak{L}$.

Corresponding to the cases indicated above, it is also possible to speak of the invariants of individual sequences of tensors, of general sequences of tensors, and of general sequences of tensors with given comitant characteristic.

If a purely covariant tensor is given, then all its polynomial comitants will also be purely covariant. However, the situation may be different if rational comitants are considered. An important example of this is the operation of raising and lowering indices, which was examined in Section 115. There, some twice covariant tensor g_{ij} was given for which $G = \det \| g_{ij} \| \neq 0$. Denoting by G^{ij} the cofactor of the element g_{ij} in the determinant G and setting

$$g^{ij} = \frac{G^{ij}}{G},$$

we obtain by Section 115 a twice contravariant tensor, whose coordinates are rational functions of the coordinates of the initial tensor g_{ij}.

In conclusion we consider the further notion of complete systems of comitants and invariants. This notion is usually used in two senses: functionally and algebraically.

A system of comitants of a given sequence of general tensors is called ***functionally complete*** if the coordinates of *every* comitant of the sequence considered are uniquely determined by the values of the coordinates of the comitants of the given system. Analogously, a system of invariants of a sequence of general tensors is functionally complete if the values of *all* the invariants of the sequence are uniquely determined by the values of the invariants of the given system.

For algebraic completeness, more is required. A system of comitants of a given sequence of general tensors is called ***algebraically complete*** if all integral comitants of the sequence can be obtained from the given comitants by means of the fundamental tensor operations. In particular, a system of invariants is algebraically complete if every integral invariant can be obtained from the given invariants by means of the fundamental tensor operations. Since we consider invariants as tensors with one coordinate, deprived of indices, the fundamental tensor operations with invariants are multiplication and the forming of linear combinations. Therefore, a system of invariants $I_1, \cdots, I_s$ is algebraically complete if and only if every integral invariant of the class considered can be represented in the form of a polynomial in $I_1, \cdots, I_s$.

For example, the coefficients of the characteristic polynomial of an affinor constitute an algebraically complete system of invariants of the affinor, since the traces of the affinor are expressed in terms of the coefficients of the characteristic polynomial, and, as will follow from the general theorem in the next section, every integral invariant of an affinor can be expressed as a polynomial in the indicated traces.

123. Integral Comitants

The notions of polynomial comitant and integral comitant were defined in the preceding sections, and it was observed that every polynomial comitant is an integral comitant. We now wish to show that the converse assertion is also true. However, to do this it is first necessary to analyze tensors having the property that the magnitude of each of their coordinates is the same in every basis of $\mathfrak{L}$.

An example of such a tensor is the identity linear transformation, whose matrix consists of the elements $a_i^j = \delta_i^j$ and constitutes a mixed tensor with constant coordinates. By means of tensor multiplication we deduce that a tensor b—with coordinates

$$b_{i_1 \cdots i_p}^{j_1 \cdots j_p} = \delta_{i_1}^{j_{1\sigma}} \cdots \delta_{i_p}^{j_{p\sigma}}, \tag{1}$$

where σ is some permutation of the numbers $1, 2, \cdots, p$—and also any linear combination of such tensors—is a tensor with constant coordinates. The somewhat more subtle converse is also true, as stated in

THEOREM 2. *If the coordinates $F_{i_1 \cdots i_p}^{j_1 \cdots j_q}$ of a tensor F have constant values not depending on the choice of a coordinate basis of $\mathfrak{L}$, then $p = q$ and*

$$F_{i_1 \cdots i_p}^{j_1 \cdots j_p} = \sum_{\sigma} \alpha_\sigma \delta_{i_1}^{j_{1\sigma}} \cdots \delta_{i_p}^{j_{p\sigma}},$$

where δ_i^j is the Kronecker symbol, the α_σ are scalars, and the σ are permutations of the numbers $1, \cdots, p$; that is a linear combination of tensors of the form (1).

To prove this, we consider instead of the tensor F the corresponding multilinear function $F(x_1, \cdots, x_p, u_1, \cdots, u_q)$, whose coordinates relative to the basis $e_1, \cdots, e_n$ are the numbers

$$F^{j_1 \cdots j_q}_{i_1 \cdots i_p} = F(e_{i_1}, \cdots, e_{i_p}, e^{j_1}, \cdots, e^{j_q}) .$$

For any $\lambda \neq 0$ the vectors $\bar{e}_1 = \lambda e_1, \bar{e}_2 = e_2, \cdots, \bar{e}_n = e_n$ are again a basis of $\mathfrak{L}$, and the vectors $\bar{e}^1 = \frac{1}{\lambda} e^1, \bar{e}^2 = e^2, \cdots, \bar{e}^n = e^n$ are the corresponding biorthogonal basis of $\mathfrak{L}'$. The equality

$$F^{j_1 \cdots j_q}_{i_1 \cdots i_p} = F(\bar{e}_{i_1}, \cdots, \bar{e}_{i_p}, \bar{e}^{j_1}, \cdots, \bar{e}^{j_q}) = \lambda^{\alpha_1 - \beta_1} F^{j_1 \cdots j_q}_{i_1 \cdots i_p} \tag{2}$$

follows from the constancy of the coordinates of the tensor F, where α_1 is the number of lower indices equal to 1, and β_1 is the number of upper indices equal to 1. If $F^{j_1 \cdots j_q}_{i_1 \cdots i_p} \neq 0$, then it follows from (2) that $\alpha_1 = \beta_1$. Similarly, the number of lower indices and the number of upper indices of the coordinate $F^{j_1 \cdots j_q}_{i_1 \cdots i_p}$ that have an arbitrary fixed value are equal. It follows in particular that $p = q$.

Thus, the equality $p = q$ is demonstrated. For brevity, we now restrict ourselves to the case $p \leqq n$. Denoting by σ some permutation of the numbers $1, \cdots, p$, we set

$$\alpha_\sigma = F(e_1, \cdots, e_p, e^{1\sigma}, \cdots, e^{p\sigma}) , \tag{3}$$

$$G^{j_1 \cdots j_p}_{i_1 \cdots i_p} = \sum_\sigma \alpha_\sigma \delta^{j_{1\sigma}}_{i_1} \cdots \delta^{j_{p\sigma}}_{i_p} , \tag{4}$$

and show that the tensor G with coordinates $G^{j_1 \cdots j_p}_{i_1 \cdots i_p}$ coincides with the tensor F.

It follows from the constancy of the coordinates of F that

$$F(x_1, \cdots, x_p, x^{1\sigma}, \cdots, x^{p\sigma}) = F(y_1, \cdots, y_p, y^{1\sigma}, \cdots, y^{p\sigma}) ,$$

where $x_1, \cdots, x_p$ and $y_1, \cdots, y_p$ are arbitrary systems of linearly independent vectors in $\mathfrak{L}$ and $x^1, \cdots, x^p$ and $y^1, \cdots, y^p$ are the corresponding biorthogonal systems in $\mathfrak{L}'$. Therefore, if the sequences $i_1, \cdots, i_p$ and $j_1, \cdots, j_p$ consist of the same *distinct* numbers of the segment $1, \cdots, n$, then

$$F(e_{i_1}, \cdots, e_{i_p}, e^{j_1}, \cdots, e^{j_p}) = \alpha_\sigma ,$$

where the permutation σ is defined by the conditions

$$j_{1\sigma} = i_1, \cdots, j_{p\sigma} = i_p .$$

Under the same conditions, (4) implies the equality

$$G(e_{i_1}, \cdots, e_{i_p}, e^{j_1}, \cdots, e^{j_p}) = \alpha_\sigma ,$$

and hence

$$F(e_{i_1}, \cdots, e_{i_p}, e^{j_1}, \cdots, e^{j_p}) = G(e_{i_1}, \cdots, e_{i_p}, e^{j_1}, \cdots, e^{j_p}) . \tag{5}$$

This equality has been proved under the supposition that $i_1, \cdots, i_p$ are distinct, and that the sequence $j_1, \cdots, j_p$ consists of the same numbers. But if the sequence $j_1, \cdots, j_p$ does not consist of the same numbers as the sequence $i_1, \cdots, i_p$, then both sides of equality (5) equal zero, in agreement with (2). Therefore (5) holds for *distinct* $i_1, \cdots, i_p$ and completely arbitrary $j_1, \cdots, j_p$. But then

$$F(e_{i_1}, \cdots, e_{i_p}, u_1, \cdots, u_p) = G(e_{i_1}, \cdots, e_{i_p}, u_1, \cdots, u_p)$$

for distinct $i_1, \cdots, i_p$ and arbitrary vectors $u_1, \cdots, u_p$ in $\mathfrak{L}'$. Since it is possible to take any linearly independent system of vectors $x_1, \cdots, x_p$ for $e_{i_1}, \cdots, e_{i_p}$, then

$$F(x_1, \cdots. x_p, u_1, \cdots, u_p) = G(x_1, \cdots, x_p, u_1 \cdots, u_p) \tag{6}$$

for linearly independent $x_1, \cdots, x_p$ and arbitrary $u_1, \cdots, u_p$ in $\mathfrak{L}'$. The condition of the linear independence of the vectors $x_1, \cdots, x_p$ in equality (6) remains to be removed. To do this, we take arbitrary vectors $x_1, \cdots, x_p$ and suppose that $x_1, \cdots, x_m$ are linearly independent and $x_{m+1}, \cdots, x_p$ are linear combinations of the preceding ones. We supplement the system $x_1, \cdots, x_m$ with vectors $y_{m+1}, \cdots, y_n$ to form a basis of $\mathfrak{L}$, and represent x_λ in the form $x_{\lambda_1} + x_{\lambda_2}$, where

$$x_{\lambda_1} = x_\lambda - y_\lambda, \quad x_{\lambda_2} = y_\lambda \qquad (\lambda = m+1, \cdots, p) .$$

By the linear independence of each sequence of vectors

$$x_1, \cdots, x_m, x_{(m+1)\alpha}, \cdots, x_{p\gamma} \qquad (\alpha, \cdots, \gamma = 1, 2)$$

and the multilinearity of the functions F and G we have

$$\begin{aligned} F(x_1, \cdots, x_p, u_1 \cdots, u_p) &= \sum F(x_1, \cdots, x_m, x_{(m+1)\alpha}, \cdots, x_{p\gamma}, u_1, \cdots, u_p) \\ &= \sum G(x_1, \cdots, x_m, x_{(m+1)\alpha}, \cdots, x_{p\gamma}, u_1, \cdots, u_p) \\ &= G(x_1, \cdots, x_p, u_1, \cdots, u_p) , \end{aligned}$$

or $F = G$.

THEOREM 3. *Every integral rational invariant I of a sequence of general tensors $x, y, \cdots, z$ may be obtained as a linear combination of full contractions of tensor products, each factor of which is one of the given tensors.*

By assumption, the invariant I is a polynomial in the coordinates of the tensors $x, \cdots, z$, satisfying the relation

$$I(x, \cdots, z) = I(\bar{x}, \cdots, \bar{z}) , \tag{7}$$

where the overbars denote the coordinates in a new coordinate basis. Since I is an invariant of general tensors, relation (7) must still hold when the tensor x is replaced by the tensor λx:

$$I(\lambda x, \cdots, z) = I(\lambda \bar{x}, \cdots, \bar{z}) . \tag{8}$$

Collecting the terms of the polynomial I of the 0th, 1st, tth degree in the coordinates of the tensor x, we obtain the decomposition

$$I = I_0 + I_1 + \cdots + I_t .$$

From (8) we have

$$I(\lambda x, \cdots, z) = I_0(x, \cdots, z) + \lambda I_1(x, \cdots, z) + \cdots + \lambda^t I_t(x, \cdots, z)$$
$$= I_0(\bar{x}, \cdots, \bar{z}) + \lambda I_1(\bar{x}, \cdots, \bar{z}) + \cdots + \lambda^t I_t(\bar{x}, \cdots, \bar{z}) ,$$

or

$$I_k(x, \cdots, z) = I_k(\bar{x}, \cdots, \bar{z}) \qquad (k = 0, 1, \cdots, t) .$$

Thus the invariant I turns out to be decomposable into the sum of invariants I_k, which are *homogeneous* in the coordinates of the first tensor x. The invariants I_k may in turn be decomposed into the sum of invariants homogeneous in the coordinates of the tensor y, and so on. Continuing this process, we decompose the original invariant I into the sum of invariants which are homogeneous in the coordinates of each tensor $x, y, \cdots, z$. Consequently, it is only necessary to prove the theorem for such invariants.

Suppose that I is an invariant polynomial in the coordinates of the tensors $x, y, \cdots, z$, each term of which has degree t_1 in the coordinates of x, degree t_2 in the coordinates of y, and so on. We construct the tensor product

$$F = x \times \cdots \times x \times y \cdots \times y \times \cdots \times \cdots \times z \times \cdots \times z$$

where the factor x occurs t_1 times, the factor y occurs t_2 times, and so on. Each coordinates $F^{j_1 \cdots j_q}_{i_1 \cdots i_p}$ of the tensor F is a monomial in the coordinates of the tensors $x, y, \cdots, z$. We now introduce the coefficients $A^{i_1 \cdots i_p}_{j_1 \cdots j_q}$ as follows: if the monomial $F^{j_1 \cdots j_q}_{i_1 \cdots i_p}$ is not a part of the invariant, we set $A^{i_1 \cdots i_p}_{j_1 \cdots j_q} = 0$. If the indicated monomial does occur in the invariant I with coefficient $C^{i_1 \cdots i_p}_{j_1 \cdots j_q}$, then we set

$$A^{i_1 \cdots i_p}_{j_1 \cdots j_q} = \frac{1}{N} C^{i_1 \cdots i_p}_{j_1 \cdots j_q} ,$$

where N is the number of coordinates of the tensor F equal to the coordinate $F^{j_1 \cdots j_q}_{i_1 \cdots i_p}$. We now have

$$I = \sum A^{i_1 \cdots i_p}_{j_1 \cdots j_q} F^{j_1 \cdots j_q}_{i_1 \cdots i_p} .$$

We show that the coefficients $A^{i_1 \cdots i_p}_{j_1 \cdots j_q}$ are the coordinates of a tensor with constant coordinates. Take a coordinate basis of $\mathfrak{L}$ and denote by A the tensor whose coordinates coincide with the numbers $A^{i_1 \cdots i_p}_{j_1 \cdots j_q}$ in this basis. Denoting by an overbar the transition to a new basis, we have

$$\sum \bar{A}^{i_1 \cdots i_p}_{j_1 \cdots j_q} \bar{F}^{j_1 \cdots j_q}_{i_1 \cdots i_p} = \sum A^{i_1 \cdots i_p}_{j_1 \cdots j_q} F^{j_1 \cdots j_q}_{i_1 \cdots i_p} . \tag{9}$$

Besides this, since I is invariant,

$$\sum A^{i_1 \cdots i_p}_{j_1 \cdots j_q} \bar{F}^{j_1 \cdots j_q}_{i_1 \cdots i_p} = \sum A^{i_1 \cdots i_p}_{j_1 \cdots j_q} F^{j_1 \cdots j_q}_{i_1 \cdots i_p} , \tag{10}$$

By interchanging the roles of the original and the new basis, and comparing equalities (9) and (10), we obtain

$$\sum \bar{A}^{i_1 \cdots i_p}_{j_1 \cdots j_q} F^{j_1 \cdots j_q}_{i_1 \cdots i_p} = \sum A^{i_1 \cdots i_p}_{j_1 \cdots j_q} F^{j_1 \cdots j_q}_{i_1 \cdots i_p} . \tag{11}$$

On the right and left sides of the equality sign stand polynomials in independent variables — the coordinates of the tensors $x, y, \cdots, z$. Therefore, after collecting similar terms the coefficients must be equal. However, the coefficients $A^{i_1\cdots i_p}_{j_1\cdots j_q}$ were chosen beforehand in such a way that similar terms have identical coefficients; therefore it follows from (11) that

$$\bar{A}^{i_1\cdots i_p}_{j_1\cdots j_q} = A^{i_1\cdots i_p}_{j_1\cdots j_q},$$

that is, the tensor A has unchanging coordinates. By Theorem 2 we have $p = q$ and

$$A^{i_1\cdots i_p}_{j_1\cdots j_q} = \sum \alpha_\sigma \delta^{i_{1\sigma}}_{j_1} \cdots \delta^{i_{p\sigma}}_{j_p},$$

hence

$$I = \sum \sum \alpha_\sigma \delta^{i_{1\sigma}}_{j_1} \cdots \delta^{i_{p\sigma}}_{j_p} F^{j_1\cdots j_p}_{i_1\cdots i_p},$$

and this means that the invariant I is a linear combination, with coefficients α_σ, of suitable full contractions of the tensor F, which was to be proved.

It is now easy to prove also the fundamental.

THEOREM 4. *Every integral rational comitant of a system of general tensors is a linear combination of products of some number of copies of the tensor δ^j_i with contractions of suitable products of the given tensors; that is, it is a polynomial comitant in the given tensors and the tensor δ^j_i in the sense of Section 121.*

Let $F^{j_1\cdots j_q}_{i_1\cdots i_p}$ be the coordinates of an integral comitant of the sequence of general tensors $x, y, \cdots, z$. We adjoin to the sequence p *general* contravariant vectors $\overset{1}{a}, \cdots, \overset{p}{a}$ and q *general* covariant vectors $\overset{1}{c}, \cdots, \overset{q}{c}$, and construct the expression

$$I = \sum F^{j_1\cdots j_q}_{i_1\cdots i_p} \overset{1}{a}{}^{i_1} \cdots \overset{p}{a}{}^{i_p} \overset{1}{c}_{j_1} \cdots \overset{q}{c}_{j_q}.$$

Since I is an integral rational invariant of the tensors $x, y, \cdots, z$, then by Theorem 3 it can be represented as a linear combination of contractions of the form

$$J = \sum G^{j_1\cdots j_{q-s}}_{i_1\cdots i_{p-s}} \overset{m_1}{a}{}^{i_1} \cdots \overset{m_{p-s}}{a}{}^{i_{p-s}} \overset{n_1}{c}_{j_1} \overset{m_{p-s+1}}{a}{}^{k_1} \overset{n_{p-s+1}}{c}_{k_1} \cdots \overset{m_p}{a}{}^{k_s} \overset{n_q}{c}_{k_s}$$

or

$$J = \sum G^{j_{1\sigma}\cdots j_{(q-s)\sigma}}_{i_{1\rho}\cdots i_{(p-s)\rho}} \delta^{j_{(q-s+1)\sigma}}_{i_{(p-s+1)\rho}} \cdots \delta^{j_{q\sigma}}_{i_{p\rho}} \overset{1}{a}{}^{i_1} \cdots \overset{p}{a}{}^{i_p} \overset{1}{c}{}^{j_1} \cdots \overset{q}{c}{}^{j_q},$$

where ρ, σ are permutations of the numbers of the segments $1, \cdots, p$ and $1, \cdots, q$ defined by the conditions

$$\lambda\rho = m_\lambda, \quad \mu\sigma = n_\mu, \qquad (\lambda = 1, \cdots, p, \ \mu = 1, \cdots, q),$$

and G is some linear combination of suitable contractions of the product $x\cdots xy\cdots y\cdots\cdots z\cdots z$. From the equality $I = \sum J$, which is an identity in the variables $\overset{1}{a}{}^i, \cdots, \overset{p}{a}{}^i, \overset{1}{c}_j, \cdots, \overset{q}{c}_j$, we obtain, by comparing corresponding coefficients,

$$F^{j_1\cdots j_q}_{i_1\cdots i_p} = \sum_{\sigma} G^{j_{1\sigma}\cdots j_{(q-s)\sigma}}_{i_{1\rho}\cdots i_{(p-s)\rho}} \delta^{j_{(q-s+1)\sigma}}_{i_{(p-s+1)\rho}} \cdots \delta^{j_{q\sigma}}_{i_{p\rho}} .$$

This completes the proof.

Theorems 3 and 4 are concerned with invariants and comitants of general tensors. However, these theorems remain true also for general tensor with given conditions of symmetry. The necessary changes in the proofs are insignificant are transparent.

124. Relative Tensors

Having established in Section 123 the forms of integral rational comitants, we now wish to solve the analogous problem for *fractional* rational comitants. However, to do this it is necessary to give a slightly more general notion of tensor.

In distinction to the tensors considered in the preceding section, which we will now call ***absolute*** or ***ordinary*** tensors, a ***relative*** or ***weighted*** tensor of weight g and valence $p+q$, p times covariant and q times contravariant, is a geometrical object characterized in each coordinate basis $e_1, \cdots, e_n$ of the space $\mathfrak{L}$ by a system of numbers $F^{j_1\cdots j_q}_{i_1\cdots i_p}$, enumerated in the indicated way, with the condition that in a new coordinate basis $e'_1, \cdots, e'_n$, connected to the old by the formulas

$$e'_i = \sum \tau^j_i e_j , \quad e_i = \sum \sigma^j_i e'_j \qquad (||\tau^j_i|| \cdot ||\sigma^j_i|| = E) ,$$

the object F is characterized by the numbers

$$F'^{j_1\cdots j_q}_{i\ \cdots i_p} = \Delta^g \sum \tau^{\lambda_1}_{i_1} \cdots \tau^{\lambda_p}_{i_p} \sigma^{j_1}_{\mu_1} \cdots \sigma^{j_q}_{\mu_q} F^{\mu_1\cdots\mu_q}_{\lambda_1\cdots\lambda_p} , \tag{12}$$

where Δ is the determinant of the matrix of the transformation of coordinates $T = ||\tau^j_i||$.

Analogously, the object F, characterized in each basis by a single number F which changes under a transformation to a new basis according to the law

$$F' = \Delta^g F ,$$

is called a ***relative scalar of weight*** g.

Relative scalars of weight g will be considered formally as tensors of weight g and valence 0.

Comparing these new definitions with the definition of the ordinary tensor given in Section 112, we see that ordinary tensors coincide with relative tensors of weight 0.

It is easy to verify, using formula (12), that by adding the corresponding coordinates of two relative tensors of the same weight and identical type, we obtain the coordinates of a new relative tensor of the same weight and type, and by multiplying the coordinates of tensors $G^{j_1\cdots j_q}_{i_1\cdots i_p}$ and $H^{j_1\cdots j_s}_{i_1\cdots i_r}$ of weights g and h according to the formula

$$F^{j_1\cdots j_q j_{q+1}\cdots j_{q+s}}_{i_1\cdots i_p i_{p+1}\cdots i_{p+r}} = G^{j_1\cdots j_q}_{i_1\cdots i_p} H^{j_{q+1}\cdots j_{q+s}}_{i_{p+1}\cdots i_{p+r}} ,$$

we obtain a relative tensor of weight $g + h$.

Similarly, given a relative tensor $G^{j_1\cdots j_q}_{i_1\cdots i_p}$ of weight g it is easy to see that the objects characterized by the numbers

$$F^{j_1\cdots j_{q-1}}_{i_1\cdots i_{p-1}} = \sum_{\lambda} G^{j_1\cdots\lambda\cdots j_{q-1}}_{i_1\cdots\lambda\cdots i_{p-1}},$$

$$H^{j_1\cdots j_q}_{i_1\cdots i_p} = G^{j_{1\sigma}\cdots j_{q\sigma}}_{i_{1\rho}\cdots i_{p\rho}},$$

where ρ, σ are permutations of the numbers $1, \cdots, p$ and $1, \cdots, q$, are again relative tensors of weight g. Thus, all the operations defined above for absolute tensors may be applied also to relative tensors.

The situation is made completely obvious by attention to the following immediate connection between weighted and ordinary tensors.

Suppose that

$$F(x_1, \cdots, x_p, u_1, \cdots, u_q, v_1, \cdots, v_n, \cdots, w_1, \cdots, w_n)$$

is a multilinear function of type $(p, q+gn)$, antisymmetric in each of the sets of variable vectors $v_1, \cdots, v_n, \cdots, w_1, \cdots, w_n$, or in each of the last g systems.

The ***relative coordinates*** of the function F in the basis $e_1, \cdots, e_n$ are the ordinary coordinates in this basis of the multilinear function

$$F(x_1, \cdots, x_p, u_1, \cdots, u_q, e^1, \cdots, e^n, \cdots, e^1, \cdots, e^n)$$
$$= F_0(x_1, \cdots, x_p, u_1, \cdots, u_q):$$
$$F^{j_1\cdots j_q}_{(0)i_1\cdots i_p} = F(e_{i_1}, \cdots, e_{i_p}, e^{j_1}, \cdots, e^{j_q}, e^1, \cdots, e^n, \cdots, e^1, \cdots, e^n).$$

Knowing the relative coordinates, it is possible to recover the ordinary coordinates by the formula

$$F^{j_1\cdots j_q k_1\cdots k_n\cdots l_1\cdots l_n}_{i_1\cdots i_p} = F^{j_1\cdots j_q}_{(0)i_1\cdots i_p}\varepsilon_\rho\cdots\varepsilon_\sigma \qquad (\lambda\rho = k_\lambda, \cdots, \lambda\sigma = l_\lambda). \qquad (13)$$

Changing to a new basis $e'_1, \cdots, e'_n$ and denoting the new coordinates with an overbar, we have

$$\bar{F}^{j_1\cdots j_q}_{(0)i_1\cdots i_p} = \Delta^{-g} F^{j_1\cdots j_q}_{(0)i_1\cdots i_p},$$

that is, the relative coordinates of the function F are the coordinates of a weighted tensor of weight $-g$. If we had taken contravariant vectors $v, \cdots, w$ instead of covariant, then the relative coordinates of F would be the coordinates of a weighted tensor with positive weight $+g$.

We see that each ordinary tensor F of valence $p+q+gn$, antisymmetric in the final g segments of the covariant arguments, gives rise to a weighted tensor F_0 of weight $-g$. Conversely, given a weighted tensor F_0 whose weight is a negative integer $-g$, then, defining in any coordinate basis the tensor F by the coordinates computed from formula (13), we obtain an ordinary tensor F corresponding to F_0.

The notions of invariants and comitants of a given sequence of weighted tensors are defined just as they were for ordinary tensors; it is sufficient to understand weighted tensor for tensor in the corresponding definitions of Section 121.

In the theory of weighted tensors an important role is played by two tensors with constant coordinates: the identity covariant n-vector and the identity contravariant n-vector. These objects are defined in each basis by the same set of numbers

$$e_{i_1\cdots i_n} = e^{i_1\cdots i_n} = \varepsilon_\sigma \qquad (1\sigma = i_1, \cdots, n\sigma = i_n) ,$$

where $\varepsilon_\sigma = 0$ if the indices $i_1, \cdots, i_n$ are not all distinct, and $\varepsilon_\sigma = +1$ for even, and -1 for odd, permutations (compare Section 33). An immediate computation reveals that $e_{i_1\cdots i_n}$ is a covariant antisymmetric tensor of weight -1 and that $e^{i_1\cdots i_n}$ is a contravariant antisymmetric tensor of weight $+1$.

Let $F^{j_1\cdots j_q}_{i_1\cdots i_p}$ be the coordinates of some relative tensor with $p \geqq n$ and $q \geqq n$. The following important formulas follow immediately from the definition of the identity of n-vectors:

$$\sum F^{j_1\cdots j_q}_{i_1\cdots i_p} e^{i_1\cdots i_n} = n!\, F^{j_1\cdots j_q}_{[i_1\cdots i_n] i_{n+1}\cdots i_p} ,$$
$$\sum F^{j_1\cdots j_q}_{i_1\cdots i_p} e_{j_1\cdots j_n} = n!\, F^{[j_1\cdots j_n] j_{n+1}\cdots j_q}_{i_1\cdots i_p} .$$

It follows in particular that

$$\sum e^{i_1\cdots i_n} e_{i_1\cdots i_n} = n! .$$

The operation of multiplying by an identity n-vector and following it with a full contraction in the indices of the n-vector is sometimes called the operation of ***full covariant*** (respectively ***contravariant***) ***alternatization.***

Unlike the ordinary operation of alternatization, under which the weight and type of the tensor are not changed, under the operation of full covariant or contravariant alternatization the weight is changed by $+1$ or -1 and the number of covariant or contravariant indices is diminished by n.

The identity n-vectors are examples of weighted tensors with constant coordinates. With the help of these n-vectors it is easy to find in general all weighted tensors with constant coordinates and integral weight. Let $C^{j_1\cdots j_q}_{i_1\cdots i_p}$ be the coordinates of a weighted tensor with constant coordinates and integral weight $g > 0$. Then the tensor with coordinates

$$D^{j_1\cdots j_q}_{i_1\cdots i_p i_{p+1}\cdots i_{p+n}\cdots i_{p+gn-n+1}\cdots i_{p+gn}} = C^{j_1\cdots j_q}_{i_1\cdots i_p} e_{i_{p+1}}\cdots e_{i_{p+n}}\cdots e_{i_{p+gn-n+1}}\cdots e_{i_{p+gn}}$$

is an *absolute tensor* with fixed coordinates, therefore by Theorem 3 there are constants α_σ such that

$$D^{j_1\cdots j_q}_{i_1\cdots i_p i_{p+1}\cdots i_{p+gn}} = \sum_\sigma \alpha_\sigma \delta^{j_1\sigma}_{i_1}\cdots \delta^{j_q\sigma}_{i_q} \qquad (p + gn = q) .$$

Multiplying both sides by $e^{i_{p+1}\cdots i_{p+n}}\cdots e^{i_{p+gn-n+1}\cdots i_{p+gn}}$ and performing a full contraction on the indices of the factors we obtain

$$(n!)^g C^{j_1\cdots j_q}_{i_1\cdots i_p} = \sum_\sigma \alpha_\sigma \delta^{j_1\sigma}_{i_1}\cdots \delta^{j_p\sigma}_{i_p} e^{j(p+1)\sigma}\cdots e^{j(p+gn-n+1)\sigma\cdots j(p+gn)\sigma} \tag{14}$$

Replacing here the contravariant identity polyvector $e^{j_1\cdots j_n}$ by the corresponding covariant polyvector, we obtain a general expression for relative tensors with constant coordinates and negative integral weight $-g$.

It follows in particular from formula (14) that nonzero tensors with constant coordinates of weight $g > 0$ have gn more contravariant indices then covariant, and those with weight $-g$, for $g > 0$, conversely, have gn more covariant indices than contravariant.

It follows immediately from formula (14) and Theorem 4 that *every integral comitant* $F^{j_1 \cdots j_q}_{i_1 \cdots i_p}$ *of weight* g or $-g$, for $g > 0$, *of a sequence of general absolute tensors is a linear combination of tensors obtained by means of g full alternatizations of some number of contracted products, with suitable permutations of the indices, of the given tensors and tensors* δ^j_i.

To prove this, it is again sufficient to consider the product (in the case $g > 0$)

$$F^{j_1 \cdots j_q}_{i_1 \cdots i_p} e_{i_{p+1} \cdots i_{p+n}} \cdots e_{i_{p+gn-n+1} \cdots i_{p+gn}}$$

and apply to it Theorem 4 on absolute comitants.

Finally, the proof of Theorem 4 also carries over immediately to the general case of integral comitants of weight g of sequences of general weighted tensors with given conditions of symmetry. The result is the following proposition, which is sometimes called the fundamental theorem of tensor algebra.

Every integral rational weighted comitant of a sequence of general weighted tensors with given conditions of symmetry is a linear combination of tensors obtained by full alternatizations of contracted products of the given tensors and tensors with suitable permutations of the indices.

As an example we consider a twice covariant absolute tensor with coordinates g_{ij}. The easily verified formula

$$\det \| g_{ij} \| = \frac{1}{n!} \sum g_{i_1 j_1} g_{i_2 j_2} \cdots g_{i_n j_n} e^{i_1 \cdots i_n} e^{j_1 \cdots j_n}$$

shows that the determinant of the tensor g_{ij} is an integral invariant of weight 2.

Denoting by G^{ij} the cofactor corresponding to the element g_{ij} in the determinant of the matrix $\| g_{ij} \|$, we have

$$G^{ij} = \frac{\partial}{\partial g_{ij}} \det \| g_{ij} \| = \frac{1}{(n-1)!} \sum g_{i_2 j_2} \cdots g_{i_n j_n} e^{i i_2 \cdots i_n} e^{j j_2 \cdots j_n},$$

that is, the numbers G^{ij} are the coordinates of a twice contravariant tensor of weight 2.

125. Rational Comitants

As remarked above, the question of the structure of fractional rational comitants is easily solved with the help of integral rational weighted comitants. The point of departure is the following obvious observation: *if* $F^{j_1 \cdots j_q}_{i_1 \cdots i_p}$ *are the coordinates of an integral rational comitant of weight g of a sequence of weighted tensors and I is some integral invariant of weight h of the same sequence of tensors, then the numbers*

$$G^{j_1 \cdots j_q}_{i_1 \cdots i_p} = \frac{F^{j_1 \cdots j_q}_{i_1 \cdots i_p}}{I}$$

determine a rational comitant of weight $g - h$ of the given sequence of tensors.

Our goal is to prove the converse assertion, for which it is convenient first to prove the following

LEMMA. *Let $f(A)$ be some nonzero polynomial in the elements of the square matrix A. If the identity $f(AB) = f(A)f(B)$ holds for all A, B, then $f(A) = |A|^r$, where r is a suitable nonnegative integer not depending on A.*

From the identity $f(E)f(A) = f(A)$ for the identity matrix E it follows that $f(E) = 1$. On the other hand, for an arbitrary scalar λ let

$$f(\lambda E) = \alpha_0\lambda^m + \alpha_1\lambda^{m-1} + \cdots + \alpha_m .$$

Then the relation $f(\lambda E)f(\lambda^{-1}E) = 1$ may be written in the form

$$(\alpha_0\lambda^m + \alpha_1\lambda^{m-1} + \cdots + \alpha_m)(\alpha_0 + \alpha_1\lambda + \cdots + \alpha_m\lambda^m) = \lambda^m ,$$

which together with the equality $f(E) = 1$ gives $f(\lambda E) = \lambda^m$. In particular, we have $f(\lambda A) = f(\lambda E)f(A) = \lambda^m f(A)$. Now let A be a nonsingular matrix with arbitrary elements, $A^{-1} = |A| A^*$, where $|A|$ is the determinant of A and A^* is the matrix constructed from the adjuncts of the elements of the determinant of A arranged in the proper order. From $f(A)f(A^{-1}) = 1$ we have

$$f(A)f(A^*) = |A|^m . \tag{15}$$

By a familiar theorem of the theory of determinants, the determinant of the matrix A is an irreducible polynomial in the ring of all polynomials in the elements of A. Since equality (15) shows that $f(A)$ is a divisor of $|A|^m$, then $f(A) = \alpha|A|^r$, where α is some scalar. From the condition $f(E) = 1$ we see that $\alpha = 1$, and thus $f(A) = |A|^r$.

THEOREM 5. *Every rational comitant of a sequence of general weighted tensors $x, \cdots, z$ has the form*

$$R^{j_i \cdots j_q}_{i_1 \cdots i_p} = \frac{F^{j_1 \cdots j_q}_{i_1 \cdots i_p}}{G} ,$$

where $F^{j_1 \cdots j_q}_{i_1 \cdots i_p}$ is an integral weighted comitant, and G is an integral weighted invariant, of the given sequence of tensors.

We first prove this theorem for rational invariants. By assumption, we are given an invariant R of some type $p + q$ having the form

$$R = \frac{F}{G} ,$$

where F, G are polynomials in the independent coordinates of the fixed sequence of general tensors. We assume that the numerator and denominator of R are *without common factors*. Performing a transformation with matrix $T = ||\tau_i^j||$ to a new coordinate basis of $\mathfrak{L}$, we obtain

$$\frac{F(x, \cdots, z)}{G(x, \cdots, z)} = \frac{F(\bar{x}, \cdots, \bar{z})}{G(\bar{x}, \cdots, \bar{z})} |T|^h ,$$

where $(-h)$ is the weight of R. We will consider the expression $F(\bar{x}, \cdots, \bar{z})$ as a function of the old coordinates of the tensors $x, \cdots, z$ and the τ_i^j, which are also considered as independent variables. From the formula for the transformation of the coordinates of tensors (see Section 112) it is evident that $F(\bar{x}, \cdots, \bar{z})$ may be represented in the form

$$F(\bar{x}, \cdots, \bar{z}) = \frac{f(T)}{|T|^s} F_1(x, \cdots, z, \tau) , \tag{16}$$

where $f(T)$ is an integral polynomial in the variables τ_i^j, which is not devisible by $|T|$, and $F_1(x, \cdots, z, \tau)$ is a polynomial in the elements τ_i^j and the old coordinates of the tensors $x, \cdots, z$, not divisible by any nonconstant polynomial in the τ_i^j. In view of the uniqueness of the decomposition of polynomials in several variables into irreducible factors, the polynomials $f(T)$ and F_1 in the decomposition (16) are uniquely determined to within a constant factor. Let

$$G(\bar{x}, \cdots, \bar{z}) = \frac{g(T)}{|T|^t} G_1(x, \cdots, z, \tau)$$

be an analogous decomposition for G. From the relation

$$\frac{F(x, \cdots, z)}{G(x, \cdots, z)} = |T|^{h+t-s} \frac{f(T)}{g(T)} \frac{F_1(x, \cdots, z, \tau)}{G_1(x, \cdots, z, \tau)} \tag{17}$$

we see that F_1 and G_1 are relatively prime since if they had a common factor, this factor would depend only on the coordinates of the tensors $x, \cdots, z$, and then the fraction on the left side could also be reduced. It now follows from (17) that

$$F_1(x, \cdots, z, \tau) = \alpha F(x, \cdots, z), \quad G_1(x, \cdots, z, \tau) = \beta G(x, \cdots, z) ,$$

where α and β are constants. Absorbing them into the functions $f(T)$ and $g(T)$, we may therefore write, by (16),

$$F(\bar{x}, \cdots, \bar{z}) = \frac{f(T)}{|T|^s} F(x, \cdots, z) . \tag{18}$$

Suppose now that $T = T_1 T_2$, where T_1, T_2 are matrices with arbitrary elements. Formula (18) in complete notation yields

$$\frac{f(T_1 T_2)}{|T_1 T_2|^s} F(x, \cdots, z) = F((xT_1)T_2, \cdots, (zT_1)T_2)$$

$$= \frac{f(T_2)}{|T_2|^s} F(xT_1, \cdots, zT_1) = \frac{f(T_2)f(T_1)}{|T_2|^s |T_1|^s} F(x, \cdots, z) ,$$

and hence $f(T_1 T_2) = f(T_1)f(T_2)$. By the lemma, we have $f(T) = |T|^r$ or $F(\bar{x}, \cdots, \bar{z}) = |T|^{r-s} F(x, \cdots, z)$; that is, $F(x, \cdots, z)$ is a ***weighted invariant.*** Similarly, $G(x, \cdots, z)$ is also a weighted invariant, and the theorem is proved for invariants.

Finally, let

$$R^{j_1\cdots j_q}_{i_1\cdots i_p} = \frac{F^{j_1\cdots j_q}_{i_1\cdots i_p}}{G^{j_1\cdots j_q}_{i_1\cdots i_p}}$$

be the coordinates of some weighted comitant of the tensors $x, \cdots, z$, where $F^{j_1\cdots j_q}_{i_1\cdots i_p}$ and $G^{j_1\cdots j_q}_{i_1\cdots i_p}$ are relatively prime polynomials in the independent coordinates of the given tensors. Denoting by G the least common multiple of the polynomials $G^{j_1\cdots j_q}_{i_1\cdots i_p}$, we may represent the coordinates of the comitant in the form

$$R^{j_1\cdots j_q}_{i_1\cdots i_p} = \frac{H^{j_1\cdots j_q}_{i_1\cdots i_p}}{G} .$$

We adjoin to the sequence of tensors $x, \cdots, z$ the independent contravariant vectors $\overset{1}{a}, \cdots, \overset{p}{a}$ and covariant vectors $\overset{1}{c}, \cdots, \overset{q}{c}$, and consider the invariant

$$I = G^{-1} \sum H^{j_1\cdots j_q}_{i_1\cdots i_p} \overset{1}{a}{}^{i_1} \cdots \overset{p}{a}{}^{i_p} \overset{1}{c}_{j_1} \cdots \overset{q}{c}_{j_q} .$$

The numerator and denominator are relatively prime polynomials in the coordinates of the given tensor, and therefore, according to the proof above, the polynomial G is a weighted invariant of the sequence $x, \cdots, z$. Since

$$H^{j_1\cdots j_q}_{i_1\cdots i_p} = GR^{j_1\cdots j_q}_{i_1\cdots i_p} ,$$

where G is an invariant and R is a tensor, then H is also a tensor, and Theorem 5 is proved.

In Section 115, during the consideration of tensors in metric spaces, there was constructed, for a given twice covariant tensor g_{ij}, with matrix $\| g_{ij} \|$ having a nonzero determinant, the important dual twice contravariant tensor g^{ij}, whose coordinates are the elements of the contragredient matrix $\| g^{ij} \| = \| g_{ij} \|'^{-1}$. Thus,

$$g^{ij} = \frac{G^{ij}}{\det \| g_{ij} \|} ,$$

where G^{ij} is the cofactor of the element g_{ij} in the determinant of $\| g_{ij} \|$. Since G^{ij} and $\det \| g_{ij} \|$ are relatively prime, then by Theorem 5 the values G^{ij} must determine a weighted tensor, and $\det \| g_{ij} \|$ must be a weighted invariant. Indeed, it was shown at the end of Section 124 that G^{ij} and $\det \| g_{ij} \|$ are respectively a tensor and an invariant, each of weight 2.

126. Comitant Characteristics

As previously remarked, the coincidence of the values of all polynomial invariants of two tensors of identical types is necessary, but generally not sufficient, for the congruence of the tensors. Therefore, besides the values of the invariants it is necessary to consider other characteristics connected with tensors. One of the important characteristics of tensors is the vanishing of certain of their comitants. If all the coordinates of some tensor equal zero in one basis, then they also equal zero in any other basis. Therefore, the vanishing of a comitant is an effectively verified criterion, not depending upon the choice of coordinate basis. The indication of a number of comitants, of a sequence of general tensors, which vanish, and of a number of comitants known to be different from zero for given tensors, is called a ***comitant characteristic*** of the tensors, and the giving of all vanishing integral comitants of a sequence of tensors is called the ***complete comitant characteristic*** of the sequence.

As an example we consider two sequences $a_1, \cdots, a_s$ and $b_1, \cdots, b_s$ of vectors in a space $\mathfrak{L}$. Linear combinations $\alpha_1 a_1 + \cdots + \alpha_s a_s$ and $\alpha_1 b_1 + \cdots + \alpha_s b_s$ are the simplest comitants of these systems. The results of Section 121 show that if the vanishing of a linear combination of the vectors of one sequence always implies the vanishing of the corresponding linear combinations of the vectors in the other sequence, then the sequences are congruent. Thus, in this case the coincidence of only the *linear comitant* characteristics turns out to be sufficient for the congruence of the sequences of vectors.

We now introduce the important notion of the ***rank of a tensor*** and clarify its connection with comitant characteristics.

Let $F(x_1, \cdots, x_p, u_1, \cdots, u_q)$, where $x_i \in \mathfrak{L}$, $u_j \in \mathfrak{L}'$, be a given multilinear function. Let $\mathfrak{M}$ be the set of all vectors a of the space $\mathfrak{L}$ for which

$$F(a, x_2, \cdots, x_p, u_1, \cdots, u_q) = 0$$

for arbitrary $x_2, \cdots, x_p, u_1, \cdots, u_q$. Since F is linear in x_1, $\mathfrak{M}$ is a linear subspace, which is called the ***kernel*** of F in the first argument. The dimension d of the subspace $\mathfrak{M}$ is the ***nullity***, and $n-d$ is the ***rank***, of F in x_1. The kernel and rank in the remaining arguments are defined similarly.

Choosing a basis $e_1, \cdots, e_n$ of $\mathfrak{L}$, it is easy to see that the rank of F in x_1 equals the maximal number of linearly independent functions among

$$F(e_1, x_2, \cdots, x_p, u_1, \cdots, u_q), \cdots, F(e_n, x_2, \cdots, x_p, u_1, \cdots, u_q)\,.$$

We arrange the coordinates $F^{j_1 \cdots j_q}_{i_1 \cdots i_p}$ of the function F in a $(p+q)$-dimensional table, and divide the table into n layers; the lth layer is occupied by the coordinates whose index i_1 has the value l. It is clear that the lth layer is the table of coordinates for the function $F(e_l, x_2, \cdots, x_p, u_1, \cdots, u_q)$, and thus the maximal number of linearly independent layers equals the rank of F in x_1.

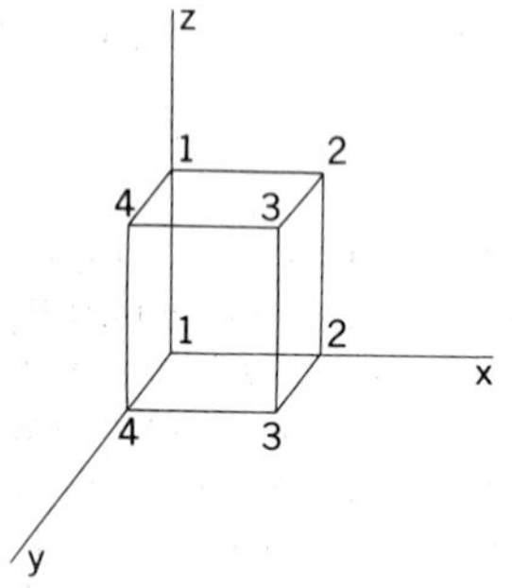

Figure 5

If $p+q=2$, then the coordinates of F may be arranged in an ordinary square matrix, and the rank of F in x_1 thus equals the maximal number of linearly independent rows, and the rank of F in x_2 equals the maximal number of linearly independent columns of the matrix of F. It is known that these two numbers coincide, and therefore we speak simply of the rank of a tensor of valence 2.

For tensors of higher valence the ranks in different arguments may be different. For example, let $\mathfrak{L}$ be a two-dimensional space. The coordinates of a tensor $F(x, y, z)$ of valence 3 may be naturally arranged on the vertices of a cube (see Fig. 5). Let these coordinates of F be 1, 2, 3, 4 in the lower and upper layers. It is evident from the figure that the rank of F in z equals 1, and the rank in x and in y equals 2.

To establish the connection between the rank and the comitant characteristics of a tensor $F(x_1, \cdots, x_p, u_1, \cdots, u_q)$, we denote $F(x_1, \cdots, x_p, u_1, \cdots, u_q)$ by $F(x_1, X)$, where X is the set of arguments $x_2, \cdots, x_p, u_1, \cdots, u_q$. The alternatized product

$$G_s(y_1, \cdots, y_s, X_1, \cdots, X_s) = \sum \varepsilon_\sigma F(y_1, X_{1\sigma}) \cdots F(y_s, X_{s\sigma}) ,$$

in which the sum is taken over all permutations σ of the numbers $1, \cdots, s$, is a comitant of the tensor F. For fixed values of the arguments in X the expression $F(y, X)$ is a linear function on $\mathfrak{L}$, or a covariant vector, and G_s, for fixed $X_1 \cdots, X_s$, is the outer product of the s vectors $F(y, X_1), \cdots, F(y, X_s)$. It follows from the results of Section 118 that $G_s \neq 0$ if these vectors are linearly independent, and $G_s = 0$ if they are linearly dependent. Thus, the assertion that the rank of F in x_1 equals r is equivalent to the comitant relation $G_{r+1} = 0$, $G_r \neq 0$.

Instead of the rank of a tensor in one argument, one may consider the rank in a pair, triple, or more, of arguments. For example, the rank of $F(x_1, \cdots, x_p, u_1, \cdots, u_q)$ in x_1, x_2 is defined as the maximal number of linearly independent functions of $x_3, \cdots, x_p, u_1, \cdots, u_q$ of the form $F(a, b, x_3, \cdots, x_p, u_1, \cdots, u_q)$. This rank evidently equals the maximal number of linearly independent layers of the table of coordinates of the function F if the layers are defined as sets of coordinates in which the first two indices have fixed values.

As an example of an application of the notion of rank we consider the problem of the classification of affinors, already solved in Chapter IV. Let $\mathscr{A}$ be a given affinor, $\mathscr{E}$ be the identity affinor, α a scalar. The affinors $(\alpha\mathscr{E} - \mathscr{A})^s$, for $s = 1, \cdots, n$, are polynomial comitants of $\mathscr{A}$. It was shown in problem 10 of Section 61, how to find the elementary divisors of $\mathscr{A}$ corresponding to the proper value α when one knows the ranks of the affinors $(\alpha\mathscr{E} - \mathscr{A})^s$. Thus, the ranks of the comitants for $s - 1, \cdots, n$ and arbitrary α determine an affinor to within congruence.

●EXAMLES AND PROBLEMS

1. Let $F^{j_1 \cdots j_q}_{i_1 \cdots i_p}$ be the coordinates of some comitant of a system of tensors and a general vector x. Show that the partial derivatives

$$\frac{\partial}{\partial x^\alpha} F^{j_1 \cdots j_q}_{i_1 \cdots i_p} = F^{j_1 \cdots j_q}_{i_1 \cdots i_p \alpha}$$

are the coordinates of a tensor. If $F^{j_1 \cdots j_q}_{i_1 \cdots i_p}$ is a comitant of a system of tensors and a covariant general tensor μ, then the numbers

$$\frac{\partial}{\partial u_\alpha} F^{j_1\cdots j_q}_{i_1\cdots i_p} = F^{j_1\cdots j_q \alpha}_{i_1\cdots i_p}$$

are also the coordinates of a tensor.

2. Let $F, \overset{1}{F}, \cdots, \overset{n}{F}$ be invariants of a system of tensors and a general vector x. Using the result of the preceding problem and the operation of full alternatization, show that the ***Jacobian***

$$J(\overset{1}{F}, \cdots, \overset{n}{F}) = \begin{vmatrix} \dfrac{\partial \overset{1}{F}}{\partial x^1} \cdots \dfrac{\partial \overset{1}{F}}{\partial x^n} \\ \cdots\cdots\cdots \\ \dfrac{\partial \overset{n}{F}}{\partial x^1} \cdots \dfrac{\partial \overset{n}{F}}{\partial x^n} \end{vmatrix}$$

is a relative invariant of weight $+1$, and the ***Hessian***

$$H(F) = \begin{vmatrix} \dfrac{\partial^2 F}{\partial x^1 \partial x^1} \cdots \dfrac{\partial^2 F}{\partial x^1 \partial x^n} \\ \cdots\cdots\cdots\cdots \\ \dfrac{\partial^2 F}{\partial x^n \partial x^1} \cdots \dfrac{\partial^2 F}{\partial x^n \partial x^n} \end{vmatrix}$$

is a relative tensor of weight $+2$.

3. For fixed p all non-zero fully decomposable p-vectors are congruent to each other. Represent the conditions for the complete decomposition of a p-vector (compare Section 119) in comitant form.

INDEX